# RADIATION AND SHIELDING IN SPACE

# NUCLEAR SCIENCE AND TECHNOLOGY

## A Series of Monographs and Textbooks

CONSULTING EDITOR

## V. L. PARSEGIAN

School of Engineering
Rensselaer Polytechnic Institute
Troy, New York

1. John F. Flagg (Ed.)
   CHEMICAL PROCESSING OF REACTOR FUELS, 1961

2. M. L. Yeater (Ed.)
   NEUTRON PHYSICS, 1962

3. Melville Clark, Jr., and Kent F. Hansen
   NUMERICAL METHODS OF REACTOR ANALYSIS, 1964

4. James W. Haffner
   RADIATION AND SHIELDING IN SPACE, 1967

# RADIATION AND SHIELDING IN SPACE

JAMES W. HAFFNER

*North American Aviation*
*Space and Information Systems Division*
*Downey, California*

ACADEMIC PRESS    New York and London    1967

ACADEMIC PRESS INC.
111 Fifth Avenue, New York, New York 10003

*United Kingdom Edition published by*
ACADEMIC PRESS INC. (LONDON) LTD.
Berkeley Square House, London W.1

LIBRARY OF CONGRESS CATALOG CARD NUMBER: 66-30084

PRINTED IN THE UNITED STATES OF AMERICA

# PREFACE

In man's quest for the stars several new technical disciplines concerned with space environment have appeared. Often these disciplines began as a branch of some established scientific field, but developed into separate entities because of their specialized nature. This has been the history of space radiation shielding, which is concerned with the extraterrestrial nuclear radiation environment and how man can protect himself from its undesirable effects.

It has been observed that when a technical discipline reaches a certain degree of development, books pertaining to that discipline become desirable. This occurs when the problems have been defined, solutions or at least avenues of approach have been developed, and the discipline becomes of interest to those outside its relatively small core of researchers. Space radiation shielding has reached such a degree of development. The nuclear radiation environment in space has been investigated sufficiently so that its major features are known. Our knowledge of these features leaves little doubt that man in space may receive dangerous or even lethal radiation doses under certain conditions. The shielding properties of matter have also been studied sufficiently so that the calculation techniques for space radiation attenuation are known. However, radiation shielding per se represents weight, and minimizing this weight while providing for the safety of man in space is of importance to the entire aerospace industry.

Two conferences[1,2] specifically concerned with space radiation shielding have been held to bring together the various parts of this technical discipline. These conferences helped establish space radiation shielding as a separate entity and to make it known to the aerospace industry. However, the conference reports are basically collections of papers whose assimilation is time consuming for the person looking for a numerical answer. At this time it is not certain if future conferences of this sort will be held.

---

[1] *Symposium on the Protection against Radiation Hazards in Space*, Rept. TID-7652, U.S. Atomic Energy Commission (1962).

[2] *Second Symposium on Protection against Radiations in Space*, Rept. SP-71, National Aeronautics and Space Administration (1964).

The major purpose of this book is to present the discipline of space radiation shielding in a structured manner for the person who has use for its conclusions as well as for those who are primarily concerned with its techniques. This first audience includes aerospace scientists engaged in the design of spacecraft and/or components thereof, those engaged in mission analysis studies, and those concerned with space environment simulation studies. Knowledge of the nuclear space radiation environment and its effects on men and materials is rapidly becoming an integral part of such investigations. The second audience, many of whose works are referenced in this volume, includes experts in space radiation and nuclear shielding. For these scientists this book presents a reference in which the discipline of space radiation shielding (as of 1966) is summarized.

There are four distinct sections in the book. The first is concerned with the nuclear radiation environment in space (Chapters 1–3). The second section (Chapter 4) is a summary of the effects of nuclear radiations on men and materials. The third section (Chapters 5–7) deals with the techniques which doses and dose rates as a function of shield thickness and other relevant parameters are calculated. In the fourth section (Chapters 8 and 9) the results of several space radiation shielding studies are presented which relate the preceeding sections to each other and to the overall design of spacecraft. In each of these four sections it was necessary to select a cutoff point, since the material covered in each section has been the subject of several books. Therefore much of the material is summarized, omitting many of the details of the techniques by which it was obtained. Tables and graphs are used to present a large part of the information. For those who desire to investigate some point in more detail, references are presented throughout the book. In addition, the reader is directed to those information centers (see Chapters 4 and 7) at which current information on shielding, radiation effects, and computer codes are accumulated.

The author wishes to express his appreciation to those whose efforts helped make this book a reality. The contributions of co-workers in the discipline of space radiation shielding to promote an understanding of and an appreciation for the subject have been invaluable. Special thanks go to E. R. Beever and D. H. Rusling who assisted in all phases of manuscript preparation.

*June 1967*

                                                        J. W. HAFFNER

# CONTENTS

# *I*

# SOLAR PARTICLE RADIATION

## A.  Historical Review

Man has observed the Sun ever since he could see, and records of these observations have been kept for centuries. Solar and lunar eclipses, comets, and planets have been noted as particularly significant. For the past two centuries, detailed observations of the Sun have been carried out using telescopes. Sunspots, prominences, and flares were among the features discovered this way. However, it has only been since 1946 that the Sun has been recognized as a source of nuclear particles. In that year, Forbush [1] noted that the output current of his ground level ionization chambers increased approximately 8% above the steady state value (due to cosmic ray background) for several hours. This ionization increase had been preceded by an observed solar flare. In addition the effect was much more latitude-dependent than the cosmic radiation was known to be, and it showed a larger diurnal (day-night) difference. When the same effects were observed less than a month later, Forbush reported that the ionization was probably due to cosmic-type radiation emitted by the Sun. Since then many observations both on Earth and in space have confirmed that the Sun is a source of nuclear particles.

Briefly the Sun is known to be the source of two types of nuclear radiation —the solar wind and solar flare particles. The solar wind is a high flux ($\sim 10^8$ particles/cm$^2$) of low-energy (kev) protons which is continually being emitted. The time variations in the density and velocity of the solar wind protons are relatively small ($\lesssim$ an order of magnitude). The solar flare particles are sporadically emitted in conjunction with optical (flares) and nonoptical (radio, X-ray bursts) electromagnetic radiation. These solar flare particles consist of protons, alpha particles, and a few heavier nuclei as well with Mev energies. As many as $\sim 10^{30}$ such particles may be emitted in conjunction with a single flare lasting as long as an hour, although most flares are smaller. Flares tend to occur in 11-year cycles, with few or no important flares in a year when the Sun is "quiet." A dozen or more may occur when the Sun is active, and many are accompanied by Mev particles which reach the Earth.

From the standpoint of space travel, the solar wind is relatively harmless, since its low energy makes shielding easy. However, materials which must be exposed to it will be affected. The solar flare particles are more dangerous because of their much greater penetrating power and because their emission cannot be accurately predicted. In this chapter the characteristics of these solar particulate radiations are discussed.

## B.   Observation of Events on the Sun

Our Sun is a rather quiet, ordinary star, one of approximately $10^{11}$ stars in our galaxy (the Milky Way). However, because of its proximity to the Earth, its influence upon the latter is all important. This proximity also has made it possible to study the Sun in some detail. Its outer portions are the only parts observable from the Earth. Its surface as we look at it is called the photosphere. It has a somewhat granular appearance, somewhat like the surface of an orange. Each grain is believed to be a convection cell, possibly indicative of magnetic domain structure. The photosphere has a diameter of $\sim 1.4 \times 10^6$ km, and a blackbody temperature of nominally $\sim 6000$ °K.

Beyond the photosphere is the chromosphere, a transition region extending $\sim 14,000$ km above the photosphere. The density decreases radically from the bottom ($\sim 1$ gm/cm$^3$) to the top ($\sim 10^{-8}$ gm/cm$^3$) of the chromosphere, and the temperature climbs from $\sim 6000$ °K to at least $10^6$ °K.

The corona is the outermost portion of the Sun, extending from the chromosphere to far beyond the Earth. The corona is subdivided into the inner (K) corona and the outer (F) corona. The inner corona extends $10^5$–$10^6$ km beyond the chromosphere, and can be seen during a total solar eclipse by the Moon. It is characterized by emission spectral lines, while the F corona exhibits Fraunhofer lines believed caused by light scattered by interplanetary dust. The corona has a temperature of $\gtrsim 10^6$ °K, and a density of $10^{-12}$ to $10^{-15}$ gm/cm$^3$, its outer portions constituting the solar wind. The surface of the Sun rotates about an axis normal to the ecliptic plane in the same direction as the planets rotate about the Sun. The period of rotation as seen from the Earth is a function of solar latitude, varying from approximately 25 days at the equator to approximately 33 days at the poles. An average figure of 27 days is often used, since many of the interesting phenomena take place at a solar latitude where the rotation period is approximately 27 days.

Various types of disturbances are observed in these outer portions of the Sun. Among these are plages, sunspots, flares, and the generation of various types of radiation.

## 1. PLAGES AND SUNSPOTS

A plage is a region on the solar surface which appears brighter than its surroundings when viewed in a particular wavelength region of the optical spectrum. The H and K lines of doubly ionized calcium (Ca II) are often used for plage observation, but the lines of iron and other heavy ionized atoms have also been used. The plages are regions of the chromosphere which have a higher temperature than their surroundings. One may grow in area and intensity for a period of days, some of them covering 0.1–0.3% of the visible solar disk at maximum extent. The large, bright plages very often give rise to sunspots.

A sunspot is a relatively cool region of the photosphere. The inner portion of a sunspot is called the umbra and has a temperature of $\sim 4000$ °K. Surrounding the umbra is the penumbra, which is often at 4500–5000 °K. Strong magnetic fields (often several thousand gauss) are associated with sunspots. A sunspot may appear in a plage region a few days after the plage. It will usually grow for a period of days, sometimes by increasing in size, sometimes by combining with adjacent sunspots, since sunspots often occur in groups. Sunspots vary in size from intergranular regions $\sim 10^3$ km in diameter to giants of $\sim 10^5$ km in diameter. Sunspots generally last a month or so, although lifetimes as short as a few days and as long as several months have been observed.

Both plages and sunspots are usually observed at moderate solar latitudes (5–35 deg) and tend to occur in 11-year cycles. The sunspot number ($R$) is defined as [2]

$$R = k(f + 10g) \tag{1.1}$$

where $g$ is the number of disturbed regions on the Sun (single sunspots or groups of sunspots); $f$ is the total number of individual sunspots; and $k$ is a factor assigned to a particular observer.

Records of sunspots have been kept for over two centuries, and in terms of the sunspot number, $R$, the results are shown in Fig. 1-1 [2]. It is seen that the 11-year cycle is only approximate, but the cyclic behavior is unmistak-

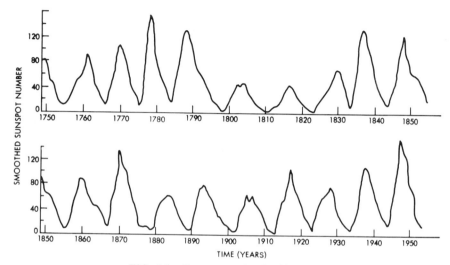

FIG. 1-1.   Sunspot number for 200 years.

able. The International Geophysical Year (IGY) of 1958–1960 was chosen to coincide with a maximum in solar activity, and 1965–1966 was designated the year of the quiet Sun for corresponding reasons. While sunspots are interesting in themselves, they often give rise to solar flares.

## 2.   FLARES

A solar flare is a sudden brightening of the chromosphere usually observed in the H$\alpha$ region of the optical spectrum, although a few large, intense flares have been observed in the white (integrated) light of the Sun. A flare nearly always originates in the vicinity of a sunspot, often propagates at 100–1000 km/sec across a portion of the solar surface, and usually only lasts a matter of minutes.

Solar flares are classed by size (corrected area) and brightness. The size classes are [2]

Class 1     $1\text{-}3 \times 10^{-4}$ of solar disk

Class 2     $3\text{-}7 \times 10^{-4}$ of solar disk

Class 3     $>7 \times 10^{-4}$ of solar disk

The class is determined on the basis of corrected area, since the apparent size of a flare near the limb (edge of the solar disk) would appear smaller than

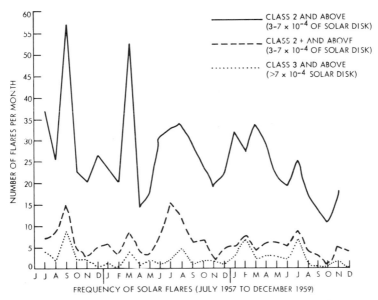

FIG. 1-2. Solar flare frequency July 1957–December 1959.

for an event of the same size near the center of the disk (as seen from Earth). The brightness may be designated by a plus $(+)$ or a minus $(-)$ for flares which are more or less bright, respectively, than the average. Thus a $3-$ flare is a relatively large, dim event, while a $2+$ flare is a bright, medium-sized one. Flare frequency by class for 1952–1960 is shown in Fig. 1-2 (see also Table 1-1).

Solar flares have been the object of considerable research. Much of our current information is presented in the publications of Smith and Smith [3], Severny [4], Hess [5], and others. The development of flares from plages and sunspots has been investigated by Howard [6], Dodsen and Hedeman [7], and others.

TABLE 1-1

BRIEF SUMMARY OF 1949–1961 SOLAR FLARE DATA

| | | | | | | | | | | | |
|---|---|---|---|---|---|---|---|---|---|---|---|
| **Observations on Sun** | | | | | | **Observation of effects on Earth** | | | | | |
| Flares characteristics | | | | | Type IV radio noise | Polar cap absorptions[f] | | | Geomagnetic storms | | |
| Date[a] | Time[b] | Position[c] | Plage no.[d] | Impor-tance[e] | Time of start | Time of start | Dura-tion (days) | Max. att. (db) | Date | Time of start | Max. intensity[g] (gammas) |
| 1/23/49 | 0103 | N25, E00 | 1795 | 3 | — | 1200 | 4 | — | 1/24/49 | 1827 | 155 |
| 4/11/49 | 0040 | N25, E70 | 1844 | 1 | — | 1400 | 4 | — | 4/11/49 | 0725 | 29 |
| | 0727 | S04, E04 | — | 1 | — | | | — | 4/12/49 | 1521 | 28 |
| 5/10/49 | 0345 | S18, E19 | 1859 | 2 | — | 2000 | 4 | — | 5/11/49 | 0204 | 15 |
| | 2011 | S20, E12 | 1859 | 3+ | — | 1800 | 4 | — | 5/12/49 | 0840 | 150 |
| 6/4/49 | 1627 | N04, W51 | 1876 | 2+ | — | 1800 | 4 | — | 6/6/49 | 2114 | 27 |
| 8/3/49 | 0051 | S20, W20 | 1924 | 1 | — | 1200 | 6 | — | 8/4/49 | 0043 | 64 |
| 8/5/49 | 0807 | S22, W55 | 1924 | 3 | — | 1200 | 3 | — | 8/6/49 | 1112 | 9 |
| 11/19/49 | 1033 | S02, W72 | 1997 | 3+ | — | 1200 | 3 | Large | 11/19/49 | 1756 | 42 |
| 2/1/50 | 2215 | N20, W79 | 2043 | 3 | — | 0200 | 2 | — | 2/2/50 | 0635 | 27 |
| 2/21/50 | 2344 | N11, W26 | 2055 | 3+ | — | 1200 | 3 | — | — | — | — |
| 2/22/50 | 0302 | N13, W29 | 2055 | 2+ | — | — | — | — | 2/23/50 | 1043 | 49 |
| 3/27/50 | — | — | — | — | — | — | 3 | — | 3/29/50 | 0721 | 14 |
| 5/27/50 | — | — | — | — | — | — | 5 | — | 5/27/50 | 1205 | 63 |
| 3/7/51 | — | — | — | — | — | 1600 | 9 | — | 3/6/51 | 0750 | 38 |
| 4/2/51 | — | — | — | — | — | 1600 | 8 | — | 4/1/51 | 2050 | 51 |
| 5/11/51 | 0830 | S09, W48 | 2341 | 2 | — | — | 9 | — | — | — | — |

| Date | Time | Position | No. | Imp. | Time | Time | Imp. | Imp. | Date | Time | No. |
|---|---|---|---|---|---|---|---|---|---|---|---|
| 5/12/51 | — | N07, W15 | 2343 | 2 | — | — | — | — | 5/14/51 | 1751 | 27 |
| 5/13/51 | — | S13, E67 | 2347 | 3 | — | — | — | — | 5/17/51 | 1702 | 54 |
| 10/27/51 | 0641 | N10, W18 | 2343 | 3 | — | — | — | — | 5/18/51 | 2314 | 37 |
| — | — | — | — | — | — | 0800 | 3 | — | 10/28/51 | 1154 | 98 |
| 3/2/53 | — | — | — | — | — | 1800 | 3 | Weak | 3/2/53 | 0429 | 88 |
| 1/16/55 | 2130 | N33, W41 | 3065 | 3 | — | — | 2 | Weak | 3/17/55 | 0300 | 43 |
| — | — | — | — | — | — | — | — | — | 3/18/55 | 1500 | 59 |
| 2/23/56 | 0342 | N23, W80 | 3400 | 3 | — | 0430 | 3 | 8.4 | 2/25/56 | 0307 | 103 |
| 3/11/56 | — | — | — | 1+ | — | 1600 | 4 | — | 3/10/56 | 0000 | 24 |
| 4/27/56 | 2100 | N15, W34 | 3474 | 3 | — | — | 2 | Weak | 4/28/56 | 1727 | 64 |
| 8/31/56 | 1241 | N16, E16 | 3643 | 3 | 1231 | 1500 | 2.5 | — | 9/2/56 | 0230 | 82 |
| 11/13/56 | 1501 | N16, W10 | 3753 | 2 | 1431 | 2100 | 2 | — | 11/13/56 | 2136 | 86 |
| 1/20/57 | 1120 | S27, W18 | 3820 | 2+ | — | 1500 | 2.5 | — | 1/21/57 | 1255 | 82 |
| 4/3/57 | 0835 | S15, W60 | 3907 | 3 | 0826 | 1500 | 2.5 | Small | 4/5/57 | 0707 | 37 |
| 5/18/57 | 0813 | S11, W15 | 3979 | 1+ | — | 0200 | 0.5 | 1 | 5/21/57 | 0910 | 13 |
| 6/22/57 | 0236 | N23, E12 | 4024 | 2 | 0231 | 0530 | 3 | — | 6/25/57 | 0046 | 84 |
| 7/3/57 | 0740 | N14, W40 | 4039 | 3+ | 0832 | 0845 | 2 | 6 | 7/4/57 | 2342 | 56 |
| 7/24/57 | 1827 | S24, W27 | 4070 | 3 | 1801 | 2051 | 0.5 | 2 | 7/27/57 | 1959 | 8 |
| 8/9/57 | 0628 | S09, E75 | 4099 | 2 | — | 2245 | 1 | 2.5 | 8/9/57 | 1347 | 16 |
| 8/28/57 | 0940 | S30, E25 | 4125 | 3+ | 0920 | 0030 | 0.5 | — | 8/29/57 | 1909 | 38 |
| 8/29/57 | 2020 | S28, E30 | 4125 | 2+ | — | — | — | — | — | — | — |
| — | 0555 | N24, E35 | 4124 | 2 | — | 1300 | 2 | 9 | 8/31/57 | 1812 | 36 |
| — | 1037 | S25, E20 | 4125 | 2 | — | — | — | — | — | — | — |
| — | 1303 | N10, W26 | 4124 | 1+ | 1257 | 1730 | 1.5 | 9 | 9/4/57 | 1300 | 145 |
| — | 1316 | S34, W36 | 4125 | 2+ | 1500 | — | — | — | — | — | — |
| 9/12/57 | 1516 | N11, W18 | 4134 | 2 | 1500 | 1200 | 1.5 | 0.5 | 9/13/57 | 0046 | 160 |
| 9/21/5 | 1338 | N10, W06 | 4152 | 3 | 1331 | 1630 | 2 | 5 | 9/22/57 | 1345 | 164 |

TABLE 1-1 (*continued*)

| | Observations on Sun | | | | | Observation of effects on Earth | | | | | |
| | Flares characteristics | | | | Type IV radio noise | Polar cap absorptions[f] | | | Geomagnetic storms | | |
| Date[a] | Time[b] | Position[c] | Plage no.[d] | Importance[e] | Time of start | Time of start | Duration (days) | Max. att. (db) | Date | Time of start | Max. intensity[g] (gammas) |
|---|---|---|---|---|---|---|---|---|---|---|---|
| 9/26/57 | 1836 | S26, E28 | 4161 | 1 | 1836 | 2315 | 1 | 2 | — | — | — |
| | 1855 | N22, E15 | 4159 | 3 | — | — | — | — | 9/29/57 | 0016 | 8 |
| 10/20/57 | 1642 | S26, W45 | 4189 | 3 + | 1636 | 0630 | 1 | 5 | 10/21/57 | 2241 | 28 |
| 2/9/58 | 2141 | S12, W14 | 4404 | 2 + | 2105 | 0700 | 1 | 12 | 2/11/58 | 0125 | 199 |
| 3/23/58 | 1005 | S14, E78 | 4476 | 3 + | 1003 | 1830 | 1.5 | 5 | 3/25/58 | 1540 | 33 |
| 3/25/58 | 0530 | N14, E25 | 4474 | 2 | — | 1300 | 4.5 | 12 | — | — | — |
| | 0603 | S15, E50 | 4476 | 2 | — | — | — | — | — | — | — |
| 4/9/58 | 1440 | N11, W41 | 4490 | 1 | — | 1000 | 2 | 4.5 | — | — | — |
| | 1450 | N24, W58 | 4485 | 1 | — | — | — | — | — | — | — |
| 4/10/58 | 0100 | N25, W63 | 4485 | 1 | — | — | — | — | — | — | — |
| | 0914 | N18, W78 | 4485 | 1 + | — | — | — | — | — | — | — |
| 6/6/58 | 0439 | N16, W78 | 4578 | 2 | 0437 | 1345 | — | — | 6/7/58 | 0046 | 77 |
| | 1056 | N43, E42 | 4597 | 1 + | — | — | — | — | — | — | — |
| 7/7/58 | 0115 | N25, W08 | 4634 | 3 + | 0026 | 0130 | 4 | 17 | 7/8/58 | 1728 | 200 |
| | 0033 | N25, E07 | 4634 | 1 + | — | — | — | — | — | — | — |
| 7/29/58 | 0056 | S17, W42 | 4659 | 2 + | — | 0405 | 1 | 1.5 | 7/31/58 | 1529 | 15 |
| | 0303 | S14, W44 | 4659 | 3 | — | — | — | — | — | — | — |
| 8/16/58 | 0440 | S14, W50 | 4686 | 3 + | 0448 | 0600 | 2.5 | 15 | 8/17/58 | 0622 | 82 |
| 8/19/58 | 2254 | N18, E26 | 4708 | 2 | 2140 | 1500 | 0.5 | 3 | — | — | — |

| Date | UT | Position | No. | Imp. | | | | | Date | | |
|---|---|---|---|---|---|---|---|---|---|---|---|
| 8/20/58 | 0044 | N16, E18 | 4708 | 2+ | — | — | — | — | 8/22/58 | 0227 | 34 |
| 8/22/58 | 1448 | N18, W10 | 4708 | 3 | 1430 | 1530 | 3.5 | 10 | 8/24/58 | 0140 | 85 |
| 8/26/58 | 0027 | N20, W54 | 4708 | 3 | 0023 | 0100 | 3 | 13 | 8/27/58 | 0243 | 64 |
| 9/22/58 | 0750 | S19, W42 | 4765 | 2 | — | 1400 | 3.5 | 4 | 9/25/58 | 0408 | 82 |
|  | 1017 | N17, W65 | 4756 | 2 | — | — | — | — | — | — | — |
| 5/10/59 | 2140 | N18, E48 | 5148 | 3+ | 2100 | 2300 | 7 | 15 | 5/11/59 | 2328 | 108 |
| 6/13/59 | 0400 | N17, E57 | 5204 | 1+ | — | 1300 | 2 | 1.5 | — | — | — |
| 7/10/59 | 0240 | N20, E66 | 5270 | 3+ | 0223 | 0400 | 4 | 15 | 7/11/59 | 1625 | 44 |
| 7/14/59 | 0349 | N16, E06 | 5269 | 3+ | 0330 | 0700 | 3 | 20 | 7/15/59 | 0803 | 236 |
| 7/16/59 | 2132 | N15, W30 | 5269 | 3 | 2118 | 0200 | 7 | 18 | 7/17/59 | 1638 | 119 |
| 9/1/59 | 1702 | S12, W52 | 5340 | 2 | — | 0400 | 2 | Small | — | — | — |
|  | 1948 | N12, E60 | 5355 | 2+ | 1914 | — | — | — | 9/3/59 | 2159 | 103 |
| 10/16/59 | 1425 | N30, E65 | 5408 | 1+ | — | — | — | — | — | — | — |
| 3/30/60 | 1540 | N12, E12 | 5615 | 2 | 1519 | 0300 | 1 | 7 | 3/31/60 | 0800 | 241 |
| 4/1/60 | 0858 | N12, W10 | 5615 | 3 | — | 0930 | 2 | 3 | 4/2/60 | 2313 | 68 |
| 4/5/60 | 0245 | N12, W61 | 5615 | 2+ | 0207 | 0800 | 2 | 3 | 4/7/60 | 1511 | 22 |
| 4/28/60 | 0137 | S05, E34 | 5645 | 3 | 0145 | 0200 | 1 | 3 | 4/27/60 | 2020 | 84 |
| 4/29/60 | 0200 | N12, W20 | 5642 | 2 | 0200 | 0350 | — | — | — | — | — |
|  | 0420 | N10, W22 | 5642 | 3 | 0350 | — | — | — | 4/30/60 | 0132 | 174 |
|  | 0554 | N14, W20 | 5642 | 2 | 0606 | 1044 | 2 | 5 | 5/6/60 | 1650 | 60 |
|  | 1015 | N14, W90 | 5642 | 2 | — | 1830 | 4 | 15 | 5/8/60 | 0421 | 128 |
| 5/4/60 | 1540 | S10, E08 | 5653 | 3 | 1414 | 0620 | 3 | 4.5 | — | — | — |
| 5/6/60 | 0521 | S10, E85 | 5663 | 1+ | 0530 | — | — | — | 5/16/60 | 1351 | 42 |
| 5/13/60 | 0550 | N29, W68 | 5654 | 3 | — | 0800 | 2 | 2.5 | 9/4/60 | 0900 | 118 |
| 9/3/60 | 0037 | N18, E88 | 5838 | 2+ | — | 1328 | 2 | Small | — | — | — |
| 9/26/60 | 0538 | S21, W64 | 5858 | 2 | 0554 | 1445 | 3 | 15 | — | — | — |
| 11/12/60 | 1330 | N26, W04 | 5925 | 3+ | 1327 | — | — | — | 11/13/60 | 1023 | 280 |

TABLE 1-1 (continued)

| | Observations on Sun | | | | | Observation of effects on Earth | | | | | |
|---|---|---|---|---|---|---|---|---|---|---|---|
| | Flares characteristics | | | | Type IV radio noise | Polar cap absorptions[f] | | | Geomagnetic storms | | |
| Date[a] | Time[b] | Position[c] | Plage no.[d] | Impor- tance[e] | Time of start | Time of start | Dura- tion (days) | Max. att. (db) | Date | Time of start | Max. intensity[g] (gammas) |
| 11/15/60 | 0221 | N26, W33 | 5925 | 3+ | 0221 | 0505 | 3.5 | 20 | 11/15/60 | 1304 | 94 |
| 11/20/60 | 2020 | N26, W113 | 5925 | 2 | — | 0500 | 1 | 5 | 11/21/60 | 0631 | 45 |
| 7/11/61 | 1700 | S07, E31 | 6171 | 3 | 1702 | — | 1 | 1.5 | 7/13/61 | 1115 | 102 |
| 7/12/61 | 1025 | S07, E24 | 6171 | 3+ | 1400 | 0700 | 2.5 | 20 | 7/14/61 | 0730 | 98 |
| 7/15/61 | 1440 | N14, E13 | 6172 | 3 | 1435 | 1545 | 3 | 3 | — | — | — |
| | 1512 | S07, W20 | 6171 | 2 | 1522 | — | — | — | 7/17/61 | 1827 | 93 |
| 7/18/61 | 1000 | S06, W58 | 6171 | 3+ | 0940 | 1135 | 2.5 | 9 | 7/20/61 | 0249 | 35 |
| 7/20/61 | 1620 | S06, W90 | 6171 | 3+ | 1607 | 0300 | 1 | 5 | 7/23/61 | 0600 | 17 |
| 9/10/61 | 2020 | N12, E90 | 6212 | 1 | 1935 | 2300 | — | 8 | — | — | — |
| 9/28/61 | 2223 | N14, E30 | 6235 | 3 | 2212 | 2335 | — | 1.8 | 9/30/61 | 2111 | 114 |
| 11/10/61 | 1444 | N08, W90 | 6264 | 2+ | 1440 | — | — | 1 | — | — | — |

[a] Date of flare on sun as observed from Earth.

[b] Universal time on Earth at which observation first reported.

[c] Latitude and Longitude on sun as observed from Earth.

[d] McMath-Hulbert Observatory serial number for location of flare.

[e] Portional area of sun covered and relative brightness (see text).

[f] Note that the times given for polar cap absorptions may fall on the date following that of flare observation.

[g] Maximum geomagnetic storm intensity is the equivalent daily complitude of geomagnetic disturbance on a 0–400 scale.

There are a number of events which are apparently related to solar flares. Bright, narrow regions on the Sun with a threadlike appearance (filaments) often disappear at the onset of a flare. The magnetic fields in the flare region are seriously disturbed, and sunspots (along with their associated magnetic fields) may disappear as a result of a flare. It is known that various types of radiations are emitted as a result of (or in conjunction with) a large solar flare. Some of these emissions constitute the major radiation hazards for interplanetary travel. Others may be useful for predicting the occurrence of solar flaring. Section D of this chapter deals with this in more detail.

### 3. RADIO, X-RAY BURSTS

Associated with solar flares are three types of electromagnetic radiation. The first class (optical) has been used to observe the time and spatial behavior of solar flares as discussed above. The other two classes (radio, X-ray) also merit discussion here.

Six types of radio emissions are associated with solar flares [8]. These types, which differ primarily in their time behavior, are as follows:

Type I lasts for $\leqslant 1$ sec; broadband; no frequency drift.
Type II lasts for a few minutes; frequency decreases slowly.
Type III lasts for approximately 1 sec; frequency decreases rapidly.
Type IV lasts for $\gtrsim 1$ hr; broadband; no frequency drift.
Type V lasts for a few minutes; narrowband; no frequency drift.
Type U lasts a few seconds; frequency drifts down then up.

These longer duration radio bursts are apparently emitted from discrete regions on the Sun, called M Regions. The short duration radio bursts do not last long enough to determine their source locations. The Type IV radio emission has a high correlation with solar flare events which result in the emission of nuclear radiations. This type of solar radiation has been investigated by Thompson and Maxwell [9], Fokker [10], Das Gupta and Basu [11], and others. The sources of the Type IV radio emission often have an appreciable angular size ($\sim 10$ sec of arc) and appear to move across the solar disk with flarelike velocities (100–1000 km/sec). In the meter wavelength region, they are almost always preceded by a Type II burst. It has been proposed that the origin of Type IV radio emission is in the synchrotron radiation of electrons accelerated during a solar flare.

Bursts of X rays also accompany solar flares. These X rays have been studied by Peterson and Winckler [12], Smith [13], Conner *et al.* [14], and others. The X rays appear to have an approximately $E^{-2}$ energy spectrum, the shape being relatively constant during the few minutes the burst lasts. The energies measured are in the kev region. As with radio bursts, the intensity increases rapidly to a maximum value, then decreases more slowly. Neither the radio nor the X-ray bursts constitute an important radiation hazard at 1 A.U. (the astronomical unit $\simeq 1.5 \times 10^8$ km). The source of the X rays is bremsstrahlung, probably due to fast electrons in the upper chromosphere [15]. The exact location is uncertain because the total number of electrons involved is not known. At high solar altitudes ($\gtrsim 50{,}000$ km), the electron density is so low that an unacceptably large volume is required to generate the observed intensity, while at low solar altitudes ($\lesssim 10{,}000$ km), the collision rate is too high to account for the observed duration.

For purposes of space radiation shielding, the major importance of radio and X-ray bursts is their possible use as warning signals. Since they travel 1 A.U. in approximately 8 min, while the dangerous solar particulate radiation requires an hour or more, observation of these bursts will provide time for astronauts to take cover.

## C.   Characteristics of the Solar Wind

Our direct experimental knowledge of the solar wind rests completely upon the few space probes which have been sent to relatively great distances from the Earth. These include Mariner II (Venus probe), Mariner IV (Mars probe), Explorers X and XII (extended elliptical Earth orbits), and the Soviet probes, Luniks I and II. The characteristics of the solar wind have been reported by Neugebauer and Snyder [16, 17], Bernstein [18], Parker [19], Gringauz [20], and others. Faraday cup ion traps, some preceded by electrostatic or magnetic filters were used for these measurements [21]. However, such direct measurements have been supplemented by several indirect ones. These involved experiments which yielded information on interplanetary magnetic fields, the galactic (cosmic) radiation, the Van Allen belts, and comets. In addition, characteristics of the zodiacal light, the Earth's upper atmosphere, and satellite drag may be related to the behavior of the solar wind. Combined with theoretical studies (discussed later in this chapter) these measurements have yielded a semiconsistent picture of the solar wind. This picture is discussed in this section.

The solar wind is really an extension of the solar corona, and extends to several astronomical units at least [22]. It plays a role in the deflection of comet tails [23, 24], the outer boundary of the geomagnetically trapped radiation (Van Allen belts) [25, 26], and may have a hand in producing the solar auroras on the Earth [18, 27]. It influences and is influenced by the interplanetary magnetic field ($\sim 10^{-4}$–$10^{-5}$ gauss) [28]. Except when the Sun is active, the solar wind constitutes the most important particulate solar radiation.

### 1.  COMPOSITION

The solar wind is a plasma, which means that a substantial fraction of the matter is ionized. The only particles definitely identified are protons, although there may be a small ($\lesssim 1\%$) alpha-particle component as well [18]. Electrons have not been identified, although presumably they are equally present in the solar wind to maintain electrical neutrality. Heavier nuclei ($Z \geqslant 3$) have not been found.

There are two problems related to the measurement of the solar wind. The first is the low-energy spectrum which makes direct measurement of the energy of a single particle impossible. One can only measure the flux of particles as a function of energy. While the electrostatic and magnetic techniques used distinguish between positive and negative particles, they do not distinguish between protons and alpha particles, for example. In order to measure two parameters of a particle (such as mass and energy), it is necessary to make two measurements (such as range and specific ionization, or range and rigidity, for example). The range of solar wind particles is too small (microns) to measure accurately unless they are accelerated by a known amount. So far this approach has not been tried.

A second problem related to solar wind measurements is the presence of optical photons (sunlight). These photons, especially in the ultraviolet wavelength region, are sufficiently energetic to produce photoelectrons. Thus a photoelectric current of $\sim 10^{-8}$ amp/cm$^2$ is produced by sunlight at 1 A.U. from most metallic surfaces. This must be compared with a solar wind current of $\sim 10^{-11}$ amp/cm$^2$. While the photoelectric current can be excluded from measurements of the electrically positive component of the solar wind, it presents a difficult obstacle which must be overcome if measurements of the negative component are to be carried out.

At the present time one can only say that the solar wind consists of protons (1–10/cc) and probably an equal density of electrons. The presence of heavier nuclei ($Z \geqslant 2$) is doubtful.

## 2. ENERGY SPECTRA

Since the solar wind is a plasma, there are two velocity (energy) distributions to be considered. One is the velocity distribution of the individual particles within the plasma (the thermal energies). The other is the directed velocity of the plasma as a whole. While these two are not independent, they are different and vary in different ways.

The directed velocity is rather high, varying from ~300 km/sec (quiet Sun) to ~1000 km/sec (active Sun) at 1 A.U. [17, 20]. The protons in the solar wind have thermal energies of ~1–10 kev. This corresponds to a temperature of ~$10^6$ °K, and a thermal velocity of ~100 km/sec. Thus the thermal velocities are small compared with the directed velocities at 1 A.U.

It is interesting to note that the directed velocity and the temperature of the solar wind plasma are apparently directly correlated. Also the plasma density apparently is inversely related to the temperature. Thus the temperature decreases and the directed velocity increases as a function of distance from the Sun, since the plasma density must decrease due to geometrical considerations.

Since electrons have not been observed in the solar wind, one can only speculate about their energy distribution. Any electrons in the solar wind would have the same directed velocity as the protons, but their thermal energies might be much less. If the solar wind is magnetically accelerated at the Sun, the electrons would probably have approximately 1/1836 the energies of the protons. These low energies (a few electron volts) would make them doubly difficult to detect.

## 3. TIME BEHAVIOR

The solar wind is continually "blowing," but its flux and directed velocity vary with solar activity [29–31]. Since the solar magnetic field is carried along with the solar wind, the same time variations are observed in the interplanetary magnetic fields as well.

There are short-term (on the order of minutes) changes during which the flux (density times directed velocity) may vary as much as by 50% [18].

These are not understood, but may be due to corresponding fluctuations in the emission of the solar wind. It is possible that they are due to hydromagnetic shock waves in the solar wind [32]. Since the solar wind is a plasma, a disturbance in one of its portions will propagate. However, it is generally believed that the flow of the solar wind is supersonic [33] (i.e., the directed velocity exceeds the disturbance propagation velocity). Therefore, a disturbance will tend to be carried along with the plasma. In any event, there are short-term semirandom fluctuations in the solar wind.

There are also longer term fluctuations in the solar wind associated with solar disturbances, especially flares [31, 34]. Such disturbances are detected on earth as geomagnetic storms approximately 4 hours later. Following an abrupt onset, the density and velocity of the solar wind increase for approxi-

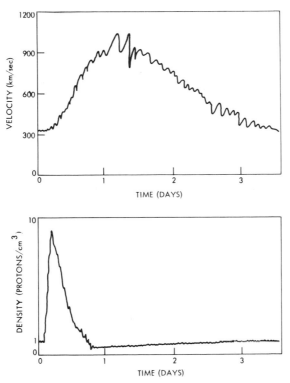

FIG. 1-3.  Behavior of solar wind during solar disturbance.

mately an hour. However, after a few hours the density decreases to less than the nominal value, while the directed velocity continues to increase, reaching a maximum about a day after the abrupt onset. The directed velocity then slowly decreases over a period of a few days and the density rises until both have returned to their previous nominal values ($\sim 1$ proton/cm$^3$ at $\sim 300$ km/sec). At their respective peaks, the density has been known to increase an order of magnitude, and the directed velocity to triple, from their nominal values. Representative behaviors for these two parameters of the solar wind during a solar disturbance (such as a flare) are shown in Fig. 1-3.

### 4.   SPATIAL DEPENDENCE

The solar wind is emitted by the Sun radially but the roughly 27-day rotation of the Sun causes the flow pattern to have a spiral appearance, somewhat like water sprayed from a rotating lawn sprinkler (Fig. 1-4).

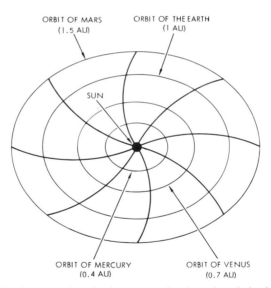

FIG. 1-4.   Inner portion of solar system, showing solar wind spirals.

Probably the solar wind is fairly well confined to the ecliptic plane. The former thus appears to follow a rather flat spiral from the Sun to several astronomical units. The theoretical radial dependence of the solar wind is shown in Fig. 1-5.

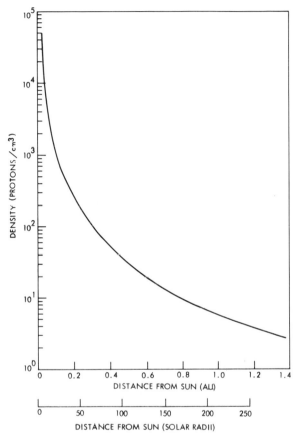

FIG. 1-5.   Density of solar wind as a function of distance from sun.

The emission of the solar wind from the Sun is apparently not spatially uniform, being greatest in the vicinity of disturbed regions. These regions are generally located between 5 and 35 deg of the solar equator. This also indicates that the solar wind may be largely confined to the region of the ecliptic plane. The spatial behavior of the solar wind in the vicinity of the Earth is of special interest. The geomagnetic field (approximately a dipole at right angles to the ecliptic plane) excludes the solar wind from a teardrop-shape region (the Chapman–Ferraro cavity) surrounding the Earth (the magnetosphere) [35]. Within this region the Earth's magnetic field is dominant; outside of it the Sun's magnetic field (carried by the solar wind) prevails. The magnetosphere varies from 8–12 Re (earth radii) on the sunward side, being compressed when the Sun is active and expanding when it is quiet. The tail of the magnetosphere probably extends for a hundred Re on the shadow side of the Earth. Additional details of the Chapman–Ferraro cavity are discussed in Chapter 3.

## D. Characteristics of Solar Flare Particulate Radiation

### 1. COMPOSITION

The solar flare particles are largely protons with important alpha particle and some heavier nuclear components as well. The proton component has been investigated by Ney *et al.* [36], Ogilvie *et al.* [37], Modisette *et al.* [38], Davis and Ogilvie [39], and others. In every case protons were found to be present in the solar particulate radiation. Tabulations of the proton fluxes received at 1 A.U. from flares over the last solar cycle (1954–1965) have been compiled by Webber [40], Lewis *et al.* [41], and others.

An important but variable alpha particle component has also been observed in solar flare particulate radiation. These alpha particles have been studied by Biswas *et al.* [42], McDonald [43], Yates [44], and others. The component is usually given as the flux above a certain energy per nucleon. On this basis, the component varies from $\sim 28\%$ (7/16/59) on down. For many flares, especially the early ones (before 1959), the component was not measured. However, if one compares the alpha particle flux with the proton flux on an energy per particle basis, the result is 0.8/1.0 [45]. (On an energy per nucleon basis, it is $\sim 0.8/4$, or $\sim 20\%$.)

It must be remembered that the analysis was based only on those events for which both proton and alpha particle fluxes were available. In addition, the assumption was made that the proton–alpha particle ratio did not change in the course of a flare. Since the comparison was carried out on a per-particle rather than a per-flare basis, the results were essentially determined by six large flares (May 10, 1959; July 10, 14, and 16, 1959; and November 12 and 15, 1960). All but one of these flares were multiple events which may have had anomalously large particle components. In any case, it seems probable that the alpha particle-proton ratio is approximately as large as the He-H ratio of the solar chromosphere ($\sim 10\%$).

The spectral lines of helium are observed to brighten an order of magnitude during a solar flare on the Sun [4], indicating that the He-H energy ratio in the chromosphere increases when the Sun is active. Thus it is not surprising that the fraction of alpha particles in flare radiation is considerably higher than in the solar wind. However, it is doubtful that the alpha particle-proton ratio would exceed the He-H ratio of the chromosphere. The minimum alpha particle energy (escape threshold) is probably about four times that for protons, and this probably accounts for surprisingly large alpha particle components on an energy per particle basis.

The presence of heavy nuclei in flare radiation has been reported by Fitchel and Guss [46], Ney and Stein [47], Biswas *et al.* [48], and others. The C, N, O group appears to constitute the major portion of these heavy nuclei, with Li, Be, and B being virtually absent. Nuclei heavier than oxygen are virtually absent also. The nuclei with $Z \geqslant 3$ constitute at most a small percentage of solar flare particulate radiation, probably less than 1%.

Electrons have been reported in solar flare radiation by Meyer and Vogt [49]. An equal number of electrons is believed to be emitted with the positively charged components as a sort of plasma cloud. However, the acceleration and propagation mechanisms believed responsible yield electron energies approximately 1/1836 those of the protons. While electrons may be considered as present in solar flare particulate radiation, their characteristics are not as well known as those of the protons and alpha particles.

## 2. ENERGY SPECTRA

The energy spectra of the particles emitted during many flares in the last solar cycle have been measured directly. In addition the observation of polar cap absorptions (PCA's) has yielded indirect information concerning the energy spectra. Investigations by Anderson *et al.* [50], Ehmert *et al.* [51], Winckler and Bhavsar [52], Ogilvie and Bryant [53], Ghielmetti [54], Stone [55], and others, have yielded a great deal of spectral energy information.

Unfortunately there are problems. The first is that each flare appears to have its own energy spectrum, and two apparently identical flares (as observed on the Sun) may have quite different particle energy spectra at 1 A.U. The interplanetary magnetic fields, the relative positions of the flare and the Earth, and previous flare history all appear to play a role.

The second problem is that the energy spectrum during any one flare is a function of time. The high-energy particles tend to arrive first, and disappear sooner than low-energy ones. Thus measurements which do not integrate over the duration of a flare must be identified by the actual time they were carried out.

In dealing with any energy spectrum, it is important to distinguish between integral energy spectra and differential energy spectra. An integral energy spectrum includes all particles of the type specified above a given energy. Thus

$$\phi_p(>10 \text{ Mev}) \quad \frac{\text{protons}}{\text{cm}^2}$$

represents all the protons above 10 Mev. A differential energy spectrum represents the number of particles per unit energy interval at the specified energy. Thus

$$\phi_p(10 \text{ Mev})dE \quad \frac{\text{protons}}{\text{cm}^2\text{-Mev}}$$

TABLE 1-2

SUMMARY OF SOLAR FLARE PROTON DATA FOR 1956–1961 INCLUSIVE[a]

| Year | $\hat{\phi}$[b] | | | $\int \phi$[c] | | |
|------|---------|---------|----------|---------|---------|----------|
|      | >10 Mev | >30 Mev | >100 Mev | >10 Mev | >30 Mev | >100 Mev |
| 1956 | $1.0(10^4)$ | $8.0(10^3)$ | $5.1(10^3)$ | $1.8(10^9)$ | $1.0(10^9)$ | $3.5(10^8)$ |
| 1957 | — | — | — | — | — | — |
| 1958 | $3.3(10^4)$ | $5.2(10^3)$ | $3.2(10^2)$ | $6.6(10^9)$ | $7.2(10^8)$ | $2.4(10^7)$ |
| 1959 | $1.13(10^5)$ | $2.6(10^4)$ | $4.9(10^3)$ | $2.1(10^{10})$ | $4.2(10^9)$ | $4.5(10^8)$ |
| 1960 | $5.6(10^4)$ | $2.2(10^4)$ | $5.3(10^3)$ | $6.8(10^9)$ | $2.0(10^9)$ | $3.7(10^8)$ |
| 1961 | $1.2(10^4)$ | $3.2(10^3)$ | $1.5(10^2)$ | $1.6(10^9)$ | $3.5(10^8)$ | $4.3(10^7)$ |
| Total | $2.2(10^5)$ | $6.4(10^4)$ | $1.6(10^4)$ | $3.8(10^{10})$ | $8.3(10^9)$ | $1.24(10^9)$ |

[a] Only those events for which the majority of data available. These events were

| | | | |
|---|---|---|---|
| 2/23/56 | 9/22/58 | 4/28/60 | 11/20/60 |
| 3/23/58 | 5/10/59 | 5/4/60 | 7/11/61 |
| 7/7/58 | 7/10/59 | 6/13/60 | 7/12/61 |
| 8/16/58 | 7/14/59 | 9/3/60 | 7/18/61 |
| 8/22/58 | 7/16/59 | 11/12/60 | 7/20/61 |
| 8/26/58 | 4/1/60 | 11/15/60 | 9/28/61 |

[b] $\hat{\phi} > E$ is the peak flux rate (protons/cm$^2$-sec) above energy $E$.

[c] $\int \phi > E$ is the total flux (protons/cm$^2$) above energy $E$.

represents the number of protons whose energies are within an energy band of width $dE$ at 10 Mev. The energy derivative of the integral energy spectrum yields the corresponding differential type.

It is possible to obtain a typical energy spectrum for a large flare by averaging the results for a number of flares. In Table 1-2 the peak flux rates and total fluxes are given for the years 1956–1961. It will be noticed that these are integral energy spectra, since the fluxes refer to the number of protons above energies of 10, 30, and 100 Mev. It is seen that for these six years, the total number of protons above 10 Mev was about 4.1 times that above 30 Mev, and about 30.6 times that above 100 Mev. This yields an approximate $E^{-1.5}$ energy dependence. Thus large flares have been observed to yield protons which have an average $E^{-1.5}$ integral energy spectrum [56] ($\sim E^{-2.5}$ differential energy spectrum).

This sort of analysis does not agree well with results reported by many authors. Integral energy spectra in the $E^{-2}$–$E^{-4}$ range are usually obtained instead. The discrepancy lies in the anomalous behavior of the protons associated with the 2/23/56 flare. The protons associated with this flare exhibited an approximate $E^{-0.7}$ integral energy spectrum, and, they constituted about 28% of the protons above 100 Mev. Thus the statistics are insufficient to obtain typical proton energy spectra for events with such widely varying characteristics.

Many authors [40, 57] prefer to express the integral spectrum as an exponential function of rigidity rather than as a power function of energy. Thus the proton spectra are written

$$\phi_p(> P) = \phi_0 \exp[-P/Po] \qquad (1.2)$$

where $\phi_0$ is the total proton flux for the event (protons/cm$^2$); $P$ the rigidity (Mv/nucleon); and $Po$ the characteristic rigidity for the solar event. Rigidity ($P$) is related to energy ($E$) by the relationship:

$$P = \frac{1}{Ze}\sqrt{E^2 + 2M_0C^2E} \qquad (1.3)$$

where $Ze$ is the charge on the particle, and $M_0$ the rest mass of the particles. Thus for low-energy paricles the rigidity is proportional to $\sqrt{E}$ while in cases of high energy the rigidity is proportional to $E$. Rigidity is a measure of how easily a particle is deflected by a magnetic field. The relationship between

TABLE 1-3

PARTICLE FLUXES (PARTICLES/CM$^2$) FOR NINE LARGE SOLAR EVENTS

| Event | Protons | | | Alpha particles | | |
|---|---|---|---|---|---|---|
| | $\int\phi > 10$ Mev | $\int\phi > 30$ Mev | $\int\phi > 100$ Mev | $\int\phi > 40$ Mev | $\int\phi > 120$ Mev | $\int\phi > 400$ Mev |
| 3/23/58 | $2 \times 10^9$ | $2.5 \times 10^8$ | $1 \times 10^7$ | $8.5 \times 10^7$ | $7 \times 10^6$ | $8 \times 10^4$ |
| 5/10/59 | $5.5 \times 10^9$ | $9.6 \times 10^8$ | $8.5 \times 10^7$ | $7.5 \times 10^8$ | $4.2 \times 10^7$ | $3.5 \times 10^5$ |
| 7/10/59 | $4.5 \times 10^9$ | $1.0 \times 10^9$ | $1.4 \times 10^8$ | $1.6 \times 10^8$ | $2.4 \times 10^7$ | $5 \times 10^5$ |
| 7/14/59 | $7.5 \times 10^9$ | $1.3 \times 10^9$ | $1.0 \times 10^8$ | $1.3 \times 10^9$ | $8 \times 10^7$ | $7 \times 10^5$ |
| 7/16/59 | $3.3 \times 10^9$ | $9.1 \times 10^8$ | $1.3 \times 10^8$ | $7.5 \times 10^8$ | $1.2 \times 10^8$ | $6 \times 10^6$ |
| 9/3/60 | $9 \times 10^7$ | $3.5 \times 10^7$ | $7 \times 10^6$ | $1 \times 10^6$ | $3.6 \times 10^5$ | $4 \times 10^4$ |
| 11/12/60 | $4 \times 10^9$ | $1.3 \times 10^9$ | $2.5 \times 10^8$ | $4 \times 10^8$ | $1.2 \times 10^8$ | $1.1 \times 10^7$ |
| 11/15/60 | $2.5 \times 10^9$ | $7.2 \times 10^8$ | $1.2 \times 10^8$ | $3.8 \times 10^8$ | $9 \times 10^7$ | $6.5 \times 10^6$ |
| 7/18/61 | $1 \times 10^9$ | $3 \times 10^8$ | $4 \times 10^7$ | $3 \times 10^7$ | $5.5 \times 10^6$ | $4 \times 10^5$ |
| Total | $3.04 \times 10^{10}$ | $6.78 \times 10^9$ | $8.82 \times 10^8$ | $3.86 \times 10^9$ | $4.88 \times 10^8$ | $2.15 \times 10^7$ |

kinetic energy and rigidity for protons and $A = 2Z$ nuclei is shown in Fig. 1-6.

If the energy spectra of solar flare protons are expressed as a rigidity exponential, the values of $Po$ range from 56 (9/29/57 and 7/12/61) to 195 (2/23/56) [40]. A $Po$ of about 100 Mv (million volts) is fairly characteristic.

However, the use of a rigidity exponential has its limitations also. The particle fluxes for most events are too high for low energies ($E \lesssim 10$ Mev) and high energies ($E \gtrsim 500$) to be fit by an exponential. These are just the

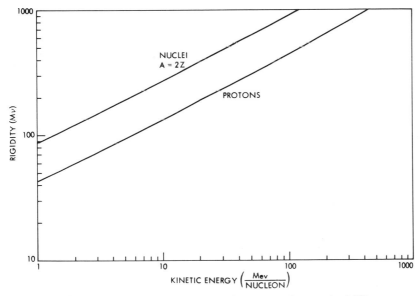

FIG. 1-6.   Relationship between kinetic energy and magnetic rigidity.

energy regions where a power law spectrum errs in the opposite direction. Both approaches require modification to include the time dependence of the energy spectrum.

Studies of the alpha particle energy spectra show that they have essentially the same shape as the proton spectra [45, 58]. The integral fluxes for protons and alpha particles observed in nine events are listed in Table 1-3. If these are plotted on an energy per particle basis, it is seen that the two spectra have essentially the same shape over the range concerned (Fig. 1-7). If peak

TABLE 1-4

PEAK FLUX RATES (PARTICLES/CM²-SEC) FOR NINE LARGE SOLAR EVENTS

| Event | Protons | | | Alpha particles | | |
|---|---|---|---|---|---|---|
| | $\phi > 10$ Mev | $\phi > 30$ Mev | $\phi > 100$ Mev | $\phi > 40$ Mev | $\phi > 120$ Mev | $\phi > 400$ Mev |
| 3/23/58 | 8000 | 1200 | 100 | 420 | 60 | 1.2 |
| 5/10/59 | 30,000 | 6000 | 1000 | 5000 | 500 | 5 |
| 7/10/59 | 15,000 | 4000 | 1200 | 800 | 160 | 5 |
| 7/14/59 | 50,000 | 10,000 | 1200 | 10,000 | 1000 | 10 |
| 7/16/59 | 18,000 | 6000 | 1500 | 5000 | 1500 | 100 |
| 9/30/60 | 450 | 200 | 60 | 6 | 3 | 0.4 |
| 11/12/60 | 32,000 | 12,000 | 2500 | 4000 | 1500 | 180 |
| 11/15/60 | 22,000 | 8000 | 2400 | 4200 | 1500 | 160 |
| 7/18/61 | 7000 | 2500 | 60 | 280 | 100 | 11 |
| Total | 182,450 | 49,900 | 10,020 | 29,706 | 6323 | 472.6 |

fluxes for these same events (Table 1-4) are compared, the same conclusion is reached.

It will be noted that the energy spectral shape is appreciably steeper for these nine events than for the twenty-five which were included in the Table 1-2 totals. The proton-alpha particle comparisons could only be carried out using those events for which both alpha particle and proton data were

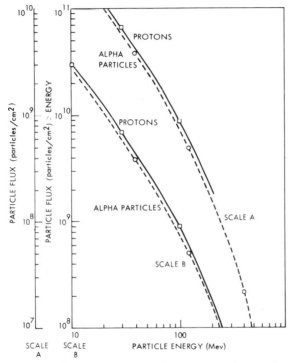

FIG. 1-7. Relationship between solar flare proton and α-particle spectra.

available. For the event of 2/23/56, no alpha particle data were available, so it was omitted here.

Very little spectral energy information is available for the heavier nuclei ($Z \geqslant 3$). What little is available suggests that on an energy per nucleon basis these nuclei have a spectrum similar in shape to those for protons and alpha particles.

### 3.  TIME BEHAVIOR

The time behavior of the particulate radiation associated with solar flares has received considerable attention. The increase in the counting rate of detectors designed to measure galactic (cosmic) radiation has been studied by Firor [59], Brode and Goodwin [60], Lockwood *et al.* [61], Winckler [62], Anderson [63], Towle and Lockwood [64], and others. It has been found that there is a fairly typical time history for the particles associated with a flare. This time history (which is energy-dependent) is illustrated in Fig. 1-8. It is seen that three intervals characterize this history.

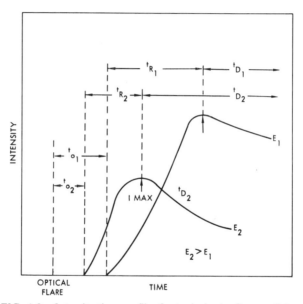

FIG. 1-8.   Intensity-time profiles for typical solar flare particles.

The onset-delay time is defined as the time from the maximum of the visible flare intensity (on the Sun) to the arrival of the particles at the detector. At 1 A.U. this onset-delay time varies considerably from event to event. Values as low as a few minutes have been observed for relativistic particles associated with some events to several hours for low-energy particles in other events. The rise time is the time interval between the first arrival of particles of a particular energy and the time at which the flux of these particles reaches its maximum intensity. This rise time is also strongly event- and energy-dependent, the high-energy particles having shorter rise times. At 1 A.U. the rise times vary from a few minutes (high-energy particles in some events) to several hours (low-energy particles in others).

The decay time is that time between maximum flux intensity and the disappearance of particles of a given energy. This is also strongly event- and energy-dependent. A considerable body of evidence indicates that the decay time varies exponentially, so that a characteristic decay time is usually used instead. This is the time for the particle flux at a given energy to decrease by a factor of $e$. At 1 A.U. the characteristic decay times vary from a few hours (high energies, some events) to a few days (low energies, other events).

Investigation shows that these three times (onset-delay, rise, characteristic decay) are strongly related. Events with short onset-delay times have short rise and short characteristic decay times, and the converse. This in turn correlates well with particle energy spectra, since events with short times have a large fraction of high-energy particles. Also, particles whose behavior is characterized by short times are generally associated with flares in the western portion of the Sun. This is undoubtedly determined by inter-planetary propagation mechanisms.

The first systematic attempt to construct a model for the nuclear radiation observed at the Earth due to a solar flare was made by Bailey in 1962 [65]. He correlated the radio PCA (polar cap absorption) data available with direct balloon, rocket, and satellite radiation measurements to arrive at a time history for the protons emitted during a typical large event. A cross-plot of the integral proton energy spectra obtained in this way is shown in Fig. 1-9.

The curves of Fig. 1-9 may be approximately fitted by the expression [66]

$$\phi(E > E_0, t) = \frac{1 \times 10^{10}\, t \, \exp[-8 \times 10^{-4} E_0 t]}{E_0^2} \tag{1.4}$$

where $\phi(E > E_0, t)$ is the flux of protons with energies above $E_0$ emitted as a function of time (protons/cm²-hr); $t$ the time since event began (hr); and $E_0$ the particle energy (Mev).

Integration of the above expression with respect to time yields the integral energy spectrum for the entire event:

$$\phi(E > E_0) = \frac{1.56 \times 10^{16}}{E_0^4} \tag{1.5}$$

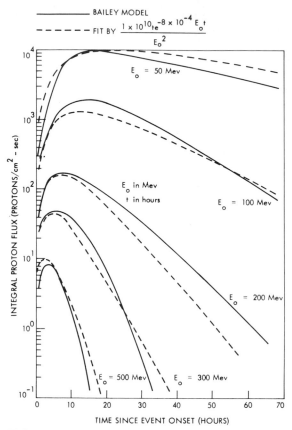

FIG. 1-9.   Time-energy fit for Bailey's model flare particles.

where $\phi(E > E_0)$ is in units of protons/cm$^2$. Differentiation of Eq. (1.4) with respect to energy yields

$$\phi(E, t) \, dE = 1 \times 10^{10} \exp[-8 \times 10^{-4} t] \left( \frac{8 \times 10^{-4} Et + 2}{E^3} \right) dE \quad (1.6)$$

where $\phi(E, t) \, dE$ is the proton flux (protons/cm$^2$-hr-Mev). The corresponding derivative of Eq (1.5) is

$$\phi(E) \, dE = \frac{6.25 \times 10^{16} \, dE}{E^5} \quad (1.7)$$

with $\phi(E) \, dE$ in units of protons/cm$^2$-Mev.

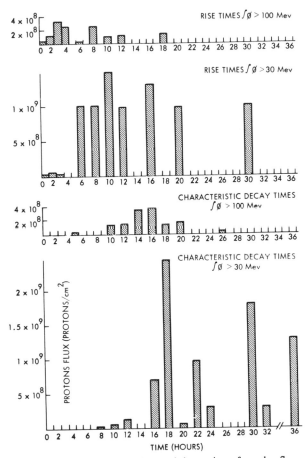

FIG. 1-10.   Size-weighted rise and decay times for solar flares.

Both Eq. (1.5) (the integral spectrum) and Eq. (1.7) (the differential energy spectrum) fit the corresponding spectra derived from Bailey's spectra very well. The Bailey model is for a very large event ($\sim 10^{10}$ protons/cm$^2$ > 30 Mev), and no single event of this magnitude has been observed. The characteristics of events which have been observed have been tabulated by Webber [40]. The rise and characteristic decay time distributions from his compilation are shown in Fig. 1-10. While many of the smaller events do not show up in Fig. 1-10, it is the large events which are of major concern in space radiation shielding. The weighted rise and decay times are

|               | $\int \phi > 30$ Mev | $\int \phi > 100$ Mev |
|---------------|----------------------|-----------------------|
| Rise time     | 12 hr                | 7 hr                  |
| Decay time    | 25 h                 | 15 hr                 |

By combining the results of Table 1-2 (which shows a $E^{-1.55}$ time integrated spectrum and a $E^{-1.15}$ behavior of the peak flux rates) with the above information, it is possible to fit the average behavior of the large events by an expression of the form.

$$\phi(E > E_0, t) = \frac{At \, \exp[-0.022E_0^{0.4t}]}{E_0^{0.75}} \qquad (1.8)$$

where $t$ is time (hr) and $E$ is energy (Mev). $A$ is a normalization constant related to the size of the event by the expression

$$\phi(E > E_0) = \frac{2100 \, A}{E_0^{1.55}} \quad (p/cm^2) \qquad (1.9)$$

The corresponding differential energy spectra may be obtained from Eqs. (1.8) and (1.9). The rise and decay times for the protons above various energy thresholds are given by the expressions

$$t_{rise} = \frac{45}{E^{0.4}} \quad hr \qquad (1.10)$$

$$\tau_{decay} = \frac{100}{E^{0.4}} \quad hr = 2.15 t_{rise}$$

Again, at least a portion of the difference between the Bailey model event and this analysis is due to the nontypical behavior of the event of 2/23/56.

It must be emphasized that these relationships are only the size-weighted averages, and many deviations are found. In addition, all of the measurements on which these relationships are based were at essentially 1 A.U. The characteristics of the particulate radiation associated with future solar flares will undoubtedly exhibit large variances, but upon analysis will hopefully yield similar size-weighted averages.

Another aspect of the time behavior of solar flare particulate radiation deals with the prediction of these events. Legrand [67], Dodson and Hedeman [68], Goedeke and Masley [69], Weddell [70], Malitson [71], and others have sought correlation between observables and the appearance of solar flare particles. These correlations are of two types—cyclical (long-term) prediction and event (short-term) prediction.

The cyclical prediction is fairly straightforward. Since sunspots occur in nearly 11-year cycles and apparently flares do also, it is almost certain that solar particulate radiation associated with flares follows an 11-year cycle. The data of Table 1-2 show this effect clearly. The maximum Mev particle fluxes received 1959–1960 were an order of magnitude above those received in 1956 and in 1961. Since the Wolf sunspot number varies approximately $1\frac{1}{2}$ orders of magnitude from solar maximum to solar minimum, it is probable that the solar particulate radiation does also.

There is an element of uncertainty concerning the magnitude of future solar cycles. The amplitudes of the past three cycles (as judged by sunspot data) have been increasing, but this trend cannot continue forever. Webber [72], Minnis [73], and others have analyzed past solar data to predict that the amplitude of the next cycle should be comparable to the 1954–1965 cycle, or perhaps somewhat smaller. For shielding studies, the past solar cycle is usually used as a model for future cycles.

Another important cycle is the roughly 27-day solar rotation as seen from the Earth. Sunspot groups have been observed to endure for a few solar revolutions, and recurrent Mev protons with a 27-day period have been observed at earth. While flares do not last for anything like 27 days, the particulate radiation emitted seems to act like a plasma cloud spiraling out from the Sun. If the emission of this cloud takes place over a period of around 27 days, it will intercept the earth each time it comes around. This phenomenon is not common, but flare particles on a given day make flare particles about 27 days later more probable than would otherwise be the case.

It is the event prediction which is of great interest for short-term (month-long) space missions. Within the Earth's magnetosphere the solar flare particulate radiation poses little danger except for positions near the poles, but for deep space missions the particles associated with large solar flares constitute a hazard to reckon with. A good analogy may be found in weather prediction. For northern latitudes, it is relatively safe to predict snow in January (cyclical prediction), but more difficult to predict whether it will snow, and how much, the week of January fifteenth (event prediction).

Analysis indicates a 14 to 35-day prediction can be made by observing the behavior of calcium plages on the Sun. The older, brighter, and larger a calcium plage is, the greater the probability a flare will occur. An analysis by Weddell [70] has yielded the following correlations:

| Expectation | All flares (at least $10^{-4}$ solar disk) | Flares at old plage |
|---|---|---|
| *S* (correct) | 0.674 | 0.901 |
| *SF* (false alarm) | 0.163 | 0.049 |
| *So* (not predicted) | 0.163 | 0.049 |

It is seen that a very good correlation exists between old plages (one that made at least one solar disk passage before the occurrence of the flare associated with it) and flares.

Observation (by Zeeman splitting of spectral lines) of the magnetically active region of the sun may be useful in predicting a flare 3–10 days in advance. The larger the area over which the magnetic field is present, the stronger the field, and the longer it lasts, the greater the probability of a flare. Weddell's analysis showed that if a magnetic field of 2–10 gauss existed for 7 or more days and extended over $\gtrsim 10^{-4}$ of the solar disk, a flare within 0.1 disk radius was highly probable. By combining the calcium plage observations with magnetic field observations, it is apparently possible to predict the Class 2 and above flares 78% of the time.

Shorter-term (approximately 7 days) predictions can apparently be made by observing magnetic null points on the solar disk. Small Forbush-type decreases in sea level neutron monitors also have been correlated with solar flares. In both cases the probability of being correct is apparently less than for plage observation.

Very-short-term predictions of the arrival of solar flare radiation in the vicinity of the Earth (in hours) can be made by monitoring the Type IV rf emission from the Sun, the polar cap absorption of galactic rf noise, and the Hα optical emission associated with the flare directly. These phenomena all indicate that a flare has taken place and that emission of particulate radiation from the sun has also probably occurred. However, the amount of the radiation and the probability it will reach the Earth can be estimated from the magnitude of these other effects and the location of the flare on the Sun. A large bright flare (e.g., 3+) near the west limb of the Sun will most probably result in a sizable flux of particles at the Earth, while for a small dim flare (e.g., 1 or 2−) near the east limb, the arrival of any particles is improbable. Similar correlations exist between the particle fluxes and the rf noise and polar cap absorptions. These effects are discussed in Section E.

## 4. SPATIAL DEPENDENCE

Our knowledge of the spatial dependence of the solar flare particulate radiation is quite limited. All of the measurements have been made in the ecliptic plane, and essentially at 1 A.U. In addition, very few measurements are available outside the geomagnetosphere. Therefore, our current concepts of such spatial dependence are quite uncertain.

Anderson [74] reported on the solar flare particles measured by the Mariner II (Venus) space probe, and Arnoldy et al. [75] observed solar particulate radiation via Pioneer V at distances of $5 \times 10^6$ km from the Earth (0.03 A.U.). More recent deep space probes had very little to observe.

The propagation of solar flare particles through space, which controls spatial dependence, has been investigated theoretically by Meyer et al. [76], Warwick [77], Parker [78], Gold [79], and others. A plasma cloud either contained in a magnetic bottle (the Gold model) or a shock wave (the Parker model) is generally assumed. Both models yield the result that the various time periods (delay-onset, rise, and characteristic decay) increase at least linearly with distance from the Sun. In addition, the total particle flux for corresponding points along the path of the plasma cloud decreases approximately linearly (if the cloud stays in the plane of the ecliptic) or quadratically (if the cloud expands equally in all directions) as a function of the distance from the Sun.

Another spatial dependence of interest is the degree of anisotropy in the solar flare particles. Relatively little information is available on this, and what is, is confusing. Raymes [80] has studied it, coming to the conclusion that a decreasing amount of anisotropy does exist during the rise time. Since the high-energy particles are relatively more important during the rise time, orientation of a space vehicle with the thick portions in the direction of arrival of the particles may effect a significant reduction in the radiation exposure of its occupants. However, the degree of anisotropy varies considerably from event to event, and for many events it amounts to a small percentage.

## E.    Effects of Solar Particulate Radiation on Earth

### 1.    MAGNETIC DISTURBANCES

The magnetic field at the surface of the Earth is $\sim 0.3$ gauss near the equator. When measured with sensitive instruments, it is observed to exhibit several kinds of fluctuations [81]. There are small—$\leqslant 1$ gamma (1 gauss = $10^5$ gammas)—fluctuations with time constants $\sim 0.1$ sec called micropulsations. Somewhat larger and slower are the geomagnetic pulsations, which have amplitudes of $\leqslant 10$ gammas and time constants of $\sim 1$ sec to $\sim 1$ min. Still larger are giant micropulsations which are observed in auroral zones, most frequently at midnight.

These magnetic disturbances are generally attributed to hydromagnetic waves in the solar wind [18]. As the boundaries of the Chapman–Ferraro cavity are disturbed, this disturbance affects the trapped radiation (Van Allen belts) inside. Disturbances of these charged particles are believed responsible for these micropulsations in the Earth's magnetic field.

Occasionally a large (a few hundred gammas) disturbance will be observed in the geomagnetic field. Such disturbances begin suddenly, are usually observed over the entire Earth, and often last for a few days. Associated with solar flares (which they follow by 1–2 days), these magnetic storms exhibit three rather distinct phases. During the initial phase, the horizontal component of the geomagnetic field increases 10–50 gammas. After several hours, it returns to its prestorm value. It continues to decrease to $\sim 50$–500 gammas below its prestorm value during this main phase, which generally lasts for roughly 1 day. Then there is a 1–3 day recovery period as the field gradually increases to its normal values.

The correlation of this behavior with that of the solar wind associated with a solar flare is fairly obvious, and has led to the postulation of a ring current by Stormer [82] and others. This is a hypothetical current of $\sim 10^6$ amp located at $\sim 8$ Re which builds up and dies out to account for the observed fluctuations in the geomagnetic field. While there is some evidence for the existence of this ring current, attempts to probe it directly have been inconclusive [81]. In any event, the geomagnetic storms are directly related to solar disturbances, especially flares. A list of these geomagnetic storms and the flares they were associated with is given in Table 1-1 of this chapter.

## 2. POLAR CAP ABSORPTIONS

The ionosphere is a portion of the Earth's upper atmosphere extending in altitude from ~50 to 1000 km. In this region, at least a portion of the atoms are ionized at all times, and these ions form an absorbing layer for radio frequency waves below the vhf range. The spatial extent and degree of ionization increase during daylight due to photoionization.

In order to measure the ionic density (ions/cm$^2$) vertically through the ionosphere, an instrument called the riometer (relative ionospheric opacity meter) has been developed [83]. This is essentially a broad band receiver which measures the galactic noise picked up in a simple antenna. As the ionization increases, the galactic noise received decreases.

Studies of riometer measurements of the Earth's ionosphere have been made during solar disturbances by Bailey [84], Collins *et al.* [85], Rose and Ziauddin [86], Reid [87], and others. Because of the geomagnetic field, the ionospheric effects associated with solar activity are greatest in the polar regions of the Earth. These polar cap absorptions (PCA) have been used extensively to investigate the radiations associated with solar disturbances.

The time history of a PCA generally begins with a SID (sudden ionospheric disturbance) a few hours after the observance of a solar flare. This SID signifies the arrival of the first particles emitted from the Sun. The spatial extent and the density of ionization increase during the rise time of the solar particulate radiation, and gradually die out with the same characteristic decay time after the maximum is reached.

The relationships between the PCA characteristics and the solar particulate radiations have been studied by Michel and Dessler [88] Parthasarathy and Venkatesan [89], Van Allen *et al.* [90], Kundu and Haddock [91], Davis *et al.* [92], and others. There is agreement that the density of ionization is directly related to the flux, and that the spatial extent is a function of the energy spectrum. A simple relationship obtained by Davis *et al.*, is

$$\phi(>E) = 6.6 \, A^2 \qquad (1.11)$$

where $\phi(>E)$ is the instantaneous flux (particles/cm$^2$-sec-ster) above the geomagnetic cutoff energy (Mev), and $A$ is riometer absorption (db).

A list of PCA's observed on Earth is included in Table 1-1. It was from details of such PCA events that Bailey [65] postulated the time energy history of the first model proton event.

3.  GALACTIC RADIATION EFFECTS

The galactic (cosmic) radiation consists of a low flux ($\sim 4$ particles/cm²-sec) of protons and bare nuclei with a very high energy ($\sim 10^2$–$10^{12}$ Mev). This radiation originates beyond the solar system; it has been studied for over fifty years. At first it was thought that the high-energy solar particle radiation was a component of cosmic radiation, but investigations within last twenty years have revealed the differences. The compositions, energies, source and acceleration mechanisms, and time behaviors for solar flare particles and galactic particles are different (see Chapter II).

This galactic radiation is affected by solar activity at 1 A.U. Such effects of solar activity are greater closer to the Sun, and presumably decrease to zero beyond the solar system.

The first effect of solar activity is to decrease the flux of galactic radiation. This behavior is most noticeable at the low end of the galactic energy spectrum ($\lesssim 1$ Bev). There is close to a factor of 2 variation associated with the 11-year solar cycle, a tiny percentage of variation (sometimes) associated with the 27-day solar rotation, and a $\lesssim 30\%$ decrease which lasts for a few days associated with solar flares (the Forbush effect). All of these solar influences on the galactic radiation are out of phase with the Sun's activity— the more active the Sun, the more the galactic radiation at the Earth is decreased. Considering the energy of galactic radiation ($\sim 10^2$–$10^{12}$ Mev), the fact that the Sun's activity can influence it at all is remarkable. These effects are discussed in more detail in Chapter III.

4.  VAN ALLEN BELT EFFECTS

The Van Allen belts consist of electrons and protons trapped in the geomagnetic field. They occupy a distorted toroid volume of space about the Earth extending from an altitude of a few hundred kilometers to the geomagnetosphere (the Chapman–Ferraro cavity). They largely lie in a region within 30 deg of the geomagnetic equator.

These Van Allen belts are spatially distorted by the solar wind, which presses upon the geomagnetosphere. When the Sun is quiet, the geomagnetosphere extends to 12 Re on the sunward side of the earth; when the Sun is active, the geomagnetosphere is compressed to $\sim 8$ Re. As might be expected, the compression of these radiation belts is not uniform, the outer portions ($r \gtrsim 3$ Re) being compressed more than the inner ($r \lesssim 3$ Re).

The Van Allen belts are apparently populated to some extent by the solar

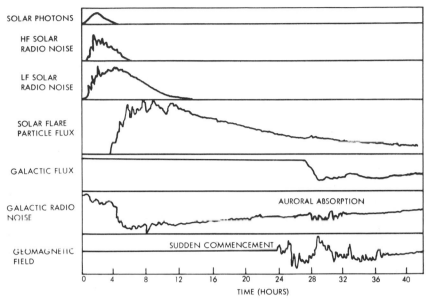

FIG. 1-11.  Schematic showing effects of a solar flare observed at Earth.

radiation. Two mechanisms may play a role. The first is that neutrons due to interactions between the solar flare protons and the Earth's atmosphere may be ejected upward to decay to an electron and a proton in the trapped radiation belts. The second proposed mechanism is that the solar flare particle plasma may sufficiently distort the geomagnetic field to allow some of this plasma to spill into the geomagnetosphere at the poles. This effect may be the source of the polar aurora observed after solar flares. These effects are discussed further in Chapter III.

An overall picture of the effects of the Sun's activity on the Earth may be seen in Fig. 1-11 [2]. It is seen that while the electromagnetic radiation associated with a solar flare has a duration of only a few hours, the particulate radiation and the effects it produces may persist for days.

## F.  Theories of Solar Particulate Radiation

### 1.  THE SOLAR WIND

An early model of the corona and the solar wind was proposed by Chapman [93], [94]. Chapman showed that thermal conduction associated with the coulomb forces in the corona would produce a specific static temperature distribution. From this a model corona was produced which revealed the extent of that portion of the Sun. Chapman's model yielded a density of 300 protons/cm$^3$ and a temperature of $2 \times 10^5$ °K for the solar wind near the Earth.

A more refined model based upon hydrodynamic streaming was proposed by Parker [95]. This model is based upon a particular solution of the fluid equations with an assumed temperature distribution which implied the existence of an approximate heat source. Such a model yielded a supersonic solar wind of 300–500 km/sec at 1 A.U.

Modifications of the Parker model have been proposed by Chamberlin [96] and Noble and Scarf [97]. The former obtained a subsonic solution to the fluid equations (the solar breeze); the latter, a supersonic solution. Comparisons with measurements seem to favor the self-consistent supersonic model.

Without delving into the details of the theories, it can be pointed out that the directed velocities follow a spiral path away from the Sun due to the 27-day solar rotation period. The anomalous behavior of the solar wind during and after solar flares is believed due to perturbations in the interplanetary solar magnetic field.

## 2. SOLAR FLARES

There appears to be general agreement that the charged particle radiation emitted during or after a solar flare consists of a relativistic and a nonrelativistic portion. The former is smaller, more directional, and arrives first. These are the time-of-flight particles which are responsible for the early time-peaking of the high-energy particles. The nonrelativistic portion consists of a nonequilibrium plasma cloud which expands to several solar diameters as it migrates away from the Sun.

The particle fluxes observed by a detector inside this plasma cloud are essentially isotropic, and these particles constitute the larger portion of the total solar flare radiation. However, occasionally the Earth will receive only one of these two portions of the solar flare radiation, and probably many of the variations in the energy and time histories of different flares are due to differing proportions of these relativistic and nonrelativistic particles.

The detailed mechanisms by which the nonrelativistic plasma cloud is held together are not known. There are two leading theories concerning this mechanism—the Gold [79] "magnetic bottle" model and the Parker [98] "kink" or blast-wave theory. The magnetic bottle model assumes a distension of the solar bipolar fields, resulting in a perturbation looking like a large blown balloon of bubble gum (see Fig. 1-12). The kink model is based on an abrupt dislocation of a uniform field akin to a jostling of a rotary lawn sprinkler. Both agree fairly well with measurements. If measurements could be made of solar flare radiations and associated magnetic fields at various positions around the Sun, it should be possible to determine if either of these theories is correct.

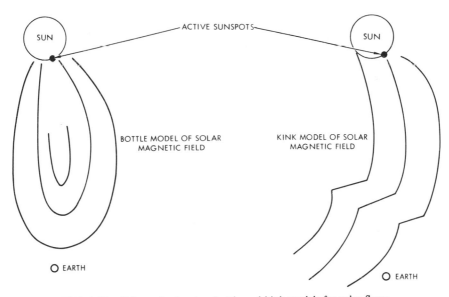

FIG. 1-12. Schematic showing bottle and kink models for solar flares.

These two models describe how the nonequilibrium plasma cloud produced during a solar flare might be held together as it migrates away from the sun. Theories pertaining to the mechanisms by which this plasma cloud is produced often involve assuming an acceleration mechanism which breaks off a portion of the chromosphere [99]. Hydromagnetic shock mechanisms which account for the observed solar Type IV radio noise and X-ray emission seem especially interesting. Unfortunately our understanding of solar dynamics must improve before we can remove major uncertainties as to why and how solar flares originate.

## REFERENCES

1. S. E. Forbush, Three Unusual Cosmic Ray Increases Possibly Due to Charged Particles from the Sun, *Phys. Rev.* **70,** 771 (1946).
2. W. P. Saylor, D. E. Winer, C. J. Eiwen, and A. W. Carriker, Space Radiation Guide, Rept. AMRL-TDR-62–86, Biomed. Lab., U.S. Air Force, Wright Patterson Air Force Base, Columbus, Ohio (1962).
3. H. J. Smith and E. V. P. Smith, "Solar Flares." Macmillan, New York, 1963.
4. A. B. Severny, Solar Flares, *Ann. Rev. Astron. Astrophys.* **2,** 363 (1964).
5. W. N. Hess (ed.), *AAS-NASA Symposium on the Physics of Solar Flares*, NASA-SP-50 (1964).
6. R. Howard, On the Relation of Major Solar Flares with Changes in Sunspot Areas, *Astrophys. J.* **138,** 1312 (1963).
7. H. Dodson and E. R. Hedeman, The Frequency and Positions of Flares within Three Active Sunspot Areas, *Astrophys. J.* **110,** 242 (1949).
8. J. P. Wild, S. F. Smerd, and A. A. Weiss, Solar Bursts, *Ann. Rev. Astron. Astrophys.* **1,** 291 (1963).
9. A. R. Thompson and A. Maxwell, Solar Radio Bursts and Low Energy Cosmic Rays, *Nature* **185,** 89 (1960).
10. A. D. Fokker, Type IV Solar Radio Emission, *Space Sci. Rev.* **2,** 70 (1963).
11. M. K. Das Gupta and D. Basu, Solar Radio Bursts in Relation to Flare Importance, *Astrophys. J.* **137,** 997 (1963).
12. L. E. Peterson and J. R. Winckler, Gamma Ray Bursts from a Solar Flare, *J. Geophys. Res.* **64,** 697 (1959).
13. H. J. Smith, Solar Perturbations of the Space Environment, *Second Symp. Protection against Radiations in Space*, p. 41, NASA-SP-71 (1964).
14. J. P. Conner, W. D. Evans, M. D. Montgomery, S. Singer, and E. E. Stogsdill, Solar Flare X-Ray Emission Measurement, *in*: "Space Research" (H. C. Van de Hulst, ed.), Vol. V, North-Holland Publ., Amsterdam, 1965.
15. K. A. Anderson, Energetic Solar Particles, *in*: "Space Physics" (D. P. LeGalley and A. Rosen, eds.), Chapt. 16. Wiley, New York, 1964.
16. M. Neugebauer and C. W. Snyder, The Mission of Mariner 2—Preliminary Observations, Solar Plasma Experiment, *Science* **138,** 1095 (1962).
17. M. Neugebauer and C. W. Snyder, Solar Wind Measurements near Venus, *J. Geophys. Res.* **70,** 1587, 1965.
18. W. Bernstein, The Solar Plasma—Its Detection, Measurement, and Significance, *in*: "Space Physics" (D. P. LeGalley and A. Rosen, eds.), Chapt. 11. Wiley, New York, 1964.
19. E. N. Parker, The Solar Wind, Radio Propagation, *J. Res Natl. Bur. Std.* **65**d, 537 (1961).
20. K. I. Gringauz, Some Results of Experiments in Interplanetary Space by Means of Charged Particle Traps on Soviet Space Probes, *in*: "Space Research" (H. C. Van de Hulst, ed.), Vol. II. North-Holland Publ., Amsterdam, 1961.
21. H. S. Bridge, C. Dilworth, B. Rossi, and F. Schub, An Instrument for the Investigation of Interplanetary Plasma, *J. Geophys. Res.* **65,** 3053 (1960).
22. W. I. Axford, A. J. Dessler, and B. Gottlieb, Termination of Solar Wind and Solar Magnetic Field, *Astrophys. J.* **137,** 1268 (1963).

23. D. E. Osterbrock, A Study of Two Comet Tails, *Astrophys. J.* **128**, 95 (1958).

24. D. Antrack, L. Biermann, and R. H. Lust, Some Statistical Properties of Comets with Plasma Tails, *Ann. Rev. Astron. Astrophys.* **2**, 327 (1964).

25. W. I. Axford, The Interaction between the Solar Wind and the Earth's Magnetosphere, *J. Geophys. Res.* **67**, 3791 (1962).

26. R. J. Slutz and J. R. Winkelman, Shape of the Magnetospheric Boundary under Solar Wind Pressure, *J. Geophys. Res.* **69**, 4933 (1964).

27. S. Chapman, Aurora and Geomagnetic Storms, *in*: "Space Physics" (D. P. Le-Galley and A. Rosen, eds.), Chapt. 7. Wiley, New York, 1964.

28. E. J. Smith, Interplanetary Magnetic Fields, *in*: "Space Physics" (D. P. LeGalley and A. Rosen, eds.), Chapt. 10. Wiley, New York, 1964.

29. E. N. Parker, Dynamical Properties of Stellar Coronas and Stellar Winds, I and II, *Astrophys. J.* **139**, 72, 93 (1964).

30. E. N. Parker, Dynamical Properties of the Stellar Coronas and Stellar Winds, III, *Astrophys. J.* **139**, 690 (1964).

31. J. Hirshberg, The Relationship between Solar Wind Velocities and Surface Magnetic Disturbances during Sudden Commencement Storms, *J. Geophys. Res.* **70**, 4159 (1965).

32. G. J. F. MacDonald, Hydromagnetic Waves in Space, *in*: "Space Physics" (D. P. LeGalley and A. Rosen, eds.), Chapt. 13. Wiley, New York, 1964.

33. F. L. Scarf, The Solar Wind and Its Interaction with Magnetic Fields, *in*: "Space Physics" (D. P. LeGalley and A. Rosen, eds.), Chapt. 12. Wiley, New York, 1964.

34. P. A. Sturrock and J. R. Sprieter, Shock Waves in the Solar Wind and Geomagnetic Storms, *J. Geophys. Res.* **70**, 5345 (1965).

35. S. Chapman and V. C. A. Ferraro, The Geomagnetic Ring Current, I—Its Radial Stability, *Terr. Magn. Atmos. Elect.* **46**, 1 (1941).

36. E. P. Ney, J. R. Winckler, and P. S. Frier, Protons from the Sun on May 12, 1959, *Phys. Rev. Letters* **3**, 183 (1959).

37. K. W. Ogilvie, D. A. Bryant, and L. R. Davis, Rocket Observations of Solar Protons during the November 1960 Events, I, *J. Geophys. Res.* **67**, 929 (1962).

38. J. L. Modisette, T. M. Vinson, and A. C. Hardy, Model Solar Proton Environments for Manned Spacecraft Design, Tech. Note NASA-TN-D-2746 (1965).

39. L. R. Davis and K. W. Ogilvie, Rocket Observations of Solar Protons during the November 1960 Events, II, *J. Geophys. Res.* **67**, 1711 (1962).

40. W. R. Webber, An Evaluation of the Radiation Hazard Due to Solar Particle Events, Rept. D2-90469, Boeing Airplane Co., Seattle, Washington (1963).

41. L. R. Lewis, G. M. Brown, J. Gabler, and R. M. Magee, Solar Flare Radiation Survey, Rept. RTD-DTR-63-3044, *USAF Weapons Lab.*, Albuquerque, New Mexico (1963).

42. S. Biswas, P. S. Frier, and W. Stein, Solar Protons and Alpha Particles from the September 3, 1960 Flares, *J. Geophys. Res.* **67**, 13 (1962).

43. F. B. McDonald, Review of Galactic and Solar Cosmic Rays, *Second Symp. on Protection against Radiations in Space*, p. 19, NASA-SP-71 (1964).

44. G. K. Yates, Solar Flare High Energy Alpha Particles and Their Storage in Interplanetary Space, *J. Geophys. Res.* **69**, 3077 (1964).

45. J. W. Haffner, The Role of Alpha Particles in Shielding against Solar Event Radiation, Rept. SID-64–1297, North American Aviation, Inc., Los Angeles, California (1964).

46. C. E. Fitchel and D. E. Guss, Heavy Nuclei in Solar Cosmic Rays, *Phys. Rev. Letters* **6**, 495 (1961).

47. E. P. Ney and W. A. Stein, Solar Protons, Alpha Particles, and Heavy Nuclei in November 1960, *J. Geophys. Res.* **67**, 2087 (1962).

48. S. C. Biswas, C. E. Fichtel, and D. E. Guss, Study of the Hydrogen, Helium, and Heavy Nuclei in the November 12, 1960 Solar Cosmic Ray Event, *Phys. Rev.* **128**, 2756 (1962).

49. P. Meyer and R. Vogt, High Energy Electrons of Solar Origin, *Phys. Rev. Letters* **8**, 387 (1962).

50. K. A. Anderson, R. Arnoldy, R. Hoffman, L. Peterson, and J. R. Winckler, Observations of Low Energy Solar Cosmic Rays from the Flare of 22 August 1958, *J. Geophys. Res.* **64**, 1133 (1959).

51. A. Ehmert, H. Erbe, G. Pfotzer, C. D. Anger, and R. R. Brown, Observations of Solar Flare Radiation and Modulation Effects at Balloon Altitudes, July 1959, *J. Geophys. Res.* **65**, 2685 (1960).

52. J. R. Winckler and P. D. Bhavsar, Low Energy Solar Cosmic Rays and the Geomagnetic Storm of May 12, 1959, *J. Geophys. Res.* **65**, 2637 (1960).

53. K. W. Ogilvie and D. A. Bryant, Solar Proton Spectrums in the Events of November 12 and 15, 1960, *J. Geophys. Res.* **69**, 393 (1964).

54. H. S. Ghielmetti, The Spectrum and Propagation of Relativistic Solar Flare Particles during July 17–18, 1959, *J. Geophys. Res.* **66**, 1611 (1961).

55. E. C. Stone, A Measurement of the Primary Proton Flux from 10 to 130 Mev, *J. Geophys. Res.* **69**, 3939 (1964).

56. J. W. Haffner, Shielding Analysis of the 1956–1961 Solar Proton Event Data, Rept. SID-64–1295, North American Aviation, Inc., Los Angeles, California (1964).

57. P. S. Frier and W. R. Webber, Exponential Rigidity Spectra for Solar Flare Cosmic Rays, *J. Geophys. Res.* **68**, 1605 (1962).

58. P. Frier, Emulsion Measurements of Solar α Particles and Protons, *J. Geophys. Res.* **68**, 1805 (1963).

59. J. Firor, Cosmic Radiation Intensity—Time Variations and Their Origin, IV, Increases Associated with Solar Flares, *Phys. Rev.* **94**, 1017 (1954).

60. R. B. Brode and A. Goodwin, Extraordinary Increases of Cosmic Radiation on February 23, 1956, *Phys. Rev.* **103**, 377 (1956).

61. J. A. Lockwood, H. E. Yingst, A. R. Calawa, and G. Sarmariote, Cosmic Ray Neutron Intensity Increase Associated with Solar Flare of February 23, 1956, *Phys. Rev.* **103**, 247 (1956).

62. J. R. Winckler, Cosmic Ray Increase at High Altitude on February 23, 1956, *Phys. Rev.* **104**, 220 (1956).

63. H. R. Anderson, Sudden Increase of Cosmic Ray Intensity, *Phys. Rev.* **116**, 461 (1959).

64. L. C. Towle and J. A. Lockwood, Cosmic Ray Increases Associated with Solar Flares, *Phys. Rev.* **113**, 641 (1959).

65. D. K. Bailey, Time Variations of the Energy Spectrum of Solar Cosmic Rays in Relation to the Radiation Hazard in Space, *J. Geophys. Res.* **67**, 391 (1962).

66. J. W. Haffner, An Attenuation Kernel for the Bailey Model Event, *Trans. Am. Nucl. Soc.* **7,** 16 (1964).

67. J. P. Legrand, Probability of Predicting Solar Phenomena and the Global Repercussions of a Study of the Intensity of Cosmic Rays, *Comp. Rend.* **248,** 70 (1958).

68. H. W. Dodson and E. R. Hedeman, An Unexpected Effect in Solar Cosmic Ray Data Related to 29.5 Days, *J. Geophys. Res.* **69,** 3965 (1964).

69. A. D. Goedeke and A. J. Masley, Observations in the Antarctic of Solar Cosmic Ray Events of 1962 and 1963, *J. Geophys. Res.* **69,** 4166 (1964).

70. J. B. Weddell, Prediction of Probability of Occurrence of Solar Flares, *Astronautica Acta* **10,** 339 (1964).

71. H. H. Malitson, Predicting Large Solar Cosmic Ray Events, *Astronaut. Aerospace Eng.* **1,** 70 (1963).

72. W. R. Webber, An Evaluation of Solar Cosmic Ray Events During Solar Minimum, Rept. D2-84274-1, *Boeing Airplane Co*, Seattle, Washington (1965).

73. C. M. Minnis, An Estimate of the Peak Sunspot Number in 1968, *Nature* **186,** 462 (1960).

74. H. R. Anderson, Energetic Particles Measured Near Venus by Mariner 2, *J. Geophys. Res.* **69,** 2651 (1964).

75. R. L. Arnoldy, R. A. Hoffman, and J. R. Winckler, Solar Cosmic Rays and Soft Radiation Observed 5,000,000 kilometers from Earth, *J. Geophys. Res.* **65,** 3004 (1960).

76. P. Meyer, E. N. Parker, and J. A. Simpson, Solar Cosmic Rays of February 1956 and Their Propagation through Interplanetary Space, *Phys. Rev.* **104,** 768 (1956).

77. C. S. Warwick, Propagation of Solar Particles and the Interplanetary Magnetic Field, *J. Geophys. Res.* **67,** 1333 (1962).

78. E. N. Parker, The Passage of Energetic Charged Particles through Interplanetary Space, *Planetary Space Sci.* **13,** 9 (1965).

79. T. Gold, Plasma and Magnetic Fields in the Solar System, *J. Geophys. Res.* **64,** 1665 (1959).

80. F. Raymes, Apollo Spacecraft Nuclear Radiation Protection Status Report, *Second Symp. Protection against Radiations in Space*, p. 365, NASA-SP-71 (1964).

81. L. J. Cahill, The Geomagnetic Field, *in*: "Space Physics" (D. P. LeGalley and A. Rosen, eds.), Chapt. 9. Wiley, New York, 1964.

82. C. Stormer, "The Polar Aurora." Oxford Univ. Press (Clarendon), London and New York, 1955.

83. C. G. Little and H. Leinbach, The Riometer—A Device for the Continuous Measurement of Ionospheric Absorption, *Proc. IRE* **47** (2), 315 (1959).

84. D. K. Bailey, Abnormal Ionization in the Lower Ionosphere Associated with Cosmic Ray Flux Enhancements, *Proc. IRE* **47,** 255 (1959).

85. C. Collins, D. H. Jelly, and A. G. Mathews, High Frequency Radio Wave Blackouts at Medium and High Latitudes during a Solar Cycle, *Can. J. Phys.* **39,** 35 (1961).

86. D. C. Rose and S. Ziauddin, The Polar Cap Absorption Effect, *Space Sci. Rev.* **1,** 115 (1962).

87. G. C. Reid, A Study of the Enhanced Ionization Produced by Solar Protons during a Polar Cap Absorption Event, *J. Geophys. Res.* **66,** 4071 (1961).

88. F. C. Michel and J. A. Dessler, Physical Significance of Inhomogeneities in Polar Cap Absorption Events, *J. Geophys. Res.* **70,** 4305 (1965).

89. R. Parthasarathy and D. Venkatesan, An Empirical Relationship between Particle Flux, Energy Spectrum, and Radio Wave Absorption during a Polar Cap Event, *J. Geophys. Res.* **69,** 549 (1964).

90. J. A. Van Allen, W. C. Lin, and H. Leinbach, On the Relationship between Absolute Solar Cosmic Ray Intensity and Riometer Absorption, *J. Geophys. Res.* **69,** 4481 (1964).

91. M. R. Kundu and F. T. Haddock, A Relation between Solar Radio Emission and Polar Cap Absorption of Cosmic Noise, *Nature* **186,** 610 (1960).

92. L. R. Davis, C. E. Fitchel, D. E. Guss, and K. W. Ogilvie, Rocket Observations of Solar Protons on September 3, 1960, *J. Phys. Soc. Japan* **17** (*Suppl.* A-I, Part II), 326 (1962).

93. S. Chapman, Smithsonian Contributions to Astrophysics, **2,** 1 (1957).

94. F. L. Scarf, The Solar Wind and Its Interaction with Magnetic Fields, *in*: "Space Physics" (D. P. LeGalley and A. Rosen, eds.), Chapt. 12. Wiley, New York, 1964.

95. E. N. Parker, Dynamics of the Interplanetary Gas and Magnetic Fields, *Astrophys. J.* **128,** 664 (1958).

96. J. Chamberlin, Interplanetary Gas, III—A Hydrodynamic Model of the Corona, *Astrophys. J.* **133,** 675 (1961).

97. L. Nobel and F. L. Scarf, Conductive Heating of the Solar Wind, I, *Astrophys. J.* **138,** 1169 (1963).

98. E. N. Parker, Sudden Expansion of the Corona Following a Large Solar Flare and the Attendant Magnetic Field and Cosmic Ray Effects, *Astrophys. J.* **133,** 1014 (1961).

99. J. B. Weddell, Interaction of Hydrodynamic Shocks with Charged Particles in the Solar Corona, Rept. SID-64–1500, North American Aviation, Inc., Los Angeles, California (1964).

# *II*

# GALACTIC (COSMIC) RADIATION

## A. Brief History

The discovery of galactic (cosmic) radiation was made by Hess in 1911 [1]. He became curious to learn why an electroscope, well insulated from all material objects in its vicinity, would gradually lose its charge as reported by C. T. R. Wilson. One theory was that radioactivity from the Earth was responsible. If this were so, Hess reasoned, the electroscope discharge rate should decrease with altitude above the surface of the Earth. However, when carried aloft in a balloon, the electroscope was observed to lose its charge more rapidly than at ground level, this effect increasing with altitude. Clearly the radiation which discharged the electroscope was of extra-terrestrial origin, and not due to radioactivity of the Earth.

World War I (1914–1918) interrupted Hess's experiments, but he resumed his work in 1922. He observed that flights over water produced the same altitude dependence as flights over land. Because of the geographical independence of the effect, Hess concluded that the extraterrestrial radiation was isotropically distributed. Millikan called this radiation "cosmic rays," and the name has stuck [2].

Following the discovery of cosmic rays, their nature became the object of increasing investigation. Early speculation suggested that these were gamma rays, since the only radiations known to be emitted by radioisotopes with the ability to penetrate the walls of an electroscope were gamma type. However, in 1928, Clay discovered that the ionization produced by these cosmic rays increased as one went away from the Earth's equator [3]. This "latitude effect" was explainable only on the basis that at least a portion of the cosmic rays were electrically charged. The latitude effect also made spectral estimates of energy possible.

The sign of the electrical charge was not definitely established until 1938, when Johnson [4] discovered that more of the radiation arrived from the west than from the east (the east-west asymmetry effect). That protons were the major component of the cosmic radiation was shown by a series of high-altitude balloon flights carried out by Schein and his co-workers in 1941 [5].

Following World War II (1939–1945), several measurements were carried out with rockets and Earth satellites. In addition, a series of flights with improved (skyhook) high-altitude balloons was made. In 1948 Frier *et al.* [6], discovered the presence of nuclei heavier than protons in the primary cosmic radiation. The interactions of cosmic radiation with the atmosphere were studied with large arrays of ground-based detectors, of which the Agassiz Experiment [7] 1955–1958 was one of the best known.

The international Geophysical Year of 1958–1960 was a concerted effort by scientists of many nations to investigate the Earth and its surroundings. As a result, our knowledge of the Sun and its influences on cosmic radiation increased tremendously [8–10]. It was found that the magnetic fields present in the solar system were greatly influenced by solar activity, and that the Sun emitted particulate radiation of its own. The term "cosmic radiation" has, therefore, become somewhat ambiguous, since it has been used in some cases to refer to solar radiation (solar cosmic rays) as well as to galactic radiation (galactic cosmic rays). In this book, the term "cosmic radiation" will be used only to refer to galactic radiation, a convention that is apparently becoming universally adopted.

Briefly, galactic (cosmic) radiation consists of a low flux ($\sim 4$ particles/$cm^2$-sec) of energetic ($\sim 10^8$–$10^{19}$ ev) bare nuclei which appear to fill our galaxy isotropically. They have a mass distribution very approximately that of the universe (there are important differences, however). Their time behavior in our solar system is apparently controlled by the Sun, exhibiting both long-term (11-year solar cycle) and short-term (Forbush effect) variations. Their integral energy spectrum is approximately $E^{-1.5}$, except for low energies where solar activity perturbs it. When interacting with the Earth's atmosphere, they produce "showers" of secondary particles—mesons, neutrons, electrons, photons, and so forth. Their origin has been the subject of several theories but remains unknown. In this chapter, our current knowledge of the galactic (cosmic) radiation is discussed.

## B. Mass Distribution

Most of our information concerning the mass distribution of galactic radiation comes from recovered photographic emulsion plates carried aloft by balloons and rockets. If the particle is not relativistic, the ionization density along the emulsion track yields a good estimate of the particle's charge. By preparing "sandwiches" consisting of alternate layers of absorbing material (e.g., lead) and emulsion plates, estimates of the energies of the penetrating particles can also be obtained.

TABLE 2-1

COMPARISON OF CHARGE DISTRIBUTIONS IN GALACTIC
RADIATION AND GALACTIC MATTER (ESTIMATED)

| Element group | Intensity[a] (particles/cm$^2$-sec) | Atomic abundance (% by number) | Universal abundance (% by number) |
|---|---|---|---|
| Hydrogen (protons) | 3.6 | 88 | 90 |
| Helium (alpha particles) | $4 \times 10^{-1}$ | 9.8 | 9 |
| Light nuclei (Li, Be, B) | $8 \times 10^{-3}$ | 0.2 | $10^{-4}$ |
| Medium nuclei (C, N, O, F) | $3 \times 10^{-2}$ | 0.75 | 0.3 |
| Heavy nuclei ($10 \leqslant Z \leqslant 30$) | $6 \times 10^{-3}$ | 0.15 | 0.01 |
| Very heavy nuclei ($Z \geqslant 31$) | $5 \times 10^{-4}$ | 0.01 | $10^{-5}$ |
| Electrons and photons ($E > 4$ Bev) | $4 \times 10^{-2}$ | 1 | — |

[a] At solar minimum.

The approximate free space particle fluxes by nuclear charge are listed in the first column of Table 2-1 [3, 9, 11]. The entries have uncertainties ranging from $\lesssim 10\%$ for hydrogen to at least a factor of 3 for very heavy nuclei. It has been possible to measure this mass distribution only for relatively low energies $E \lesssim 10^{10}$ ev/nucleon, because relativistic particles become minimum-ionizing, making mass assignment difficult.

Estimates of the relative abundances of the various nuclear groups in our galaxy are listed in column 3 of Table 2-1 [3, 9, 11]. It must be appreciated that obtaining such estimates is difficult, since the Earth has a very atypical mass distribution and comprises (even in our solar system) a negligible fraction of the mass. It has been possible to estimate the composition of the outer portions of the Sun from optical spectra and the inner portions from theories of stellar processes and evolution. In a similar manner, the compositions of various classes of stars in our galaxy can be estimated to yield the composition of the galaxy. The composition of the interstellar dust (which contains an important fraction of the total galactic mass) can also be estimated. The result is usually something like that presented in column 3 of Table 2-1. The uncertainties vary from about 10% for hydrogen to at least an order of magnitude for very heavy nuclei for these entries.

It will be noticed that the relative abundance of hydrogen in galactic radiation and in the galaxy are essentially equal. In fact, the assumption is often made that these abundances are equal, which is important from a theoretical standpoint. The proton component of galactic radiation has been studied more than any other. McDonald and Webber [12], Vogt [13], and others have carried out studies especially concerned with this proton component.

Following the discovery of alpha particles in the galactic radiation by Frier *et al.* [6], they have been the subject of several investigations. Meyer [14], Rao [15], Engler *et al.* [16], and others studied this component under various conditions. McDonald [17] investigated the flux relationships of protons and alpha particles, while Lohrman and Teucher [18] examined the relationships between alpha particles and heavier nuclei in galactic radiation. Particularly interesting are the similarities and differences in the alpha particle-proton relationships in galactic and solar radiations. This is discussed in the section of this chapter dealing with theory.

One of the most striking comparisons between the mass distribution in galactic radiation and that in our galaxy is the great difference in the relative abundance of the light nuclei—Li, Be, and B. This has been investigated by Waddington [19], Webber [20], Rao *et al.* [21], Frier *et al.* [22], and others. The discrepancy is attributed to usage of these nuclei in thermonuclear processes in stars. Depending upon what initial assumptions one is willing to make, it is possible to estimate the age of our galaxy from the remaining amount of these light nuclei. Ages of approximately $10^{10}$ years have been obtained this way, in general agreement with estimates obtained by other approaches. Spallation (cascade type) reactions in matter the heavier galactic nuclei encounter prior to being detected are believed to be the source of this anomalously large light nuclear component. From our current knowledge of such reactions (mean free path 1–100 gm/cm$^2$), it appears that the galactic radiation has encountered $\sim 2.5$ gm/cm$^2$ between its creation at relativistic energies and its encounter with a man-made detector [23]. If the average density of matter in our galaxy is $\sim 0.1$ amu/cm$^3$, each galactic particle must have traveled a distance of $\sim 10^{25}$ cm. At the speed of light ($3 \times 10^{10}$ cm/sec), traveling this distance requires $\sim 3 \times 10^{14}$ sec ($\sim 10^7$ years). This estimate of the time to produce the observed light nuclear contribution is very important theoretically and accounts for a large amount of the study the Li, Be, and B group has received.

TABLE 2-2

APPROXIMATE ABUNDANCE OF ELEMENTS IN THE HEAVY
PRIMARY COSMIC RADIATION

| Element | Atomic number Z | Abundance (%) |
|---------|-----------------|---------------|
| Ne | 10 | 23.1 |
| Na | 11 | 14.7 |
| Mg | 12 | 16.3 |
| Al | 13 | 11.5 |
| Si | 14 | 7.2 |
| P | 15 | 5.1 |
| S | 16 | 2.5 |
| Cl | 17 | 2.6 |
| A | 18 | 2.0 |
| K | 19 | 2.5 |
| Ca | 20 | 1.8 |
| Sc | 21 | 2.0 |
| Ti | 22 | 2.0 |
| V | 23 | 1.4 |
| Cr | 24 | 1.7 |
| Mn | 25 | 0.6 |
| Fe | 26 | 1.3 |

The heavy component of galactic radiation has been investigated by Aizu *et al.* [24, 25], Young and Chen [26], Koshiba *et al.* [9], and others. The approximate abundance of the heavy nuclei in the galactic radiation is listed in Table 2-2 [3].

It will be noted that the galactic radiation appears to contain a progressively greater percentage of high Z nuclei than our galaxy, the discrepancy exceeding an order of magnitude for nuclei heavier than iron. As yet no satisfactory explanation of this discrepancy for the heavy nuclei has been found. It has been proposed that the primary cosmic radiation was initially composed solely of heavy nuclei. As time passed, these nuclei were supposedly broken down into the lighter nuclei by interacting with interstellar dust. The trouble with this theory is that the mean free path for high-energy bare nuclei decreases approximately as

$$\lambda(\text{gm/cm}^2) \sim 70/Z \qquad (2.1)$$

Thus the fraction of heavy nuclei surviving in a medium of 0.1–1.0 amu/cm$^3$ for the approximate age of the universe ($\sim 10^{10}$ years) is much smaller than the observed abundance.

Electrons in the galactic radiation have been investigated by Hayakawa and Okuda [27], Earl [28] Meyer and Vogt [29], Jones [30], and others. One of the problems connected with the mass distribution of the galactic radiation is that it appears to consist almost completely of positively charged particles. Only about 1% of the measured galactic radiation has been identified as electrons and/or photons. If the galactic radiation does not consist of equal numbers of positive and negative charges, large electrostatic potentials could conceivably be built up between various bodies of our galaxy. On the other hand, it is quite possible that the numbers of positive and negative particles are comparable, but that the negative particles are less readily detected. This would be the case if the negative particles were much lower in energy than their positive counterparts. It will be seen that the most promising acceleration mechanisms are far less efficient for electrons than for bare nuclei. This is discussed later in this chapter.

## C.  Energy Spectra

The galactic radiation is known to cover an energy range from $\sim 0.1$ Bev to $\sim 10^{10}$ Bev, approximately eleven decades. Because of this enormous energy range, a series of different techniques has been used to compile our current picture of the galactic spectra.

The proton energy spectrum has been extensively investigated. For relatively low energies, $\lesssim 15$ Bev, the geomagnetic field acts as a spectrometer, since a proton of less than $\sim 15$ Bev cannot reach the magnetic equator. For each energy between 0 and 15 Bev, there is a cutoff latitude.

This low-energy portion of the proton spectrum has been studied by Neher [31], Meyer and Simpson [32], McDonald [33], and others. The proton energy spectrum in this region is more dependent upon solar activity than that at higher energies. Above 15 Bev, a variety of techniques has been employed. Lal [34], Kaplon and Ritson [35], Fowler *et al.* [36], and many others have used nuclear photographic emulsions to measure the proton flux up to $\sim 10^3$ Bev. Above this energy the measurements become more difficult. Barrett *et al.* [37], have measured the $\mu$ meson flux produced by galactic protons in underground chambers. This techniques extends the upper energy range to $\sim 10^6$ Bev. Beyond this, the observation of large air showers has been used [38]. By summing the energies of secondaries produced in the earth's atmosphere, the energy of the primary particle, which presumably initiated the shower, can be estimated. Linsley *et al.* [39],

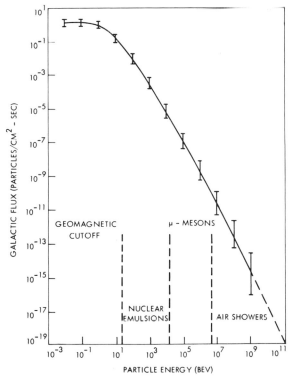

FIG. 2-1.   Integral energy spectrum for total galactic radiation.

Cranshaw *et al.* [40], Brennan *et al.* [41], and others have used this approach to estimate the primary flux to $\sim 10^{10}$ Bev. It may be noted in passing that $10^{10}$ Bev is $\sim 1$ joule, which is a fantastic energy for a particle of $\sim 10^{-24}$ gm rest mass.

The resultant proton integral energy spectrum is shown in Fig. 2-1. It will be noted that above $\sim 10$ Bev the spectrum is monotonic with a slope of about $-1.5$. Below 10 Bev the integral energy spectrum flattens out, suggesting a peak in the differential energy spectrum at $\sim 1$ Bev. Such differential energy spectra have been measured, [42, 43] and are shown in Fig. 2-2. The solar cycle variations are discussed later.

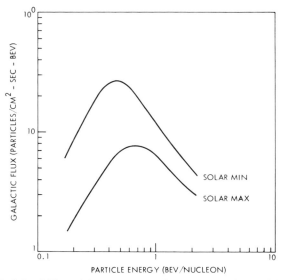

FIG. 2-2.   Differential energy spectra for protons and $\alpha$ particles.

The energy spectra of the heavier component of the galactic primary radiation have been measured only up to $\sim 10$ Bev/nucleon, using scintillation and stacked emulsion techniques. The alpha particle energy spectrum has been measured by McDonald [44], Frier *et al.* [45], Fan *et al.* [46], and others. For heavier nuclei, the energy spectra have been measured by Jain [47], Kaplon and Ritson [35], and others. The resulting integral energy spectra for the various nuclear components of the galactic radiation are shown in Fig. 2-3.

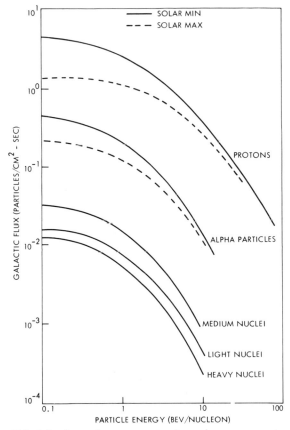

FIG. 2-3.   Integral energy spectra for various components.

It is seen that the various components all exhibit approximately the same energy spectra up to ~ 10 Bev, and it seems reasonable to assume that this may be true above 10 Bev. Various mathematical fits to these integral energy spectra have been made by Fowler and Waddington [48], Hilberry [49], Kaplon *et al.* [50], Ney [8] and others. There seems to be general agreement that the spectra can be represented by expressions of the form

$$\phi(E > E_0) = \frac{A}{(M_0 c^2 + E_0)^n} \qquad (2.2)$$

where $\phi$ is the integral flux above $E_0$ in particles/cm²-sec, $E$ is the particle kinetic energy (Bev/nucleon), $M_0 C^2$ is the rest energy of the particle (Bev), and $A$ and $n$ are constants. While there is some disagreement pertaining to the values of $A$ and $n$, the following numbers are fairly typical for the energy spectra during solar minimums:

| | | |
|---|---|---|
| Protons $(Z = 1)$ | $A = 4.0$ | $n = 1.5$ |
| Alpha particles $(Z = 2)$ | $A = 3.5 \times 10^{-1}$ | $n = 1.5$ |
| Light nuclei $(Z = 3, 4, 5)$ | $A = 1.2 \times 10^{-2}$ | $n = 1.5$ |
| Medium nuclei $(6 \leqslant Z \leqslant 9)$ | $A = 2.5 \times 10^{-2}$ | $n = 1.5$ |
| Heavy nuclei $(Z \geqslant 10)$ | $A = 3.0 \times 10^{-2}$ | $n = 1.5$ |

However, this fit has two limitations. The first is that both $A$ and $n$ are functions of the solar cycle. For protons, the effects appear to be largest, decreasing $A$ by nearly a factor of 3 at solar maximums. The value of $n$ also decreases about 30% at solar maximums for protons. For alpha particles the decreases are approximately a factor of 2 $(A)$ and roughly 20% $(n)$ respectively. The energy spectral variations for the heavier nuclei are smaller, and not as well known.

The second limitation to Eq. (2.2) is that the primary galactic energy spectrum apparently becomes steeper as the energy increases. It has thus been proposed that $n$ should be a function of $E$. One such expression is [3]

$$n = 0.67 + 0.037 \log E \qquad (2.3)$$

where $E$ is in electron volts.

The energy spectrum of the galactic (cosmic) radiation is quite important. The extremely high energy of the radiation is fortunately compensated by its relatively low flux rate, or else space travel would be more hazardous than it is.

## D.  Time Variations

### 1.  LONG-TERM VARIATIONS

The long-term (more than a century) behavior of galactic radiation has been investigated only indirectly, since direct measuring techniques have existed for only fifty years. However, there is strong evidence that galactic radiation at the Earth has undergone no long-term changes of more than a minute percentage within the last few thousand years at least.

The main evidence for the long-term constancy of the galactic radiation comes from the success of the $C^{14}$ dating technique, pioneered by Libby [51]. This technique presumes that $C^{14}$ is constantly being produced in the atmosphere of the Earth. Thus a living organism always has an equilibrium concentration of $C^{14}$ in the carbon in its body. When the organism dies, the carbon exchange with the atmosphere stops, with the result that the $C^{14}$ present decreases slowly with a half-life of about 5500 years. Thus the $C^{14}$/carbon ratio serves as a measure of the time since the organism died. This technique, under certain conditions, can be applied to inanimate objects as well. By correlating the ages obtained from $C^{14}$ dating with ages established from historical records, the general accuracy of $C^{14}$ dating has been established [52]. This could not have been the case if the $C^{14}$ concentration in the atmosphere had not remained approximately constant. Since the $C^{14}$ in the atmosphere is believed to be largely due to galactic radiation, this radiation must have remained approximately constant also.

Another technique involves measuring the radioactivity of meteorites which have been found on the Earth. If the age of the meteorite can be estimated independently, information concerning the constancy of the galactic radiation which produced the radioactivity can be obtained [53]. Conversely, if the galactic radiation is assumed to have remained constant for the life of the meteorite in space, the age of the meteorite can be measured [54]. The technique has been used both ways with reasonably consistent results [55]. This constitutes additional evidence that there have been no major long-term variations in the cosmic ray flux for the past several thousand years.

A third argument is largely theoretical, but supports the same view. Since the Li, Be, and B nuclei presumably were formed from heavier galactic radiation nuclei, the required path length in interstellar space is $\sim 10^{25}$ cm. Traveling this distance requires about $10^7$ years. If the galactic radiation had a storage time of $10^7$ years, the leakage rate would not be expected to change radically in a time short compared to this.

## 2. SOLAR CYCLE MODULATION

The Sun follows a semiregular 11-year cycle, as discussed in Chapter I. Since alternate solar cycles apparently have a few more characteristics in common than successive cycles, a 22-year solar cycle is sometimes referred to instead. In any event, the major periodic behavior of galactic radiation as measured on or near the Earth is due to this solar cycle.

The solar cycle modulation was reported by Forbush [56, 57]. Since then it has been investigated by Neher and Forbush [58], Parker [59], McDonald [60], Nerurkar and Webber [61], Manzano and Winckler [62], and others. The work carried out during the IGY was quite important in clarifying some of the solar cycle modulation effects.

The Sun's activity acts to limit the intensity of galactic radiation on the Earth. In 1954, when solar activity as measured by the sunspot number was a minimum, the flux of galactic radiation was unusually large. Conversely, the galactic radiation flux dropped as the solar maximum (1959) approached [3, 9] (see Fig. 2-4). It will be noticed that the flux (as measured by the

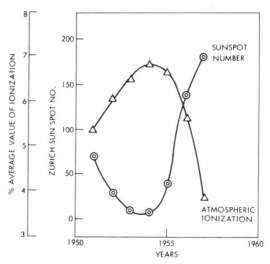

FIG. 2-4.   Anticorrelation between sunspot number and cosmic radiation.

ionization it produced) varies roughly as a factor of 3 from solar minimum to solar maximum. This is considerably less than the sunspot number, which varies over an order of magnitude in the course of a solar cycle. Another interesting point is that there may be a time lag between solar activity and galactic radiation flux [57, 63]. The problem here is that we measure solar activity only indirectly by sunspot number, solar flares, magnetic field fluctuations, and the like. None of these is necessarily a true measure of solar activity, and these do not all reach a maximum at the same time. For example, the sunspot number was maximal in 1957, but solar flare activity was maximal in 1959. Therefore, the existence and magnitude of a possible time lag (probably in the neighborhood of a year) between solar cycle maximum and galactic flux minimum is uncertain and depends upon the solar and galactic parameters observed.

As we have seen, the solar activity has its most profound effect upon the low energy ($\lesssim 10$ Bev) portion of the galactic energy spectra. This effect has been investigated by McCracken [64, 65], Storey [66], Kane *et al.* [67], Manzano and Winckler [62], and others. This decrease of the low-energy portions of the galactic spectra shows up in the altitude dependence of the

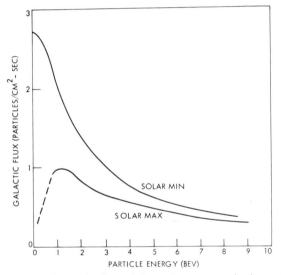

FIG. 2-5. Effects of solar activity on low-energy galactic spectra.

ionization produced in the Earth's atmosphere (see Fig. 2-5). It must be pointed out that because of this effect, the ionization produced is not necessarily a good measure of the galactic flux intensity variations due to solar cycle modulation. Since the lower energy particles produce relatively more ionization than the relativistic (minimum-ionizing) particles, the flux intensity variations may be less than about a factor of 2 from solar maximum to solar minimum.

It has been seen that the largest solar cycle effects take place in the proton energy spectrum. The alpha particle spectrum is affected nearly two-thirds as much as the proton spectrum, and the heavier components are presumably affected less.

### 3. FORBUSH EFFECT

Occasionally the galactic flux in the vicinity of the Earth will decrease rapidly within a few hours in response to transient disturbances on the Sun (Forbush effect) [56]. As these transient disturbances die away, the galactic flux slowly returns to its previous value. It is generally believed that solar flares are responsible, and the correlation between Forbush decreases and solar flares is excellent. The recovery time (a few days) also suggests Forbush decreases are due to solar flares.

The Forbush effect is named after its discoverer, S. E. Forbush. The effect has also been studied by Storey [68], Lockwood [69], Escobar *et al.* [70], Laster *et al.* [71], Gosling [72], and others. While the low-energy portions of the spectrum appear to be primarily affected, this effect is less dependent

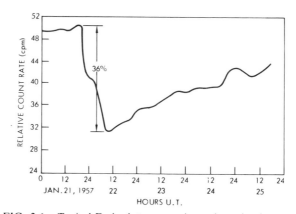

FIG. 2-6.   Typical Forbush-type cosmic ray intensity decrease.

upon particle energy than for the 11-year solar modulation [73]. The protons are disturbed more than the other components, but evidence has been obtained that the heavier nuclei are also disturbed. The usual effects are on the order of a scant percentage, but 30% flux decreases have been observed (see Fig. 2-6).

The explanation for the Forbush effect is believed to lie in the plasma cloud which the Sun ejects during a solar flare [74]. As this cloud envelopes the Earth, the magnetic screening effects inherent in plasmas act to shield the Earth from galactic radiation (while contributing far more radiation of their own). As the plasma cloud continues to expand and migrate away from the Sun, this magnetic screening action decreases. Confirmation of this explanation may be obtained by having two or more solar satellites monitor the same Forbush decrease at great distances from the Earth.

### 4. QUASI-PERIODIC 27-DAY VARIATION

The intensity of the galactic radiation has been observed to undergo 27-day periodic fluctuations [75, 76]. These fluctuations (observed during

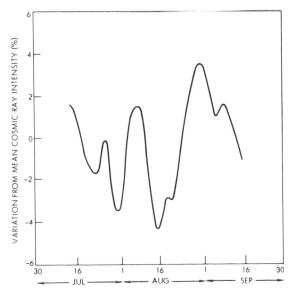

FIG. 2-7.  Typical 27-day cosmic ray intensity variation.

years when the Sun is active) persist for a few rotations of the Sun, and then disappear. The magnitude of these fluctuations is typically $\pm 1-2\%$. In Fig. 2-7 an example of the galactic flux behavior during one of these quasi-periodic variations is shown [3].

The explanation for such 27-day fluctuations in the galactic flux as observed at the Earth is believed to lie in the magnetic fields associated with active regions on the Sun. Such active regions may be emitting streams of plasma more or less continually, in which case the time variation may be considered as a low-intensity, long-term Forbush effect. Even if the magnetic fields on the Sun act directly to perturb the galactic flux, the correlation with solar activity is excellent.

5.   DIURNAL EFFECTS

The diurnal (day-night) time fluctuation is small ($\lesssim 0.3\%$), and its establishment is not beyond question. Most of the measurements of this effect have been made with detectors in the Earth's atmosphere, and the diurnal and seasonal effects of the atmosphere are difficult to rule out. However, this effect is very important theoretically, and has been the object of considerable study, Simpson *et al.* [77], Fonger [78], Sarabhai and Nerurkar [79], Sandstrom [80], Neher [9], and others have carried out investigations of the diurnal effects on galactic radiation. A typical diurnal effect, averaged

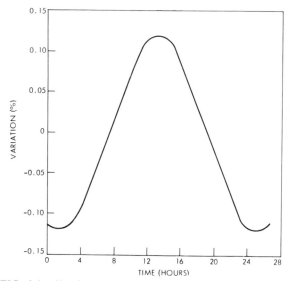

FIG. 2-8.   Yearly average of daily cosmic ray intensity variation.

over a year, is shown in Fig. 2-8. The significance of the diurnal effect is that its existence virtually precludes the isotropy of the galactic radiation in space. This in turn provides strong evidence concerning the source(s) of the galactic radiation.

It should be pointed out that efforts have been made to detect two types of diurnal effects. One is the solar diurnal effect, which is of importance in proving that the Sun is not apparently a source of galactic radiation. The other is sidereal diurnal effect, which is concerned with from what portions of the galaxy the radiation may be coming. Compton and Getting [81] pointed out that in the absence of magnetic fields, the radiation intensity should be slightly greater in the direction of the Milky Way, since most of stars in our galaxy lie in that direction. However, if a sidereal diurnal effect exists at the Earth, it is quite small ($\lesssim 0.1\%$) and must be considered very doubtful. The interstellar magnetic fields in our galaxy most probably act to make the radiation isotropic even if the source(s) are not.

## E. Spatial Distribution

To a very good first approximation, the galactic radiation in space is isotropic. However, in our solar system the galactic radiation is spatially dependent upon the distance from the Sun. In other words, the anisotropy of the galactic radiation in our solar system, while small, is not zero, and this small anisotropy results in a spatial dependence. Theoretical and experimental studies of this effect have been carried out by Elliot [82], Neher and Anderson [83], Anderson [84], and others. The general behavior of the spatial effect is shown in Fig. 2-9.

The expected relations between the spatial behavior and the other parameters of galactic radiation can be briefly stated. Since it is the Sun which perturbs galactic radiation on this scale, the same effects as observed on the Earth for the 11-year modulation should result. Thus the lower portion of the energy spectrum should be progressively depressed as one approaches the Sun, the time variations should become more severe, and the protons should be progressively affected more than the heavier components.

On the galactic scale, it is quite possible that a spatial dependence might be found. If all stars were as relatively inactive as our Sun, the resultant galactic radiation flux would be some six orders of magnitude lower than it is observed to be [11]. Therefore there must be active sources of galactic radiation (perhaps novae or other relatively localized objects). The observed radio frequency sources are relatively localized, and it has been proposed that these may be sources of galactic particulate radiation as well [76, 85].

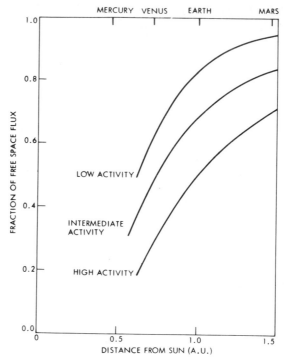

FIG. 2-9.   Variation of galactic radiation intensity with distance from Sun.

## F.   Interactions with the Earth

Since the majority of our measurements of galactic radiation have taken place on or near the Earth, a brief discussion of the effects of the Earth on such radiation is appropriate. Basically, there are two types of effects—geomagnetic and atmospheric.

### 1.   GEOMAGNETIC FIELD EFFECTS

As already mentioned, the geomagnetic field acts like a spectrometer, limiting the low-energy portions of the galactic radiation that can reach a given latitude. For vertical incidence, the minimum momentum $P_{min}$ required to reach a given geomagnetic latitude $\lambda$ is [3, 10]

$$P_{min}(\text{Bev}/c) \sim 15Z \cos^4 \lambda \qquad (2.4)$$

where $Z$ is the effective charge of the nucleus in units of $e$.

This latitude effect has been studied by Storey [86], Danielson and Frier [87], Ray [88], Simpson *et al.* [89], and others. The result is a latitude intensity distribution as shown in Fig. 2-10. The "knee," which shows up most prominently at ~60 deg at solar maximum is due to the depression of the low-energy particles.

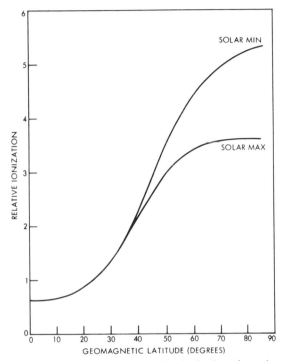

FIG. 2-10.   Latitude effect exhibited by ionization of cosmic rays.

It will be noted the coordinates of significance are magnetic, not geographical. The geomagnetic equator is inclined at an angle of ~7 deg with respect to the geographic equator. In addition, the magnetic field of the Earth is slowly shifting with respect to the geographic coordinates. Within the last century, the magnetic north pole has apparently migrated over a hundred miles. Therefore, the latitude effect may be time-dependent on a long-term basis. If so, the success of the $C^{14}$ dating technique is undoubtedly due to the winds and ocean currents which allow the carbon to diffuse around the Earth.

A second magnetic effect is the east-west one, which at a given latitude makes it easier for a positively charged particle to approach the Earth from the west. This effect, greatest at the equator, is shown in Fig. 2-11. Thus the

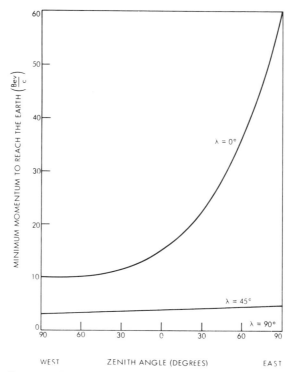

FIG. 2-11. East-west effect as shown by minimum momentum necessary to reach the Earth.

observed intensity of galactic radiation in the vicinity of the Earth is strongly anisotropic.

These magnetic directional properties have been investigated by Bostrom [90], Lamartre and Vallarta [91], Johnson [92], and others. It is seen that for particles of a given energy three situations exist. For some directions as viewed from the Earth (within the full cone) all particles of that energy can penetrate the geomagnetic field. For other directions (outside the simple Stormer cone) no particles of that energy will penetrate. Between these two concentric cones, the fraction of particles arriving varies in a complicated manner. In addition, the Earth acts as a shadow shield, and if the measurements are made in the atmosphere the cones are further distorted. However, it must be pointed out that since the galactic energy spectrum is continuous and isotropic in free space, some particles will always be able to arrive at any point within the geomagnetic field.

## 2. ATMOSPHERIC EFFECTS

For those radiation measurements made within the Earth's atmosphere, the effects of that atmosphere must be considered. The first obvious effect is to provide matter with which the radiation interacts. The very energetic galactic radiation produces "air showers" of energetic secondaries (nucleons, mesons, photons, electrons, and so on), many of which produce secondaries of their own, which in turn propagate. The entire process generally expands conically downward, lasting for a few microseconds [38].

In order to measure these "air showers," various radiation detectors have been set up. Vast arrays of scintillators covering a few square kilometers have been set up at ground level [39–41]. Neutron monitors, meson detectors, and ion chambers have been sent aloft in balloons and rockets, as well as being used at and below ground level. The roles these detectors have played in measuring various parameters of galactic radiation have been briefly mentioned.

A second effect of the atmosphere is the reflecting some of the secondaries upward (the albedo effect). Thus even radiation measurements carried out beyond the Earth's atmosphere ($\gtrsim 100$ km) are perturbed by the effects of the atmosphere. Some of the uncertainties in galactic radiation measurements are due to this effect [9]. In addition, the albedo neutrons are apparently an important source of at least a portion of the Earth's trapped (Van Allen) radiation belts (see Chapter III).

A third effect of the Earth's atmosphere lies in producing variations in radiation measurements due to meteorological disturbances. As the temperature, pressure, moisture and/or dust content, and so on, of the air change, the various parameters of galactic radiation measured in or near the atmosphere may also appear to change. Thus seasonal, diurnal and other radiation correlations have been reported [93–95] which are probably due to meteorological disturbances. These effects are almost always observed for the low-energy portion of the energy spectrum.

Cosmic radiation "air showers" have been investigated by Narayan [96], Wilson [97], Ozaki [98], Goldberg [99], Greisen [100], Boley [101], and many others. Neutron measurements have been carried out by Gabbe [102], Soberman [103], Miles [104], Hess *et al.* [105], Haymes and Korff [106], and others. Leprince-Ringuet [107], Bennett and Greisen [108], Fafarman [109], Fotino [110], and others studied meson production in showers, while Chartres and Messel [111], Lohrmann [112], Anderson [113], and others investigated photons in air showers. The directional properties of air showers have been reported by Clark [114], McCusker [115], Chitnis *et al.* [116], and others. It is easy to get bogged down with the details of air shower

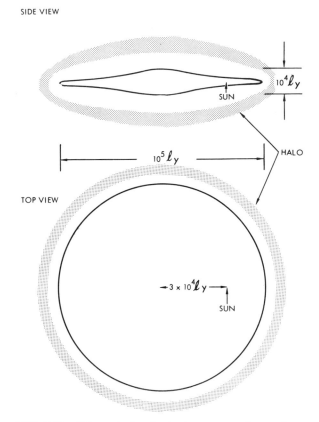

FIG. 2-12.   Schematic showing basic geometry of our galaxy.

studies, and only brief mention can be made here of some of them. For additional information the reader is referred to the references.

## G.   Theories

Various theories have been proposed to account for the observed galactic radiation. A brief review of our current ideas concerning our galaxy is in order to provide a background for a discussion of some of these.

Our galaxy is believed to be disk-shaped, approximately $10^5$ light years in diameter and $\sim 10^4$ light years thick at its center (1 light year $= \sim 10^{13}$ km; see Fig. 2-12). It contains about $10^{11}$ stars, essentially all of which rotate around the center of mass of the galaxy in the same direction. Our Sun is a rather unexciting star located at a radius of $\sim 3 \times 10^4$ light years from the galactic center. At this radius our Sun will make a trip around the galaxy in $\sim 5 \times 10^6$ years. The Milky Way is what we see when we look toward the center of our galaxy.

The stars in our galaxy are divided into two classes according to age. The more numerous young stars (Population I) are located primarily in the galactic plane, while the older stars (i.e., stars that have moved farther along the evolutionary sequence) form a sort of "halo" around the galaxy [117, 118]. This halo is much less disk-shaped than the main portion of the galaxy. Beyond this halo is even emptier space, since the closest other galaxies are $\sim 10^6$ light years distant.

Within our galaxy are clouds of dust ($\sim 10^{-1}$ to $10^3$ amu/cm$^3$), magnetic fields ($\sim 10^{-6}-10^{-5}$ gauss), and various particulate and nonparticulate (photons and neutrinos) radiations. It is interesting to note that average energy densities of visible photons (starlight), magnetic fields, and galactic radiation (cosmic rays) are all approximately 1 ev/cm$^3$.

### 1.   SOURCE THEORIES

At the present time, there is no satisfactory theory for the source of galactic nuclear radiation. It has been proposed that stars like our Sun emit this radiation. In addition to great differences in the temporal, directional, and energy distributions, the Sun is not nearly active enough [11]. If the particles emitted by the Sun were all converted into galactic radiation by some acceleration mechanism, and every other star in the galaxy acted in a similar manner, the resulting particle flux would be less than observed by about a factor of $10^6$. Thus stars like our Sun cannot be important sources of galactic radiation.

An alternative approach is to speculate that the galactic radiation is emitted by much more active stars, such as novae and supernovae [76, 85]. These events yield so much more energy than quiet stars that it is reasonable to assume that they also yield a correspondingly greater flux of charged particles. Synchrotron radiation from such events is quite evident, indicating the presence of relativistic particles (almost certainly electrons). The Crab Nebula, a recent (about $10^3$ years ago) supernovae approximately 3 light years in diameter and $\sim 5 \times 10^3$ light years distant in our galaxy is one of the strongest radio sources in our sky. By comparing the synchrotron radiation of the Crab Nebula and our Sun, it is apparent that one such event a century is more than adequate to provide the observed galactic particle flux.

A third approach has been proposed. This is that the galactic radiation was produced nearly $10^{10}$ years ago when our galaxy was created (the "Big Bang"). Here the problem is that the density of interstellar dust is sufficient to have broken up essentially all of the heavy nuclei in the galactic radiation by now [11]. Therefore some mechanism for the continuous or semicontinuous creation of galactic radiation is required.

At the present time, unusually active stars such as novae and supernovae appear to be the most likely sources of galactic particular radiation. Fan [119], Tidman [120], Biermann [121], Parker [122], Garmie and Kraushaar [123], and others have discussed various mechanisms by which this may take place.

There are two possibilities once the requisite number of particles is available. One is that the particles are created with their observed energies. A more probable situation is that they are created at lower energies and are accelerated during the nearly $10^7$ years they travel about in our galaxy.

## 2.  STORAGE THEORIES

From the observed mass distribution, one concludes that the galactic nuclear radiation has a lifetime between creation and destruction (interacting with enough matter to lose its energy) of about $10^7$ years. During this time, it most probably is contained within our galaxy by interstellar magnetic fields. Since it travels approximately $10^2$ galactic diameters in that time, it would otherwise escape. The requisite source strength to account for the observed galactic flux in that event appears to be even beyond the capability of supernovae.

The region(s) of space in which the galactic radiation is stored have been the subject of some speculation. At one time, storage in a solar "halo" was proposed [124]. However, the galactic radiation energies observed are too large for containment by our Sun. At an energy of $\sim 10^{19}$ ev (observed in air showers) a proton requires galactic dimensions for storage in a 1-gamma ($10^{-5}$ gauss) field. The lack of observed energies much above this has been used as an argument for the average magnetic field strength in our galaxy.

At the present time, we can only speculate about the trajectories of galactic radiation during its lifetime of approximately $10^7$ years. The galactic halo may play a role in preventing the particles from leaking out the top and bottom of the galactic disk. It is quite probable that, while in storage, the particles are accelerated so the trajectories may resemble cyclotronlike spirals. All we can do for the present is speculate.

### 3. ACCELERATION THEORIES

At the present time there are two main theoretical approaches to the acceleration of bare nuclei to galactic radiation energies. These approaches deal with the induction mechanism and the Fermi acceleration mechanism.

As is well known, a charged particle can gain (or lose) energy if placed in a time-dependent magnetic field (the betatron principle). It has been shown that a proton could conceivably gain several Bev energy by circumscribing an active solar region as it developed [9, 125]. In more active stars presumably larger energies could be obtained. However, there is real doubt that energies of $\sim 10^{19}$ ev would be possible this way.

Fermi proposed an acceleration theory based upon the interaction of a moving magnetic field and a charged particle [126, 127]. If the two approach each other, the charged particle will tend (on the average) to be reflected with a gain in energy. On the other hand, if the charged particle overtakes the moving magnetic field, it will tend to lose energy. Fermi showed that gains would outweigh losses providing the particle had a relativistic energy and that there were enough moving magnetic fields. Energies to the observed $10^{19}$ ev are theoretically obtainable this way.

In a sense, these two approaches complement each other. Both work much better for protons and heavier nuclei than for electrons. Each tends to make the particle flux anisotropic, but together an essentially isotropic flux may very well result. The induction theory has a much lower energy threshold (ev range) than the Fermi theory (Bev range). Together one may apparently account for many of the observed properties of the galactic nuclear radiation.

## REFERENCES

1. V. F. Hess in: "Sourcebook on Atomic Energy" (S. Glasstone, ed.), 2nd ed., p. 554 ff. Van Nostrand, Princeton New Jersey, 1958.
2. R. A. Millikan, "Electrons (+ and −), Protons, Photons, Neutrons, Mesotrons, and Cosmic Rays." Univ. of Chicago Press, Chicago, Illinois, 1947.
3. W. P. Saylor, D. E. Winer, C. J. Eiwen, and A. W. Carriker, Space Radiation Guide, Rept. AMRL-TDR-62-86, *U.S. Air Force, Biomed. Lab.* Dayton, Ohio (1962).
4. T. H. Johnson, A Note on the Nature of the Primary Cosmic Radiation, *Phys. Rev.* **54,** 385 (1938).
5. M. Schein *et al.*, The Nature of the Primary Cosmic Radiation and the Origin of the Mesotron, *Phys. Rev.* **59,** 615 (1941).
6. P. Frier, E. J. Lofgren, E. P. Ney, F. Oppenheimer, H. L. Bradt, and B. Peters, Evidence for Heavy Nuclei in the Primary Cosmic Radiation, *Phys. Rev.* **74,** 213 (1948).
7. G. Clark, J. Earl, W. Kraushaar, J. Linsley, B. Rossi, and F. Scherb, The M.I.T. Air Shower Program, *Nuovo Cimento, Suppl.* II, **8,** 623 (1958).
8. E. P. Ney, Experiments on Cosmic Rays and Related Subjects during the International Geophysical Year, *Ann. Rev. Nucl. Sci.* **10,** 461 (1960).
9. Koshiba *et al.*, *see*: H. V. Neher, The Primary Cosmic Radiation, *Ann. Rev. Nucl. Sci.* **8,** 217 (1958).
10. B. Peters, Progress in Cosmic Ray Research Since 1947, *J. Geophys. Res.* **64,** 155 (1959).
11. A. Rosen and J. L. Vogl, Cosmic Rays in Space, *in*: "Space Physics" (D. P. LeGalley and A. Rosen, eds.), Chapt. 17. Wiley, New York, 1964.
12. F. B. McDonald and W. R. Webber, Proton Component of Primary Cosmic Radiation, *Phys. Rev.* **115,** 194 (1959).
13. R. Vogt, Primary Cosmic Ray and Solar Protons, *Phys. Rev.* **125,** 366 (1962).
14. P. Meyer, The Cosmic Ray Alpha Particle Flux during Sharp Forbush Intensity Decreases, *J. Geophys. Res.* **65,** 3881 (1960).
15. M. V. K. A. Rao, Isotropic Composition of Low Energy He Nuclei in Primary Cosmic Radiation, *Phys. Rev.* **123,** 295 (1961).
16. A. Engler, M. F. Kaplon, and J. Klarmann, Flux of Cosmic Ray Particles with $Z \geqslant 2$ over Texas, *Phys. Rev.* **112,** 597 (1958).
17. F. B. McDonald, Primary Cosmic Ray Proton and Alpha Flux near Geomagnetic Equator, *Phys. Rev.* **109,** 1367 (1958).
18. E. Lohrmann and M. W. Teucher, Heavy Nuclei and Alpha Particles between 7 and 100 Bev/nucleon, *Phys. Rev.* **115,** 636 (1958).
19. C. J. Waddington, The Charge Distribution of Multiply Charged Nuclei in the Primary Cosmic Radiation, I—The Light and Medium Nuclei, *Phil. Mag.* [8] **2,** 1059 (1957).

20. W. R. Webber, New Determination of the Intensities of Primary Cosmic Ray Alpha Particles and Li, Be, B Nuclei at $\lambda = 41.5°$ Using a Cerenkov Detector, *Nuovo Cimento* [10] **4**, 1285 (1956).

21. M. V. K. A. Rao, S. Biswas, R. R. Daniel, K. A. Neelakantan, and B. Peters, Abundance of Light Nuclei in Primary Cosmic Radiation, *Phys. Rev.* **110**, 751 (1958).

22. P. S. Frier, E. P. Ney, C. J. Waddington, Li, Be, and B in Primary Cosmic Radiation, *Phys. Rev.* **113**, 921 (1959).

23. F. B. McDonald, Review of Galactic and Solar Cosmic Rays, *Second Symp. Protection against Radiations in Space*, p. 19, NASA SP-71 (1964).

24. II. Aizu *et al.*, Heavy Nuclei in Primary Cosmic Radiation at Prince Albert, Canada, I, *Phys. Rev.* **116**, 436 (1959).

25. H. Aizu *et al.*, Heavy Nuclei in Primary Cosmic Radiation at Prince Albert, Canada, II, *Phys. Rev.* **121**, 1206 (1961).

26. O. B. Young and H. Y. Chen, Heavy Primary Cosmic Rays at Geomagnetic Latitude of 41°N, *Phys. Rev.* **115**, 1719 (1959).

27. S. Hayakawa and H. Okuda, Electronic Component in Galactic Cosmic Rays, *Progr. Theoret. Phys.* (Kyoto) **28**, 517 (1962).

28. J. A. Earl, Cloud Chamber Observations of Primary Cosmic Ray Electrons, *Phys. Rev. Letters* **6** (3), 125 (1961).

29. P. Meyer and R. Vogt, Electrons in the Primary Cosmic Radiation, *Phys. Rev. Letters* **6** (4), 193 (1961).

30. F. C. Jones, The Energy Spectrum of Galactic Electrons Produced by Cosmic Rays, *J. Geophys. Res.* **68**, 4399 (1963).

31. H. V. Neher, Low Energy Primary Cosmic Ray Particles in 1954, *Phys. Rev.* **103**, 228 (1956).

32. P. Meyer and J. A. Simpson, Changes in Low Energy Particle Cutoff and Primary Spectrum of Cosmic Rays, *Phys. Rev.* **106**, 586 (1957).

33. F. B. McDonald, Study of Primary Cosmic Ray Alpha and Proton Energy Spectra, Geomagnetic Cutoff Energies, and Temporal Variations, *Nuovo Cimento, Suppl.* II, **8**, 500 (1958).

34. D. Lal, Flux Determination of High Energy Protons by Photographic Emulsion Method, *Proc. Indian Acad. Sci.* **A38**, 93 (1953).

35. M. F. Kaplon and D. M. Ritson, Emulsion–Cloud Chamber Observations on the Interactions of High Energy Primary Cosmic Radiation, *Phys. Rev.* **88**, 386 (1952).

36. P. H. Fowler, C. J. Waddington, P. S. Frier, J. Naugle, and E. P. Ney, The Low Energy End of the Cosmic Ray Spectrum of Alpha Particles, *Phil. Mag.* [8] **2**, 157 (1957).

37. P. H. Barrett, L. M. Bollinger, G. Coccoui, Y. Eisenberg, and K. Greisen, Interpretation of Cosmic Ray Measurements Far Underground, *Rev. Mod. Phys.* **24**, 133 (1952).

38. K. Greisen, Cosmic Ray Showers, *Ann. Rev. Nucl. Sci.* **10**, 63 (1960).

39. J. Linsley, L. Scarsi, and B. Rossi, Energy Spectrum and Structure of Large Air Showers, *J. Phys. Soc. Japan* **17**, *Suppl.* A-III, 91 (1962).

40. T. E. Cranshaw, W. Galbraith, N. A. Porter, J. DeBeer, and M. Hillar, Harwell Air Shower Experiment, *Nuovo Cimento, Suppl.* II, **8**, 567 (1958).

41. M. H. Brennan, A. J. Lebane, J. Malos, D. D. Millar, C. S. Wallace, and M. M. Winn, The Sidney Air Shower Experiment, *Nuovo Cimento, Suppl.* II, **8,** 653 (1958).

42. G. W. McClure, Composition of the Primary Cosmic Radiation at $\lambda = 10°$ N, *Phys. Rev.* **96,** 1391 (1954).

43. F. B. McDonald, Primary Cosmic Ray Intensity near Solar Maximum, *Phys. Rev.* **116,** 462 (1959).

44. F. B. McDonald, Direct Determination of Primary Cosmic Ray Alpha Particle Energy Spectrum by New Method, *Phys. Rev.* **104,** 1723 (1956).

45. P. S. Frier, E. P. Ney, and C. J. Waddington, Flux and Energy Spectrum of Cosmic Ray Alpha Particles during Solar Maximum, *Phys. Rev.* **114,** 365 (1959).

46. C. Y. Fan, G. Glockler, and J. A. Simpson, Cosmic Radiation Helium Spectrum below 90 Mev per Nucleon Measured on Imp I Satellite, *J. Geophys. Res.* **20,** 3515 (1965).

47. P. L. Jain, Energy Determination of Heavy Primaries in Nuclear Emulsion, *Phys. Rev.* **120,** 293 (1960).

48. P. H. Fowler and C. J. Waddington, The Energy Distribution of Cosmic Ray Particles over Northern Italy, *Phil. Mag.* [8] **1,** 637 (1956).

49. N. Hilberry, Extensive Cosmic-Ray Showers and the Energy Distribution of Primary Cosmic Rays, *Phys. Rev.* **60,** 1 (1941).

50. M. F. Kaplon, D. M. Ritson, and E. P. Woodruff, Primary Flux of High Energy Protons and Alpha Particles, *Phys. Rev.* **85,** 933 (1952).

51. W. F. Libby, "Radiocarbon Dating," Univ. of Chicago Press, Chicago, Illinois, 1952.

52. H. E. Suess, The Radioactivity of the Atmosphere and the Hydrosphere, *Ann. Rev. Nucl. Sci.* **8,** 243 (1958).

53. J. Geiss, H. Oeschger, and U. Schwartz, The History of Cosmic Radiation as Revealed by Isotopic Changes in the Meteorites and on Earth, *Space Sci. Rev.* **1,** 197 (1962).

54. F. Begemann, J. Geiss, and D. C. Hess, Radiation Age of Meteorite from Cosmic Ray-Produced He$^3$, *Phys. Rev.* **107,** 540 (1957).

55. J. R. Arnold, Nuclear Effects of Cosmic Rays in Meteorities, *Ann. Rev. Nucl. Sci.* **11,** 349 (1961).

56. S. E. Forbush, Worldwide Cosmic Ray Variations, 1937–1952, *J. Geophys. Res.* **59,** 525 (1954).

57. S. E. Forbush, Cosmic Ray Intensity Variations during Two Solar Cycles, *J. Geophys. Res.* **63,** 651 (1958).

58. H. V. Neher and S. E. Forbush, Correlation of Cosmic Ray Intensity and Solar Activity, *Phys. Rev. Letters* **1,** 173 (1958).

59. E. N. Parker, Modulation of Primary Cosmic Ray Intensity, *Phys. Rev.* **103,** 1518 (1956).

60. F. B. McDonald, Primary Cosmic Ray Intensity near Solar Maximum, *Phys. Rev.* **116,** 462 (1959).

61. N. W. Nerurkar and W. R. Webber, Observations of Primary Cosmic Ray Variations Using Ion Chamber and Geiger Counters I–A Comparison of the Long Term and Forbush Variation, *J. Geophys. Res.* **69,** 815 (1964).

62. J. R. Manzano and J. R. Winckler, Modulation of the Primary Spectrum during the Recent Solar Cycle for Rigidities between 4 and 12 Bv, *J. Geophys. Res.* **70,** 4097 (1965).

63. H. V. Neher and H. R. Anderson, Cosmic Rays at Balloon Altitudes and the Solar Cycle, *J. Geophys. Res.* **67**, 1309 (1962).

64. K. G. McCracken, Variations in Cosmic Ray Rigidity Spectrum, *Phys. Rev.* **113**, 343 (1959).

65. K. G. McCracken, Energy Dependence of Transient Changes in Primary Cosmic Ray Spectrum, *Phys. Rev.* **117**, 1570 (1960).

66. J. R. Storey, Changes in Differential Rigidity Spectrum of Primary Cosmic Rays Associated with Long Term and Short Term Intensity Variation, *Phys. Rev.* **117**, 573 (1960).

67. S. R. Kane, J. R. Winckler, and R. L. Arnoldy, Response of Ion Chambers in Free Space to the Long Term Cosmic Ray Variation from 1960–1965, *J. Geophys. Res.* **70**, 4107 (1965).

68. J. R. Storey, Latitude Dependence of Forbush-Type Cosmic Ray Intensity Decrease Observed at Aircraft Altitude, *Phys. Rev.* **113**, 302 (1959).

69. J. A. Lockwood, An Investigation of the Forbush Decrease in the Cosmic Radiation, *J. Geophys. Res.* **65**, 3859 (1960).

70. I. Escobar, E. Maldonado, N. W. Nerurkar, and R. Romero, Cosmic Ray Characteristics Registered in Chacaltaya during Unusually High Solar Activity, *J. Geophys. Res.* **65**, 1385 (1960).

71. H. Laster, A. M. Lenchek, and S. F. Sieger, Forbush Decreases Produced by Diffusive Deceleration Mechanism in Interplanetary Space, *J. Geophys. Res.* **67**, 2639 (1962).

72. J. T. Gosling, A Study of the Relationship between Absorption Time Profiles of Polar Cap Absorption Events and Forbush Decreases of Cosmic Ray Intensity, *J. Geophys. Res.* **69**, 1233 (1964).

73. J. A. Simpson, The Cosmic Radiation and Solar-Terrestrial Relationships, *Ann. Geophys.* **11**, 305 (1955).

74. P. Morrison, Solar Origin of Cosmic Ray Time Variations, *Phys. Rev.* **101**, 1397 (1956).

75. J. A. Simpson, H. W. Babcock, and H. D. Babcock, Association of a Unipolar Magnetic Region on the Sun with Changes of Primary Cosmic Ray Intensity, *Phys. Rev.* **98**, 1402 (1955).

76. V. L. Ginzburg, The Origin of Cosmic Radiation, *Progr. Elem. Particle Cosmic Ray Phys.* **4**, 339 (1958).

77. J. A. Simpson, W. H. Fonger, and L. Wilcox, Solar Component of the Primary Cosmic Radiation, *Phys. Rev.* **85**, 366 (1952).

78. W. H. Fonger, Cosmic Ray Intensity-Time Variations and Their Origin II—Energy Dependence of 27-Day Variations, *Phys. Rev.* **91**, 351 (1953).

79. V. Sarabhai and N. W. Nerurkar, Time Variations of Primary Cosmic Rays, *Ann. Rev. Nucl. Sci.* **6**, 1 (1956).

80. A. E. Sandstrom, Some Geophysical Aspects of Cosmic Rays, *Am. J. Phys.* **29** (3), 187 (1961).

81. A. H. Compton and I. A. Getting, Apparent Effect of Galactic Rotation of the Intensity of Cosmic Rays, *Phys. Rev.* **47**, 817 (1935).

82. H. Elliot, Cosmic Ray Intensity in Interplanetary Space, *Nature* **186**, 299 (1960).

83. H. V. Neher and H. R. Anderson, Change of Cosmic Ray Intensity with Distance from the Sun, *J. Geophys. Res.* **69**, 1911 (1964).

84.  H. R. Anderson, Ionizing Radiation Measured between Earth and Venus by Mariner 2, *Space Res.* **5**, 521 (1965).
85.  S. A. Colgate, W. H. Grasberger, and R. H. White, The Dynamics of a Supernova Explosion, *J. Phys. Soc. Japan* **17**, *Suppl.* A-III, 157 (1963).
86.  J. R. Storey, Cosmic Ray Latitude Survey along 145° East Longitude Using Airborne Neutron Monitor, *Phys. Rev.* **113**, 297 (1959).
87.  R. E. Danielson and P. S. Frier, Geomagnetic Effects of Heavy Primary Cosmic Radiation at 42°N, *Phys. Rev.* **109**, 151 (1958).
88.  E. C. Ray, Effects of Ring Current on Cosmic Radiation-Impact Zones, *Phys. Rev.* **104**, 1459 (1956).
89.  J. A. Simpson, K. B. Fenton, J. Katzman, and D. C. Rose, Geomagnetic Coordinates Derived from Cosmic Ray Observations, *Phys. Rev.* **102**, 1648 (1956).
90.  R. Bostrom, Geomagnetic Effects on Anisotropic Cosmic Radiation, *J. Geophys. Res.* **69**, 1217 (1964).
91.  G. Lemartre and M. S. Vallarta, On the Allowed Cone of Cosmic Radiation, *Phys. Rev.* **50**, 493 (1936).
92.  T. H. Johnson, Cosmic Ray Intensity and Geomagnetic Effects, *Rev. Mod. Phys.* **10**, 193 (1938).
93.  K. Maeda and V. L. Patel, Seasonal Variations of Cosmic Ray Intensity in Polar Regions, *J. Geophys. Res.* **66**, 1389 (1961).
94.  J. A. Lockwood and H. E. Yingst, Correlation of Meteorological Parameters with Cosmic Ray Neutron Intensities, *Phys. Rev.* **104**, 1718 (1956).
95.  U. R. Rao, K. G. McCracken, and D. Venkatesan, Asymptotic Cones of Acceptance and Their Use in the Study of the Daily Variation of Cosmic Radiation, *J. Geophys. Res.* **68**, 345 (1963).
96.  D. S. Narayan, Lateral Structure of Extensive Air Showers, *Phys. Rev.* **101**, 1815 (1956).
97.  R. W. Wilson, Atmospheric Signals Caused by Cosmic Ray Showers, *Phys. Rev.* **108**, 155 (1957).
98.  S. Ozaki, Latitude Effect on Extensive Air Showers of Cosmic Ray, *Phys. Rev.* **117**, 1125 (1960).
99.  A. Goldberg, Flux at Sea Level of Heavy Charged Particles Pair-Produced in Cosmic Ray Showers, *Phys. Rev.* **117**, 1128 (1960).
100.  K. Greisen, Cosmic Ray Showers, *Ann. Rev. Nucl. Sci.* **10**, 63 (1960).
101.  F. I. Boley, Atmospheric Cerenkov Radiation from Cosmic Ray Air Showers, *Rev. Mod. Phys.* **36**, 792 (1964).
102.  J. D. Gabbe, Some Measurements of Atmospheric Neutrons, *Phys. Rev.* **112**, 497 (1958).
103.  R. K. Soberman, High Altitude Cosmic Ray Neutron Intensity Variations, *Phys. Rev.* **102**, 1399 (1956).
104.  R. F. Miles, Density of Cosmic Ray Neutrons in the Atmosphere, *J. Geophys. Res.* **69**, 1277 (1964).
105.  W. N. Hess, H. W. Patterson, R. Wallace, and E. L. Chupp, Cosmic Ray Neutron Energy Spectrum, *Phys. Rev.* **116**, 445 (1959).
106.  R. C. Haymes and S. A. Korff, Slow Neutron Intensity at High Balloon Altitudes, *Phys. Rev.* **120**, 1460 (1960).

107. L. Leprince-Ringuet, Mesons and Heavy Unstable Particles in Cosmic Rays, *Ann. Rev. Nucl. Sci.* **3**, 39 (1953).

108. S. Bennett and K. Greisen, Energy Spectrum and Positive Excess of Mesons in Cosmic Ray Showers, *Phys. Rev.* **124**, 1982 (1961).

109. A. Fafarman, Absolute Intensity of Low Energy Cosmic Ray $\mu$ Mesons, *Phys. Rev.* **104**, 1116 (1956).

110. M. Fotino, Low Energy $\pi$ Mesons in Cosmic Radiation, *Phys. Rev.* **117**, 243 (1960).

111. B. A. Chartres and H. Messel, Angular Distribution in Electron-Photon Showers without Landau Approximation, *Phys. Rev.* **104**, 517 (1956).

112. E. Lohrman, Investigation of Bremsstrahlung and Pair Production at Energies $> 10^{11}$ eV, *Phys. Rev.* **122**, 1908 (1961).

113. K. A. Anderson, Secondary Cosmic Ray Photons below Cascade Energy, *Phys. Rev.* **123**, 1435 (1961).

114. G. W. Clark, Arrival Directions of Cosmic Ray Air Showers from Northern Sky, *Phys. Rev.* **108**, 450 (1957).

115. C. B. A. McCusker, Measurement of Primary Directions in Extensive Air Showers, *Phys. Rev.* **116**, 177 (1959).

116. E. B. Chitnis, V. A. Sarabhai, and G. Clark, Arrival Direction of Cosmic Ray Showers from Equatorial Sky, *Phys. Rev.* **119**, 1085 (1960).

117. E. N. Parker, Cosmic Rays and Their Formation in a Galactic Halo, *Astrophys. J.* **142**, 584 (1965).

118. L. Davis, Interplanetary Magnetic Fields and Cosmic Rays, *Phys. Rev.* **100**, 1440 (1955).

119. C. Y. Fan, Origin of Cosmic Radiations, *Phys. Rev.* **101**, 314 (1956).

120. D. A. Tidman, Suprathermal Particle Production by Binary Stars, *Phys. Rev.* **112**, 1759 (1958).

121. L. Biermann, Origin and Propagation of Cosmic Rays, *Ann. Rev. Nucl. Sci.* **2**, 335 (1953).

122. E. N. Parker, Origin and Dynamics of Cosmic Rays, *Phys. Rev.* **109**, 1329 (1958).

123. G. Garmie and W. L. Kraushaar, High Energy Cosmic Gamma Rays, *Space Sci. Rev.* **4**, 123 (1965).

124. R. D. Richtmyer and E. Teller, On the Origin of Cosmic Rays, *Phys. Rev.* **75**, 1729 (1949).

125. H. Alfven, "Cosmical Electrodynamics," Oxford Univ. Press, London and New York, 1950.

126. E. Fermi, On the Origin of the Cosmic Radiation, *Phys. Rev.* **75**, 1169 (1949).

127. E. Fermi, Galactic Magnetic Fields and the Origin of Cosmic Radiation, *Astrophys J.* **119**, 1 (1954).

# *III*

# THE EARTH'S TRAPPED
# RADIATION BELTS

## A.  Introduction

The Earth's trapped radiation belts (Van Allen belts) were discovered in 1958 by Van Allen *et al.* [1]. Two of the early satellites—Explorer I (1958α) and Explorer III (1958δ2)—each carried a small geiger counter to measure the cosmic radiation in space. The telemetered signals at first showed the expected radiation increase with altitude up to $\sim 600$ km. However, at higher altitudes ($\sim 1000$ km) the counting rate decreased to abnormally low values, unexplainable on the basis of expected cosmic radiation behavior. Van Allen was forced to conclude that the observed abnormally low counting rate was due to saturation effects of his detector, caused by a very large radiation flux. This conclusion has been confirmed by several dozen subsequent measurements of the radiation environment in the vicinity of the Earth. A summary of the rocket and satellite measurements of the Earth's trapped radiation belts up through 1961 is presented in a table by O'Brien [2, 3]. More recent measurements are similar and are quite numerous.

Basically the Van Allen belts consist of kev electrons and Mev protons trapped by the Earth's magnetic field. These belts occupy a distorted toroid about the Earth, lying in the plane of the geomagnetic equator. The energy and spatial distributions undergo both regular and irregular variations with time. While theoretical studies have accounted for the particle motions which make trapping possible, no completely satisfactory explanations of the source and loss mechanisms for the trapped particles have been made.

In this chapter the current (as of 1966) status of our knowledge concerning the Earth's trapped radiation belts is summarized.

## B. Theories of Particle Motion in a Magnetic Field

Birkeland [4] was among the first to investigate the effects of a magnetic field upon cathode rays (electrons). The results of his experiments were suggestive of the polar auroras, and stimulated Stormer [5] to undertake a series of theoretical investigations of the latter. Stormer's work is of sufficient importance to warrant a brief review of it here.

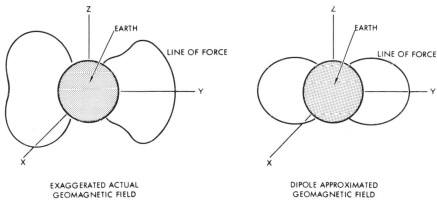

EXAGGERATED ACTUAL
GEOMAGNETIC FIELD

DIPOLE APPROXIMATED
GEOMAGNETIC FIELD

FIG. 3-1.    Representations of the Earth's magnetic field.

Approximating the geomagnetic field by a dipole (Fig. 3-1), Stormer set up the differential equation for the motion of a charged particle in the vicinity of the Earth. That equation is

$$\frac{R}{B}\left(\frac{dv}{ds}\right) = v \times B \tag{3.1}$$

where $B$ is the local magnetic flux density. For a dipole,

$$B = -\nabla\left(\frac{M \sin \lambda}{r^2}\right)$$

where $M$ is the magnetic dipole moment of the Earth $= \sim 8 \times 10^{25}$ gauss-cm$^2$, $\lambda$ is the geomagnetic latitude, $r$ is the radius from the magnetic center of the Earth, $R$ is the magnetic rigidity of the particle, and $R = pc/Ze$—where $p$ is the particle momentum, $e$ the charge of an electron, $Ze$ the charge of the particle, $c$ the velocity of light, and $v$ the velocity of the particle.

Since a time-independent magnetic field cannot change the kinetic energy of a charged particle, $R$ is a constant of the motion.

The solution of Eq. (3.1) obtained by Stormer may be written

$$\frac{r}{b} = \frac{\cos^2 \lambda}{-(\gamma/b) \pm \sqrt{(\gamma/b)^2 + \sin A \cos^3 \lambda}} \tag{3.2}$$

where $b = \sqrt{ZeM/pc}$, $A$ is the angle the velocity vector $v$ makes with the meridian plane through the particle, and $\gamma$ is a constant of integration.

It was found that a necessary and sufficient condition for the particle to be trapped in a finite volume is (for all practical purposes)

$$-\infty < (\gamma/b) < -1 . \tag{3.3}$$

For any value of $\gamma$ there are allowed and forbidden regions of space within which particle motion is possible and impossible, respectively. These are illustrated for three values of $\gamma$ in Fig. 3-2. It is seen that values of $\gamma$ on the

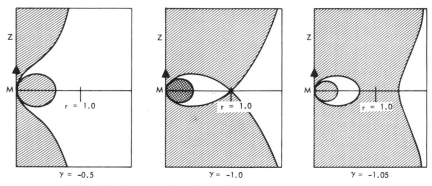

FIG. 3-2.  Stormer allowed and forbidden regions in a dipole field.

order of $-1.05$ result in an allowed region with an approximately toroid shape. However, Stormer concluded that while charged particles could be trapped in a toroid about the Earth, lack of a suitable source mechanism would probably preclude the existence of such a radiation belt.

A clear picture of the motions of a magnetically trapped charged particle was given by Alfven [6]. He showed that three essentially independent kinds of motion are possible, and that in general a trapped charged particle will take part in all of them. The first type of motion is gyromagnetic revolution about the field line with the Larmor frequency $v_L$

$$v_L = \frac{v_\perp}{2\pi r} = \frac{ZeB}{2\pi m} \qquad (3.4)$$

where $v_\perp$ is the component of particle velocity perpendicular to the field line. This relationship assumes that the magnetic field $B$ is uniform along the circular path of radius $r$. This circular component of the trapped particle's motion acts like an elementary magnetic dipole of moment $\mu$, where

$$\mu = \frac{mv_\perp^2}{2B} = \frac{mv^2 \sin^2 \alpha}{2B} ; \qquad m = \frac{m_0}{\sqrt{1-(v/c)^2}} \qquad (3.5)$$

Alfven was able to show that $\mu$ is a constant of the motion of a charged particle in a magnetic field, $B$, even if the field is a slowly varying function of position and time. Mathematically, this is equivalent to satisfying the following two conditions:

$$\left|\frac{\nabla B}{B}\right| \ll r ; \qquad \left|\frac{\partial B}{\partial t}\right| \ll Bv_L \qquad (3.6)$$

Under these conditions $\mu$ is a constant of the motion, and is called the first invariant. This requires that

$$\frac{\sin^2 \alpha}{B} = \text{const} \qquad (3.7)$$

where $\alpha$ is the angle between the total velocity vector of the particle and the magnetic field line (the pitch angle). As the magnetic field increases, the perpendicular component of the particle's velocity also increases, reaching a maximum when $\alpha = 90$ deg. For the electrons and protons in the geomagnetic field, the calculated gyro periods are shown in Figs. 3-3 and 3-4. In general, electrons have gyro periods on the order of a microsecond and protons have ones on the order of a millisecond. It will be noted that these periods are independent of particle energy (cyclotron resonance condition) so long as they do not have relativistic energies.

The second type of particle motion discussed by Alfven and others concerns the velocity component $(v_\parallel)$ parallel to the magnetic field. In an infinite homogenous magnetic field this component will remain unchanged, but in a spatially dependent magnetic field, it is restricted by the relationship

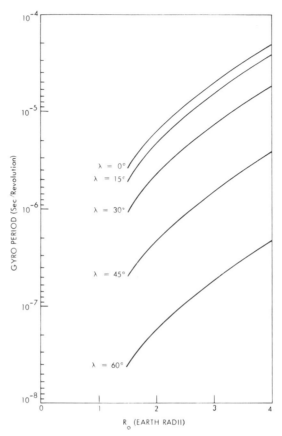

FIG. 3-3.   Gyro-periods for electrons trapped in the geomagnetic field.

$$v_{\parallel}^2 = v^2 - v_{\perp}^2 \qquad (3.8)$$

where $v$ is the total particle velocity. Since $v$ is a constant of the motion in a time-independent magnetic field, $v_{\parallel}$ decreases whenever a positive gradient in the field is encountered. If the field becomes sufficiently strong, the pitch angle becomes 90 deg and the particle motion parallel to the field lines ceases. The magnetic field strength, $B_{\max}$ at which this occurs, represents the limiting value for the particle, since regions of greater magnetic field strength are inaccessible to it. The particle approaching such a limiting field strength thus will be reflected. If two oppositely directed gradients are present in a magnetic field, it is possible for a particle to become trapped between them.

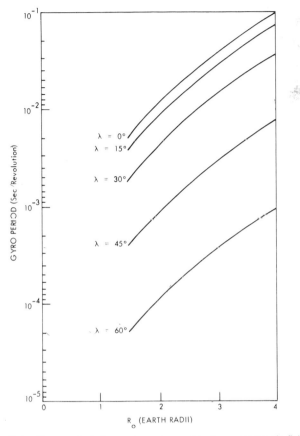

FIG. 3-4.  Gyro-periods for protons trapped in the geomagnetic field.

This is the principle of the magnetic mirror approach to controlled fusion. It also takes place in the magnetic field of the Earth.

The period of oscillation for a charged particle trapped between two oppositely directed magnetic field gradients which act as mirror points is

$$\tau_2 = 2 \int_{\text{mirror point 1}}^{\text{mirror point 2}} \frac{dl}{v_{\parallel}} \tag{3.9}$$

where $dl$ is the path length along the magnetic field line between the mirror points. This period of oscillation is often called the bounce period.

Rosenbluth and Longmire [7] showed that the action integral for this

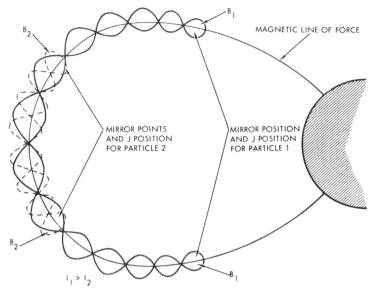

FIG. 3-5.   Schematic illustrating the first and second adiabatic invariants.

"bouncing" is also an invariant of the motion. This integral is

$$I = \int_{\text{mirror point 1}}^{\text{mirror point 2}} \sqrt{1 - \frac{B}{B_{\text{max}}}}\, dl \qquad (3.10)$$

where $B_m$ is the limiting magnetic field strength where $\alpha = 90$ deg. Thus $I$ remains constant even if $B$ is not a constant.

It is possible to visualize the path of a particle simultaneously undergoing gyrorotation and bouncing in the geomagnetic field. The path will resemble a curved spiral spring compressed at the ends (Fig. 3-5). For a particle with a large pitch angle at the geomagnetic equator $(\alpha_0)$, the mirror points lie lower than for a particle with a small $\alpha_0$. The bounce period $\tau_2$ for a particle with a large value of $\alpha_0$ is correspondingly smaller, unlike the second invariant $I$. In Fig. 3-5, the gyro radii for the two particles shown are approximately equal, implying approximately equal energy (assuming they are the same kind of particles). It must be remembered that there are particles with a continuous distribution of energies (and hence gyro radii) trapped in the geomagnetic field.

For the particles trapped in the geomagnetic field, Hamlin *et al.* [8], obtained the expression,

$$\tau_2(\text{sec}) = 0.085 \left(\frac{R}{\beta}\right) T(\alpha_0) \tag{3.11}$$

where $T(\alpha_0) \sim 1.30 - 0.56 \sin \alpha_0$, $R$ is the equatorial distance to flux line (earth radii), and $\beta = v/c$. It is seen that $\tau_2$ is on the order of seconds, so that electrons make on the order of $10^6$ revolutions about the field line (the guiding center for its gyrorotation) while undergoing one "bounce." For protons the ratio is $\sim 10^3$. This great difference in periods facilitates treating the motions independently.

The third type of motion discussed by Alfven is a longitudinal drifting of the guiding center for the gyro and bouncing motions. The gradient of the magnetic field along the particle's path results in a change of gyroradius which leads to a Lorentz force. (The radius is larger on the space side of the gyro-orbit than on the Earth side.) Since electrons and protons rotate in opposite directions about their guiding centers, they drift in opposite directions. In the geomagnetic field, electrons drift eastward, protons westward.

Associated with this longitudinal drifting is the flux invariant, presented by Northrop and Teller [9]. This invariant may be expressed by

$$\phi = \int B \, dA = \text{const} \tag{3.12}$$

where $\phi$ is the magnetic flux contained within the spiral path of the particle as it gyrates and bounces. This invariant is the weakest of the three and is disturbed, if not temporarily destroyed, during magnetic storms (Fig. 3-6).

The drift periods of trapped electrons and protons have been investigated by Spitzer [10], Welch and Whitaker [11], Hamlin *et al.* [8], Lew [12], Hassitt [13], Newkirk and Walt [14], and others. While the drift period has been observed to vary somewhat, it may be represented by Lew's expression [12]:

$$\tau_{3(\text{min})} = 172.4 \left(\frac{\gamma}{\gamma^2 - 1}\right)\left(\frac{1}{m_0 r_0}\right)\left(\frac{G}{F}\right) \tag{3.13}$$

where $\gamma = (1 - \beta^2)^{-\frac{1}{2}}$ $(\beta = v/c)$, $m_0$ is the rest mass of the particle in electron masses $(= 1$ for electron, $= 1836$ for proton), $r_0$ the radius of geomagnetic field line at geomagnetic equator in earth radii, and $G/F$ the ratio of drift period of particles mirroring at same geomagnetic latitude $\lambda_m$ to those mirroring at $\lambda = 0$ $(= \sim 1 + 0.5 \sin^2 \lambda_m)$.

SAME FIELD LINE AT DIFFERENT TIMES

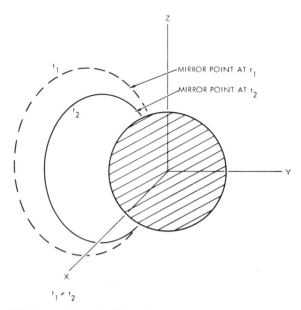

FIG. 3-6.   Schematic illustrating the third adiabatic invariant.

A somewhat simpler (and somewhat less accurate) expression is

$$\tau_{3(min)} \sim \frac{10 + 5 \sin^2 \lambda_m}{E(\text{Mev})} \tag{3.14}$$

This expression is accurate to within 50% for electrons and protons at 3 Re. Since the drift velocity decreases as equatorial distance from the Earth increases, Eq. (3.14) predicts low for $r > 3$ Re and high for $r < 3$ Re.

Thus it is seen that particles trapped in the geomagnetic field undergo three distinct types of motion—gyrotation, latitude bouncing, and longitudinal drift—with quite distinct periods for each type of motion. In this way particles are trapped in the regions of space as Stormer calculated they could be.

## C.   Characteristics of the Trapped Radiation Belts

### 1.   COMPOSITION

Early measurements of the Van Allen radiation were made with geiger counters, which yielded little information concerning the type or energy of that radiation. Sputnik II, Explorers I and III, and Pioneers III and IV carried geiger counters, and Pioneer I had only an ionization chamber on board. Later flights, such as of Explorers IV and VI, carried scintillation detectors and Discoverers 17 and 18 carried recoverable nuclear photographic emulsions. Several sounding rockets also carried nuclear emulsions which were recovered. It has been these emulsions which have definitely established the particle type in the Van Allen belts.

Freden and White [15] established that high-energy (Mev) protons were responsible for many of their emulsion tracks. One deuteron and five tritons were detected among nearly 500 protons. Heckman and Armstrong [16] carried out a similar experiment, obtaining five deuterons and no tritons among ∼800 protons. Naugle and Kniffen [17], Yagoda [18], and others carried out similar experiments to determine that protons were present in the inner trapped radiation belt.

The low-energy (kev) electrons were harder to measure than the high-energy (Mev) protons because of their inferior penetrating ability in matter. In order to separate electrons from protons, magnetic deflection techniques were used. Holly and Johnson [19], Cladis *et al.* [20], and others have carried out this type of experiment to establish the presence of electrons throughout the trapped radiation region.

It was thought that the outer Van Allen region ($r \gtrsim 2.5$ Re) was populated only by electrons. However, scintillation measurements by Bame *et al.* [21], and others established that low-energy ($\gtrsim 1$ Mev) protons are found in the outer belts as well.

Currently it is believed that electrons and protons are both found throughout the Van Allen belts. Alpha particles and other heavy nuclei have not been found. This evidence is of importance in attempts to determine the sources of these trapped particles.

## 2. Spatial Extent

As discussed in the chapter on solar flares, the geomagnetic field deflects the solar wind around the Earth, creating an approximately teardrop shaped region (the Chapman–Ferraro cavity). It is within this cavity that the energy density of the geomagnetic field exceeds that of the solar wind, and hence within which the geomagnetic field is compressed. Since the existence of the geomagnetic field is the prime requisite for the existence of the Van

Allen belts, the spatial extent of these belts is limited by the extent of the Chapman–Ferraro cavity.

The radiation fluxes as functions of particle type and particle energy are spatially dependent within this cavity. The fine structure has not been completely mapped by any means, but the gross features of the flux intensity are known.

Early results of Van Allen *et al.* [22] showed the existence of a peak counting rate, called the $P_1$ peak, at $\sim 10^4$ km from the center of the Earth. This intensity maximum has been interpreted as the inner proton belt. Later, Fan *et al.* [23], O'Brien *et al.* [24], and others reported a radiation maximum at $\sim 22 \times 10^4$ km which was found to be due to electrons. Dessler and Karplus [25] and others showed that this electron peak may be split into two, the $E_2$ peak at $\sim 16 \times 10^4$ km and the $E_3$ peak at $\sim 22 \times 10^4$ km. Dessler and Karplus and others attempted to account for the "slot" between the inner and outer belts. Some of the other investigators did not find these maximums, however.

The problem is twofold. The spatial distribution one measures depends upon the instrumentation used. Hence a peak observed at one energy will not necessarily be located the same place as the corresponding peak observed at a different energy. In addition, as is discussed later, the particle fluxes one measures are time-dependent. Hence the same instrumentation flown along the same trajectory at two different times may measure different fluxes. This is especially true in the outer portions of the Van Allen radiation.

Information concerning spatial distribution of the trapped (Van Allen) radiation is obtained every time a measurement is made at two or more places. Van Allen *et al.* [22], McIlwain [26], Bostrom *et al.* [27], Valerio [28], Temmy [29], and others too numerous to mention have all obtained information which has contributed to our current understanding of the spatial distributions of the trapped radiation. Vette [30] is currently engaged in an effort to obtain as complete a picture as possible by correlating all available information on this trapped radiation.

The general features of the spatial extent and distribution of the Earth's trapped radiation belts are shown in Figs. 3-7 and 3-8. Figure 3-7 shows the approximate time-averaged spatial distributions of high-energy protons ($E > 100$ Mev) and low-energy electrons ($E > 40$ kev) in the day-night plane, which is at right angles to the direction of the solar wind. Of course these electrons and protons both surround the Earth in a distorted torus.

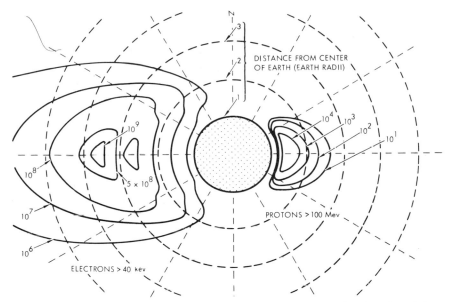

FIG. 3-7.  Spatial extent of trapped radiation belts in plane normal to the solar wind.

They are merely shown on opposite sides of the Earth for convenience.

Figure 3-8 shows the general shape of the electron flux contours in the plane of the geomagnetic equator. The boundary of the magnetosphere has been investigated by Freeman [31], Frank *et al.* [32], Cahill and Amazeen [33], Rosen [34], Slutz and Winkelman [35], and others. They find that the effects of the solar wind are quite apparent, compressing the trapped radiation belts on the sunny side and producing a long tail on the shadow side of the Earth. During periods of solar activity, this magnetosphere is compressed on the Sunward side, and when the Sun is quiet, it expands. The geomagnetosphere on the Sunward side generally varies from ∼8 Re (solar max) to ∼12 Re (solar min).

The tail of the geomagnetosphere has been investigated by Van Allen [36], Fejer [37], Anderson [38], Dessler [39], and others. They find that it is unexpectedly long, extending past the Moon. However, it appears that much of this tail is relatively devoid of trapped particles. The bulk of the geomagnetically trapped particles undoubtedly lie within ∼1–12 Re.

Another feature of the spatial distribution which has attracted much interest is the South Atlantic anomaly. Because the magnetic center of the

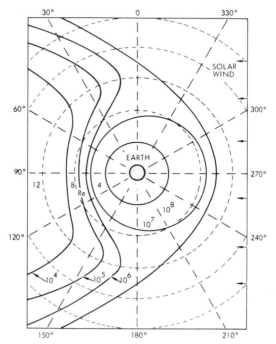

FIG. 3-8.   Spatial extent of trapped radiation belts in plane of the solar wind.

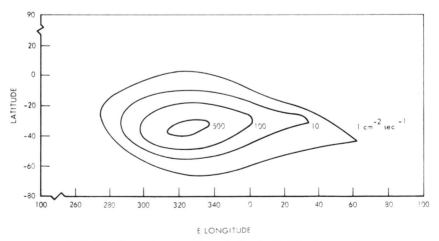

FIG. 3-9   Trapped proton fluxes in the South Atlantic anomaly.

Earth is displaced from the geographic center, the fluxes of the trapped particles are larger at low altitudes (a few hundred kilometers) over the South Atlantic Ocean than anywhere else at the same altitude. The proton fluxes in this region have been investigated by Freden and Paulikas [40], Pieper *et al.* [41], Heckman and Nakano [42], and others. The proton flux contours obtained at an altitude of 200 nautical miles for the energy range of 40–110 Mev are shown in Fig. 3-9. The trapped electrons at the South Atlantic anomaly have been measured also and have a similar spatial distribution.

The spatial distribution of trapped radiation is often described using one of two coordinate systems. The first is the $R$–$\lambda$ coordinate system where $R$ is

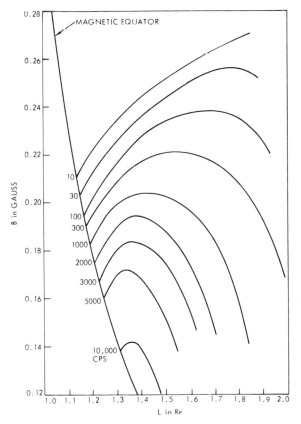

FIG. 3-10.   Explorer IV measurements in $B$–$L$ coordinates.

the distance from the center of mass of the Earth and $\lambda$ is the geographic latitude. A modification of this system based on geomagnetic rather than geographic $R$–$\lambda$ coordinates has been used.

The second coordinate system is the $B$–$L$ system introduced by McIlwain [43]. Here each magnetic field line has an $L$-value in earth radii (its approximate equatorial distance from the magnetic center of the Earth) and positions along this $L$-line are distinguished by the $B$-value magnetic field strength). The logic here was simple—to describe the spatial distribution in terms of the parameters which control the particles' motion. It avoids difficulties due to the fact the Earth's magnetic field is only approximately an off-center dipole, which has led to spherical harmonic expansions of the geomagnetic field [44].

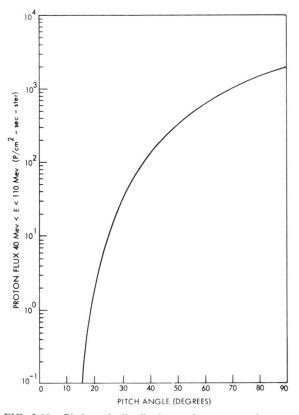

FIG. 3-11.   Pitch angle distribution at the geomagnetic equator.

In terms of B–L coordinates, the flux patterns have a different appearance (Fig. 3-10). This is essentially the same proton data as shown in Fig. 3-7.

The pitch angle distribution fits naturally into the B–L coordinate system. Such distributions have been measured [32, 45] and a typical result is shown in Fig. 3-11. From pitch angle distributions the calculation of the particle intensity along a field line is straightforward. By flying rockets along a field line, such distributions have been measured. The processing and correlation of such data is readily accomplished using the B–L coordinate system.

Unfortunately the motions of spacecraft are controlled by gravitational rather than magnetic forces (excluding magnetically oriented spacecraft) and the B–L system has its limitations. Methods of converting from R–λ to B–L systems have been devised [46], and computer programs for integrating the Van Allen flux along a given trajectory have been coded (see Chapter IX).

3. ENERGY DISTRIBUTIONS

The first measurements of the proton energy spectrum were obtained by Freden and White from recoverable emulsions flown in a sounding rocket [15]. The resulting differential energy spectrum, most of which is believed due to protons at 1000–1200 km, had an $E_p^{-1.8}$ slope between 75 and 700 Mev. Measurements by Naugle and Kniffen yielded an $E_p^{-4.5}$ slope between 10 and 50 Mev, showing that the proton energy spectrum was spatially dependent. In terms of McIlwain's parameter L, the above measurements and others were found by McIlwain and Pizzella [47] to vary as

$$\phi(E)\, dE = \text{const}\, \exp[- E/E_0]\, dE \qquad (3.15)$$

where $E_0 = 306\, L^{-5.2}$ Mev. The proton differential energy distribution at its maximum ($r \sim 1.5$ Re) is shown in Fig. 3-12.

Recently Imhof and Smith [48] analyzed scintillation detector data from rockets and satellites to obtain the relationship,

$$\phi(E)\, dE = \text{const}\, \exp[- E/E_0]\, dE \qquad (3.16)$$

where $E_0 = 406\, L^{-4.8}$. These expressions have been used for several shielding calculations.

The measurements are not all in agreement with the preceding. Heckman and Armstrong [49], Armstrong *et al.* [50], and others adduce proton spectral shapes which agree with Freden and White, but at about one-third the intensity. Other measurements yield spectral shapes which are somewhat different. The explanation appears to be partially dependent upon the time at which the measurements were made. The Freden-White spectrum has been used as the basis of more Van Allen belt shielding calculations than any other, and represents a conservative estimate of the proton energy spectrum at lower $L$-values. As the analytical expressions given above show, the proton spectron softens as $L$ increases.

The energy spectra of the naturally trapped electrons is more uncertain than those of the trapped protons. This is due to the following:

1. In the inner belt, the presence of high-energy protons makes measurement of the naturally trapped electrons difficult.

2. The fission electrons injected into the inner belt are more energetic and were initially about as numerous as the naturally trapped electrons.

3. The electron fluxes and energy spectra in the outer belt are subject to appreciable time fluctuations.

The result has been some degree of confusion. Russak [51] reviewed the various electron energy spectra obtained up to 1962, and Vette [30] summarized spectrum measurements for electrons up to 1964. Based upon their work and review articles by O'Brien [2, 3], the electron energy spectrum at the nominal heart of the outer belt ($L \sim 3.5$) is often used for shielding studies (Fig. 3-12). The electron spectrum softens as $L$ increases, so a conservative (i.e., high) estimate of radiation doses and effects is obtained by its use, and for lower $L$-values the protons produce greater doses.

It is interesting to note that, in terms of $E/m$, the electron and proton energy spectra are similar in shape. As of 1965, no simple mathematical expression (comparable to the McIlwain and Pizzella formula) for the $L$-dependence of the electron energy spectra has been published. During the next few years, our improved knowledge of the trapped electron energy spectra will undoubtedly produce such formulas.

### 4. TIME VARIATIONS

The various properties of the trapped radiation belts are quite dependent upon the solar activity. The effects of the solar wind in compressing the Earth's magnetosphere have already been mentioned. Just prior to a solar flare, the increased flux and velocity of the solar wind compress the Van Allen belts perhaps as much as 40%. This compression is not uniform—the outer portions of the trapped radiation are disturbed much more than the inner. However, even the inner portions of the Van Allen belts apparently fluctuate by a factor of 2–3 due to this disturbance. Rosen and Farley [52] observed that the locations of the peak(s) in the outer electron belt move inward some 16% (to $\sim 2.5 \times 10^4$ km) during magnetic disturbances which apparently accompany flares. Forbush *et al.* [53], Fan *et al.* [23], and others observed similar intensity variations during magnetic storms.

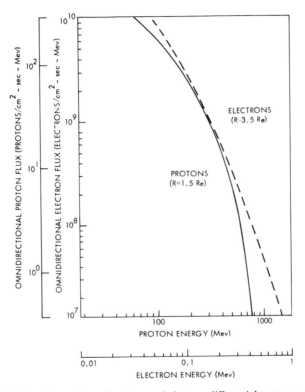

FIG. 3-12. Comparison of proton and electron differential energy spectra.

After a solar flare, the flux of particles in the Van Allen belts is increased. This has been observed by Rothwell and McIlwain [54], Pizzella *et al.* [55], and others. The electron fluxes in the outer regions are enhanced as much as an order of magnitude, while increases in the high-energy proton fluxes are appreciably smaller. Polar auroras are observed to occur during and after the late stages of solar flare disturbances. Several theories have been advanced to account for these phenomena. These theories are discussed in the next section.

In addition to the large time variations due to solar activity, other time variations are also observed in the Van Allen belts. A large diurnal variation for electrons has been reported by O'Brien [56], Frank [57] and others; it is undoubtedly due to the shape of the geomagnetosphere. Since the tail always points away from the Sun, the fact that the fluxes are greater during local noon than at local midnight is not surprising. Perhaps less to be expected are the smaller apparent seasonal variations. These are probably due to the inclination of the Earth's equator relative to the Sun, although the seasonal variation in the scale height of the atmosphere may also play a role. Several correlation studies of these seasonal variations with aurora seasonal variations have been carried out.

Several attempts [58, 59] have been made to correlate these natural time variations with the lifetimes of the trapped particles. These studies involve observing the time decay of particle fluxes after a magnetic storm, and yield lifetimes varying from less than a day for low-energy electrons at high $L$-values to several years, possibly decades, for high-energy protons at low $L$-values. Several theories pertaining to the source and loss mechanisms for the trapped particles which yield the temporal variations have been proposed. So far no complete understanding of these variations has resulted.

## D.   Theories Pertaining to the Trapped Radiation Belts

### 1.   SOURCE MECHANISMS

Two basic types of source mechanisms have been proposed. One is direct particle injection. If by some mechanism a particle finds itself in the trapped radiation region with its energy and direction of motion within the theoretically acceptable limits, it will be trapped. Possible sources of such particles are the solar wind, solar flares, and galactic (cosmic) radiation. However, the solar wind particles and many of the solar flare particles are not sufficiently energetic to reach the trapped radiation zones under normal conditions, while most of the galactic particles are too energetic to be trapped. One way out of this difficulty is to postulate a sufficient distortion of the geomagnetic field during solar activity so that solar wind and/or solar flare particles can "spill" into the trapped radiation belt region near the magnetic poles. After the field reestablishes itself, the particles may become trapped.

There are two not necessarily insurmountable difficulties with this approach. The first is that these particles, even if they are trapped, will not have the observed energy distribution of the Van Allen radiation. This objection is usually answered by postulating betraton acceleration due to the fluctuations in the magnetic field during a magnetic disturbance. It has been used to account for the low-energy trapped protons and electrons on the basis of the solar wind as the source.

The second difficulty with the direct injection theory is that only protons and electrons (for all practical purposes) have been observed in the trapped radiation belts. Solar flare radiations are known to include alpha particles and probably a few heavier nuclei as well; galactic radiations include sizable alpha particle and heavier nuclear components up to iron. Some of these alpha particles would almost certainly be trapped if direct injection were an important source of the Van Allen belts; yet they have not been observed. It is extremely difficult to postulate a mechanism which would trap a proton for years while not trapping alpha particles of comparable energies for comparable times.

In spite of these difficulties, the direct injection approach has been tried. Pizzella, McIlwain, and Van Allen [55] reduced the Explorer VII data to obtain inner belt fluctuations of factors of 2–3. They concluded that direct solar injection could be the temporary cause of this increase, with acceleration of low-energy protons already trapped contributing. Indirect injection was not ruled out, however.

Coleman [60] attempted to account for the energy spectrum of the outer belt electrons by assuming direct injection from the Sun followed by betatron acceleration. He obtained an $E^{-n}$ type integral energy spectrum, but Rosen and Farley [52] found the approach incompatible with the Explorer VI data.

One aspect of the work of Coleman and others is quite interesting. Coleman postulated that the fluctuations in the outer electron belt might be due to reversible betatron action. Thus the electron fluxes might not change at all, but only appear to change because our detectors are energy sensitive. Dessler and Karplus [25] suggested that the requisite magnetic field oscillations might be due to a ring current which is important only during magnetic storms. This ring current would act to oppose the geomagnetic field beyond $\sim 6$ Re, allowing injection of the particles.

At the present time, it appears that direct injection from the solar wind may be a source mechanism for the low-energy trapped particles. Direct injection of solar flare or galactic particles appears to be only a negligible source of the Van Allen belts.

The second basic type of source mechanism is indirect particle injection via neutron albedo. As the energetic solar flare and galactic particle radiation interacts with the Earth's atmosphere, secondary nucleons are produced. Some of these secondaries are neutrons, and some of these secondary neutrons will be ejected upward. The flight path of the neutron is unaffected by the geomagnetic field, allowing it to readily penetrate the Van Allen belts. However, the neutron, being unstable outside of a nucleus, decays with a half-life of about 800 sec into a proton and an electron. In order to conserve momentum, the protons receive nearly all of the neutron's kinetic energy, while the electron receives only approximately 1/1836 as much. Thus the existence of electrons and protons in the trapped radiation belts can be accounted for in one stroke which yields the approximate energy distributions as well. At first it looks as if here were the answer. However, when detailed calculations are made, some difficulties appear.

Singer [61], Hess [62], and others proposed that neutron albedo might account for the trapped particles. Freden and White [63] found good agreement with the inner proton belt energy spectrum from ~ 75 to 300 Mev. Lenchek and Singer [64] improved the high-energy calculations by taking into account the anisotropic distribution of the albedo neutrons. Other refinements of the calculation of the trapped proton fluxes based on the albedo theory have been carried out by Lenchek [65], Seward and Hess [66], and others.

Walt and MacDonald [67], Lenchek and Singer [64], Kellogg [68], and others used the albedo theory to calculate the electron fluxes and energy spectra in the outer Van Allen belt. Uncertainties in the atmospheric mode, reaction cross sections, and loss mechanisms made comparisons with experiments difficult, but it appears that only a portion of the outer electron belt is due to neutron albedo. Both solar flare and galactic radiations were considered. Since particle lifetimes are apparently much lower for the outer belts than for the inner, loss mechanisms are correspondingly more important. Until the quantitative behavior of the loss mechanisms is better known, uncertainties concerning the neutron albedo theory will remain.

In conclusion, however, it appears that neutron albedo is an important, but probably not the only, source of particles in the trapped radiation belts.

## 2. LOSS MECHANISMS

According to the simpleminded theory of particle motions, a particle trapped in the geomagnetic field might remain trapped forever. The time fluctuations indicate that each particle has a finite life expectancy in the Van Allen belts. Here we consider some of the mechanisms by which particles may be lost from the Van Allen belts.

The first mechanism is interaction with the atmosphere. If a particle has too large a pitch angle $\alpha_0$ at the geomagnetic equator, it will have a mirror point which lies in the Earth's atmosphere. Such a particle may be scattered so that its energy or direction remove it from the Van Allen belts. The Fokker–Plank equation is usually used to calculate the interactions of charged particles in the atmosphere. Such particles may be directly related to the production of the polar auroras. O'Brien *et al.* [69], McIlwain [70], McDiarmid *et al.* [71], Sharp *et al.* [72], and others have investigated this relationship, and it appears that, while there are direct correlations, the trapped radiation may not be sufficiently intense to produce the auroras singlehanded. However, it is beyond question that one of the loss mechanisms for geomagnetically trapped particles is interaction with the atmosphere.

Coulomb interactions constitute a second loss mechanism. If a trapped charged particle passes sufficiently close to another charged particle (trapped or untrapped), it may be scattered sufficiently to escape the Van Allen belts. Alternatively, if the relative velocity of two oppositely charged particles is not too great, they may neutralize each other. For particles with small equatorial pitch angles, this class of interactions constitutes the main loss mechanism.

Hydromagnetic waves should be mentioned here. Since the Van Allen belts constitute a plasma, a disturbance in one portion of the Van Allen belts will tend to propagate to the other portions. Thus, hydromagnetic waves in the solar wind will produce hydromagnetic disturbances in the Van Allen belts, which may in turn temporarily lower the mirroring points of trapped particles (leading to atmospheric losses) or compress portions of the belts (leading to increased coulomb losses).

## E. Artificial Trapped Radiation

Thus far this chapter has been primarily concerned with the natural trapped radiation belts. It has been demonstrated that the injection of electrons (and possibly protons) into the trapped radiation belts is also possible by nuclear detonations. Nuclear detonations which are known to have produced observable effects in the trapped radiation zones are listed in Table 3-1.

TABLE 3-1

LIST OF KNOWN HIGH-ALTITUDE NUCLEAR WEAPON BURSTS

| Event | Location | | Date | Yield (kt) | Altitude (km) |
|---|---|---|---|---|---|
| Teak | Johnston Island | (16.7°N; 169.4°W) | 8/1/58 | ? | 76 |
| Orange | Johnston Island | (16.7°N; 169.4°W) | 8/12/58 | ? | 44 |
| Argus 1 | So. Atlantic | (38°S; 12°W) | 8/27/58 | 1 | 480 |
| Argus 2 | So. Atlantic | (50°S; 8°W) | 8/30/58 | 1 | 480 |
| Argus 3 | So. Atlantic | (50°S; 10°W) | 9/6/58 | 1 | 480 |
| Starfish | Johnston Island | (16.7°N; 169.4°W) | 7/9/62 | 1.4 Mt | 400 |
| USSR | Siberia | | 10/22/62 | ? | ? |
| USSR | Siberia | | 10/28/62 | ? | ? |
| USSR | Siberia | | 11/1/62 | ? | ? |

1.  EFFECTS

The high-altitude detonation of a nuclear device produces a plasma which acts like a bubble, excluding the geomagnetic field. This magnetic bubble rises and expands in the geomagnetic field until it collapses due to the reduced temperature and pressure of the plasma inside. Any charged particles produced by the nuclear detonation may in this way find themselves trapped in the geomagnetic field. Thus the detonation can take place at an altitude considerably lower than the altitude at which injection takes place. In addition, the Argus detonations were in the region of the South Atlantic anomaly where the natural trapped radiation belts are relatively near the Earth.

The injection mechanisms are different for fission devices and for fusion devices. For fission types each of the fragments emits approximately six electrons (beta decay) before becoming stable. The first electron is generally emitted within 1 sec following the detonation; with the remaining five electrons being emitted approximately according to the $t^{-1.2}$ law of fallout activity decay ($t$ = time in seconds). Thus if the fission fragments become trapped in the geomagnetic field, they will be emitting electrons for days after the detonation. However, the majority of these artificial electrons will be emitted within a minute of the detonation, and the trapping of fission fragments for extended periods of time is uncertain.

For pure fusion devices, no fission fragments are produced and the end products of the fusion reactions are stable. However a copious supply of 14 Mev neutrons is emitted during the detonation of a fusion device and a small fraction ($\lesssim 1\%$) may decay within the trapped radiation regions. Thus a pure fusion device would tend to produce an artificial radiation belt of equal numbers of protons and electrons, as contrasted to a pure fission device, which tends to produce an artificial radiation belt composed essentially of electrons. Fusion devices are far less capable of producing an artificial radiation belt than fission types of comparable yields.

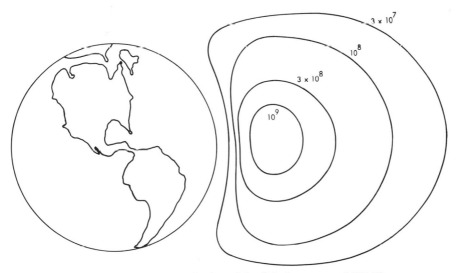

FIG. 3-13.   Spatial distribution of Starfish electrons as of 7/16/62.

The far largest source of the Earth's artificial radiation belt was the Starfish event of July, 1962. This detonation produced an artificial electron belt comparable to the natural electron belt [73] (Fig. 3-13). Since the energies of these artificially trapped electrons were greater than the energies of the naturally trapped ones, the hazards to men and materials in the trapped radiation belts were rather serious [74]. In particular, the Ariel satellite ceased to operate after about a week in the Starfish-produced electron belt, and the TRAAC and Transit 4B satellites stopped transmitting data in about a month [75].

It appears probable that the Starfish event perturbed the natural radiation belts, probably through hydromagnetic interactions. For example, the 55 Mev proton flux at 400 km altitude was observed three weeks after Starfish to be enhanced by about a factor of 5 [76]. Since there were no 55 Mev protons produced by Starfish, they must have been natural belt protons which had either been displaced in position or accelerated in energy by the event. Other similar anomalous effects were observed which suggest that the natural radiation belts are disturbed by high-altitude nuclear detonations [77].

Among the other effects of the Starfish event were artificial auroras at the conjugate points of the detonation [78, 79]. The conjugate points are the geographic locations at which the geomagnetic flux line, along which the magnetic bubble burst, enters the upper atmosphere. In addition, the electron densities of the $F_2$ layer of the ionosphere increased [80]. This resulted in increased ionospheric absorption of cosmic radio noise. Synchrotron radiation due to the artificially trapped electrons was observed [81]. By correlating the onset of these rf effects at different longitudes, the spread and drift of the artifically trapped electrons around the Earth was measured [82].

### 2. CHARACTERISTICS

The initial spatial extent of the artificial electron belt produced by Starfish is shown in the day-night plane in Fig. 3-13. The Starfish electrons were observed at the South Atlantic anomaly [75] and probably extended into the tail of the geomagnetosphere as well. These electrons are believed to have had initially a fission fragment beta decay spectrum, which can be approximately expressed by [83]

$$\phi(E)\,dE = 0.71\, \exp\left[-\left(0.575\,E + 0.055\,E^2\right)\right]dE \qquad (3.17)$$

where $E$ is the electron energy in Mev. However, this energy spectrum is perturbed with time, because the various portions of the spectrum decay unequally [75]. The same loss mechanisms operate here as for naturally trapped electrons but their relative importances are different because of the different spatial and energy distributions of the artificial electrons.

The decay of electrons with $L$-values below 1.7 is due primarily to atmos-

pheric interaction. In this region, the decay has been approximated by an expression of the form,

$$\phi(t) = \phi(0) \frac{\tau}{\tau + t} \tag{3.18}$$

where $t$ is the time since Starfish (days), and $\tau$ is a characteristic decay time (days).

At 400 km $\tau$ was initially on the order of three weeks, increasing at higher altitudes to a value of several months at $L = 1.7$. However, at even greater altitudes, the decay constant apparently decreases, becoming about a week at $L = 2.2$. The characteristic decay times as a function of $L$ as reported by

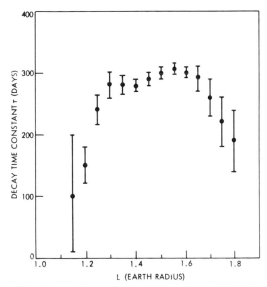

FIG. 3-14.   Characteristic decay time $\tau$ as a function of $L$ for Starfish electrons.

Walt and MacDonald [84] are shown in Fig. 3-14. Investigations of the time decay of the Starfish artificial electron belt have been carried out by Bostrom and Williams [85], Gaines and Glass [86], Allen *et al.* [87], and others.

It will be noted that the form of the above expression leads to a decreasing decay rate as time passes. Thus the Starfish electrons are decaying at a decreasing rate. However, the increased solar activity of the next few years should speed up the process. By 1970, if no additional high-altitude nuclear detonations take place, only the natural trapped radiation will be left in the Van Allen belts.

## REFERENCES

1.  J. A. Van Allen, G. H. Ludwig, E. C. Ray, and C. E. McIlwain, Observations of High Intensity Radiation by Satellites 1958, Alpha and Gamma, *Jet Propulsion* **28,** 1 (1958).
2.  B. J. O'Brien, The Trapped Radiation Zones, *in*: "Space Physics" (D. P. LeGalley and A. Rosen, ed.), Chap. 14. Wiley New York, 1964.
3.  B. J. O'Brien, Review of Studies of Trapped Radiation with Satellite-Borne Apparatus, *Space Sci. Rev.* **1,** 415 (1962).
4.  K. Birkeland, "On the Cause of Magnetic Storms and the Origin of Terrestrial Magnetism," Vol. I. (The Norwegian Aurora Polaris Expedition.) H. Aschehong & Co., Christiania, Norway, 1913.
5.  C. Stormer, "The Polar Aurora," Oxford Univ. Press (Clarendon), London and New York, 1955.
6.  H. Alfven, "Cosmical Electrodynamics," Oxford Univ. Press (Clarendon) London and New York, 1950.
7.  M. N. Rosenbluth and C. I. Longmire, Stability of Plasmas Confined by Magnetic Fields, *Ann. Phys. (N.Y.)* **1** (1957).
8.  D. A. Hamlin, R. Karplus, R. C. Vik, and K. M. Watson, Mirror and Azimuthal Drift Frequencies for Geomagnetically Trapped Particles, *J. Geophys. Res.* **66,** 1 (1961).
9.  T. G. Northrop and E. Teller, Stability of the Adiabatic Motion of Charged Particles in the Earth's Field, *Phys. Rev.* **117,** 215 (1960).
10. L. Spitzer, "Physics of Fully Ionized Gasses," Wiley (Interscience), New York, 1956.
11. J. A. Welch and W. A. Whitaker, Theory of Geomagnetically Trapped Electronics from an Artificial Source, *J. Geophys. Res.* **64,** 909 (1959).
12. J. S. Lew, Drift Rate in a Dipole Field, *J. Geophys. Res.* **66,** 2681 (1961).
13. A. Hassitt, The Drift Velocity of Trapped Particles, *J. Geophys. Res.* **70,** 535 (1965).
14. L. L. Newkirk and M. Walt, Longitudinal Drift Velocity of Geomagnetically Trapped Particles, *J. Geophys. Res.* **69,** 1759 (1964).
15. S. C. Freden and R. S. White, Protons in the Earth's Magnetic Field, *Phys. Rev. Letters* **3,** 9 (1959).
16. H. H. Heckman and A. H. Armstrong, Energy Spectrum of Geomagnetically Trapped Protons, *J. Geophys. Res.* **67,** 1255 (1962).
17. J. E. Naugle and D. A. Kniffen, Flux and Energy Spectra of the Protons in the Inner Van Allen Belt, *Phys. Rev. Letters* **7,** 3 (1961).
18. H. Yagoda, Star Production by Trapped Protons in the Inner Radiation Belt, *Phys. Rev. Letters* **5,** 17 (1960).
19. F. E. Holly and R. G. Johnson, Measurement of Radiation in the Lower Van Allen Belt, *J. Geophys. Res.* **65,** 771 (1960).

20. J. B. Cladis, L. F. Chase, W. L. Imhof, and D. J. Knecht, Energy Spectrum and Angular Distributions of Electrons Trapped in the Geomagnetic Field, *J. Geophys. Res.* **66,** 2297 (1961).

21. S. J. Bame, J. P. Conner, H. H. Hill, and F. E. Holly, Protons in the Outer Zone of the Radiation Belt, *J. Geophys. Res.* **68,** 55 (1963).

22. J. A. Van Allen, C. E. McIlwain, and G. H. Ludwig, Recent Observations with Satellite 1958E, *J. Geophys. Res.* **64,** 271 (1959).

23. C. Y. Fan, P. Meyer, and J. A. Simpson, Dynamics and Structure of the Outer Radiation Belt, *J. Geophys. Res.* **66,** 2607 (1961).

24. B. J. O'Brien, J. A. Van Allen, C. D. Laughlin, and L. A. Frank, Absolute Electron Intensities in the Heart of the Earth's Outer Radiation Zone, *J. Geophys. Res.* **67,** 1 (1962).

25. A. J. Dessler and R. Karplus, Some Properties of the Van Allen Radiation, *Phys. Rev. Letters* **4,** 271 (1960).

26. C. E. McIlwain, Redistribution of Trapped Protons during a Magnetic Storm, *Space Res.* **5,** 374 (1965).

27. C. O. Bostrom, A. J. Zmuda, and G. F. Pieper, Trapped Protons in the South Atlantic Magnetic Anomaly during July–December 1962, *J. Geophys. Res.* **70,** 2035 (1965).

28. J. Valerio, Protons from 40–110 MeV Observed on Injun 3, *J. Geophys. Res.* **69,** 4949 (1964).

29. V. V. Temmy, Atlas of the Intensity Distributions of Trapped Corpuscles Measured by the Cosmos-3 and Cosmos-5 Satellites, *Space Res.* **5,** 489 (1965).

30. J. I. Vette, "Models of the Trapped Radiation Environment," Vols. I and II, NASA Rept. SP-3024 (1966).

31. J. W. Freeman, The Morphology of the Electron Distribution in the Outer Radiation Zone and near the Magnetospheric Boundary as Observed by Explorer 12, *J. Geophys. Res.* **69,** 1691 (1964).

32. L. A. Frank, J. A. Van Allen, and E. Macagno, Charged Particle Observations in the Earth's Outer Magnetosphere, *J. Geophys. Res.* **68,** 3543 (1963).

33. L. J. Cahill and P. G. Amazeen, The Boundary of the Geomagnetic Field, *J. Geophys. Res.* **68,** 1835 (1963).

34. A. Rosen, The Radiation Belt Boundary near Solar Cycle Maximum as Determined from the Trapping of Energetic Electrons, *J. Geophys. Res.* **70,** 4793 (1965).

35. R. J. Slutz and J. R. Winkelman, Shape of the Magnetospheric Boundary under Solar Wind Pressure, *J. Geophys. Res.* **69,** 4933 (1964).

36. J. A. Van Allen, Absence of 40 keV Electrons in the Earth's Magnetospheric Tail at 3300 Earth Radii, *J. Geophys. Res.* **70,** 4731 (1965).

37. J. A. Fejer, Geometry of the Magnetospheric Tail and Auroral Current Systems, *J. Geophys. Res.* **70,** 4972 (1965).

38. K. A. Anderson, Energetic Electron Fluxes in the Tail of the Geomagnetic Field, *J. Geophys. Res.* **70,** 4741 (1965).

39. A. J. Dessler, Length of the Magnetospheric Tail, *J. Geophys. Res.* **69,** 3913 (1964).

40. S. C. Freden and G. A. Paulikas, Trapped Protons at Low Altitudes in the South Magnetic Anomaly, *J. Geophys. Res.* **69,** 1259 (1964).

41. G. F. Pieper, C. O. Bostrom, and A. J. Zmuda, Trapped Protons in the South Magnetic Anomaly, July–December 1961, *J. Geophys. Res.* **70**, 2021 (1965).

42. H. H. Heckman and G. H. Nakano, Direct Observations of Mirroring Protons in the South Atlantic Anomaly, *Space Res.* **5**, 329 (1965).

43. C. E. McIlwain, Coordinates for Mapping the Distribution of Magnetically Trapped Particles, *J. Geophys. Res.* **66**, 3681 (1961).

44. D. C. Jensen and W. A. Whitaker, A Spherical Harmonic Analysis of the Geomagnetic Field, *J. Geophys. Res.* **65**, 2500 (1960).

45. L. R. Davis and J. M. Williamson, Low Energy Trapped Protons, *Space Res.* **3**, 365 (1963).

46. C. S. Roberts, Coordinates for the Study of Particles Trapped in the Earth's Magnetic Field: A Method of Converting from $B$, $L$, to $R$, $\lambda$ Coordinates, *J. Geophys. Res.* **69**, 5089 (1964).

47. C. E. McIlwain and G. Pizzella, On the Energy Spectrum of Protons Trapped in the Earth's Inner Van Allen Zone, *J. Geophys. Res.* **68**, 1811 (1963).

48. W. L. Imhof and R. V. Smith, Proton Intensities and Energy Spectra in the Inner Van Allen Belt, *J. Geophys. Res.* **69**, 91 (1964).

49. H. H. Heckman and A. H. Armstrong, Energy Spectrum of Geomagnetically Trapped Protons, *J. Geophys. Res.* **67**, 1255 (1962).

50. A. H. Armstrong, H. Harrison, H. H. Heckman, and L. Rosen, Charged Particles in the Inner Van Allen Radiation Belt, *J. Geophys. Res.* **66**, 351 (1961).

51. S. L. Russak, Radiation Dosages from Electrons and Bremsstrahlung in the Van Allen Belts, *Proc. Symp. Protection against Radiation Hazards in Space*, AEC Rept. TID 7652, 760 (1962).

52. A. Rosen and T. A. Farley, Characteristics of the Van Allen Radiation Zones as Measured by the Scintillation Counter on Explorer VI, *J. Geophys. Res.* **66**, 2013 (1961).

53. S. E. Forbush, D. Venkatesan, and C. E. McIlwain, Intensity Variations in Outer Van Allen Radiation Belt, *J. Geophys. Res.* **66**, 2275 (1961).

54. P. Rothwell and C. E. McIlwain, Magnetic Storms and the Van Allen Radiation Belts— Observations from Satellite 1958E (Explorer IV), *J. Geophys. Res.* **65**, 799 (1960).

55. G. Pizzella, C. E. McIlwain, and J. A. Van Allen, Time Variations of Intensity in the Earth's Inner Radiation Zone, October 1959–December 1960, *J. Geophys. Res.* **67**, 1235 (1962).

56. B. J. O'Brien, A Large Diurnal Variation of the Geomagnetically Trapped Radiation, *Geophys. Union*, 43rd Ann. Meeting, Washington, D.C. (1962).

57. L. A. Frank, On the Local Time Dependence of Outer Radiation Zone Electrons ($E > 1.6$ MeV) Intensities near the Magnetic Equator, *J. Geophys. Res.* **70**, 4131 (1965).

58. H. Liemohn, The Lifetime of Radiation Belt Protons with Energies between 1 keV and 1 MeV, *J. Geophys. Res.* **66**, 3593 (1961).

59. B. J. O'Brien, Lifetimes of Outer Zone Electrons and Their Precipitation into the Atmosphere, *J. Geophys. Res.* **67**, 3687 (1962).

60. P. J. Coleman, The Effects of Betatron Accelerations on the Intensity and Energy Spectrum of Magnetically Trapped Particles, *J. Geophys. Res.* **66**, 1351 (1961).

61. S. F. Singer, Radiation Belt and Trapped Cosmic Ray Albedo, *Phys. Rev. Letters* **1**, 181 (1958).

62. W. N. Hess, Van Allen Belt Protons from Cosmic Ray Neutron Leakage, *Phys. Rev. Letters* **3**, 11, 145 (1959).

63. S. A. Freden and R. S. White, Spectrum of Trapped Particles in the Inner Radiation Belt, *J. Geophys. Res.* **65**, 1377 (1960).

64. A. M. Lenchek and S. F. Singer, Geomagnetically Trapped Protons from Cosmic Ray Albedo Neutrons, *J. Geophys. Res.* **67**, 1263 (1962).

65. A. M. Lenchek, On the Anomalous Component of Low Energy Geomagnetically Trapped Protons, *J. Geophys. Res.* **67**, 2145 (1962).

66. F. Seward and W. N. Hess, Electron Loss Rate from the Outer Radiation Belts, *Am. Geophys. Union*, *43rd Ann. Meeting* (1962).

67. M. Walt and W. M. MacDonald, Energy Spectrum of Electrons Trapped in the Geomagnetic Fields, *J. Geophys. Res.* **66**, 2047 (1961).

68. P. S. Kellogg, Electrons of the Van Allen Radiation, *J. Geophys. Res.* **65**, 2705 (1960).

69. B. J. O'Brien, J. A. Van Allen, F. E. Roach, and C. W. Gartlein, Correlation of an Auroral Arc and a Subvisible Monochromatic 6300 Å Arc with Outer Zone Radiation on November 28, 1959, *J. Geophys. Res.* **65**, 2759 (1960).

70. C. E. McIlwain, Direct Measurement of Particles Producing Visible Auroras, *J. Geophys. Res.* **65**, 2727 (1960).

71. I. B. McDiarmid, I. C. Rose, and E. Budzinski, Direct Measurement of Charged Particles Associated with Auroral Zone Radio Absorption, *Can. J. Phys.* **39**, 1888 (1961).

72. R. D. Sharp, J. E. Evans, R. G. Johnson, and J. B. Reagan, Measurement of Total Energy Flux of Electrons Precipitating on Auroral Zones, *Space Res.* **5**, 282 (1965).

73. J. W. Freeman, The Geomagnetically Trapped Radiation, *Second Symp. Protection against Radiations in Space*, p. 7, NASA-SP-71, (1964).

74. W. N. Hess, The Bomb-Produced Radiation Belt, *IEEE Trans.* **NS–10**, No 1, 8 (1963).

75. W. N. Hess, The Effects of High Altitude Explosions, *in*: "Space Physics" (D. P. LeGalley and A. Rosen, eds.), Chap. 15. Wiley, New York, 1964.

76. R. Fitz, H. Yagoda, and E. Holeman, Observations on Trapped Protons in Emulsions Recovered from Satellite Orbits, *Paper at COSPAR Meeting, Warsaw, Poland* (1963).

77. A. G. McNish, Geomagnetic Effects of High Altitude Nuclear Explosions, *J. Geophys. Res.* **64**, 2253 (1959).

78. P. J. Edwards and J. S. Reid, Effects of Nuclear Explosion Starfish Prime Observed at Hobart, Tasmania, July 9, 1962, *J. Geophys. Res.* **69**, 3607 (1964).

79. J. M. Malville, Artificial Auroras Resulting from the 1958 Johnston Island Explosions, *J. Geophys. Res.* **64**, 2267 (1959).

80. D. Rothwell, J. H. Wager, and J. Sayers, Effect of the Johnston Island High Altidude Nuclear Explosion on the Ionization Density in the Topside Ionosphere, *J. Geophys. Res.* **68**, 947 (1963).

81. R. B. Dyce and S. Horowitz, Measurements of Synchrotron Radiation at Central Pacific Sites, *J. Geophys. Res.* **68**, 713 (1963).

82. G. R. Ochs, D. T. Farley, K. L. Bowles, and P. Bandyopadlay, Observations of Synchrotron Radio Noise at the Magnetic Equator Following the High Altitude Nuclear Explosion of July 9, 1962, *J. Geophys. Res.* **68**, 701 (1963).

83.  F. L. Keller and R. G. Pruett, The Effect of Charged Particle Environment on Manned Military Space Systems, *Second Symp. Protection against Radiations in Space*, p. 265, NASA-SP-71 (1964).

84.  M. Walt and W. M. MacDonald, The Influence of the Earth's Atmosphere on Geomagnetically Trapped Particles, *Rev. Geophys.* **2** (1964).

85.  C. O. Bostrom and D. J. Williams, Time Decay of the Artificial Radiation Belt, *J. Geophys. Res.* **70,** 240 (1965).

86.  E. E. Gaines and R. A. Glass, Satellite Measurements of the Decay of the Artificial Electron Belt, *J. Geophys. Res.* **69,** 1271 (1964).

87.  L. Allen, J. L. Beavers, W. A. Whitaker, J. A. Welch, and R. B. Walton, Project Jason— Measurement of Trapped Electrons from a Nuclear Device by Sounding Rockets, *J. Geophys. Res.* **64,** 893 (1959).

# *IV*

# EFFECTS OF RADIATION ON

# MEN AND MATERIALS

The nuclear radiations present in space are important for at least two reasons. First, their presence and characteristics provide valuable information concerning the structure, behavior, and history of our Earth, solar system, and galaxy. This has been discussed to some extent in the previous three chapters. Second, these extraterrestrial radiations can produce undesirable effects on men and materials in space. This chapter is concerned with a brief review of such radiation effects.

## MEN

### A.   Interaction Mechanisms

#### 1.   ATOMIC AND MOLECULAR EFFECTS

On the atomic and molecular level, nuclear radiation interacts with matter to produce atomic ionization, atomic displacements, and nuclear reactions (atomic transformations). These effects may be produced directly or indirectly, and may be permanent or transitory. The type and energy of the radiations, as well as the characteristics of the material involved, play a role [1].

Photons (X and $\gamma$ rays) act primarily by atomic ionization [2]. Their zero rest mass makes the spatial displacement of an atom relatively improbable, and their small nuclear cross sections make nuclear interactions unlikely. However, photons can disturb electrons in the matter through which they pass, and if the electrons do not revert to their original configurations, permanent damage may result.

For low-energy photons ($\lesssim 0.1$ Mev) the chief interaction mechanism is the photoelectric effect. For this type of interaction the photon disappears, giving its energy to a bound electron. If this energy is sufficient, the electron will be able to escape the atom to which it was initially bound; otherwise it will be raised to a higher bound level. The electron may revert to its initial state by the emission of one or more photons of the same total energy in this case. However, the electron may fall into other bound states, resulting in a permanent atomic change.

For photons of intermediate energies ($0.1 \sim 10$ Mev) the Compton effect usually predominates. In this type of interaction, the photon is scattered by the electron with a loss in energy. The electron receives this "lost" photon energy with results similar to those described above. Above $\sim 10$ Mev the main interaction mechanism is pair production, in which the photon disappears, giving rise to an electron ($e^-$) and a positron ($e^+$) in its place. These particles, which share the initial photon energy $-1.02$ Mev, constitute secondary radiations that can give rise to effects of their own. Thus photons produce ionization radiation damage directly via the photoelectric and Compton effects, and indirect radiation damage via pair production.

Electrons produce primary radiation damage largely by ionization [3]. Since photons dissipate their energy by pushing electrons around, electrons and photons act much alike in producing radiation damage. However, the spatial distribution of the damage is often different. A 1 Mev electron will produce a trail of ionization of $\sim 0.3$ in. in tissue, whether the electron is a primary particle or a secondary one. If the electron is the primary particle, the outer 0.3 in. of tissue will be damaged, but the interior will not be, since 1 Mev electrons cannot travel that far. However, a $\sim 1$ Mev secondary electron may be produced by a 1 Mev photon several inches deep in tissue. The surface ionization is correspondingly less, and the depth ionization greater, for photons than for electrons of comparable energies.

Electrons can produce secondary radiation damage by bremsstrahlung. This bremsstrahlung consists of photons emitted when the electron undergoes acceleration (or deceleration). Such secondary photons may produce some ionization at depths the primary electrons cannot reach.

Neutrons act in a completely different manner [4]. Having an appreciable mass ($\sim 1$ amu) but no net charge, they can produce atomic displacements but no primary ionization. The magnitudes of the displacements increase with neutron energy (up to a few Mev) and with decreasing atomic mass.

Hydrogen displacements (knock-on protons) are especially damaging. Neutrons of all energies also have appreciable nuclear cross sections [2]. The resulting nuclear reactions generally give rise to secondary nucleons (protons and other neutrons) at high energies, and to photons (capture and activation gamma rays) and activation electrons at low energies.

Atomic displacements result in broken molecular bonds which will not re-form unless the displaced atom returns to its initial position. If the displacement is severe, the displaced atom tends to tear a hole through the matter it traverses, producing secondary displacements and ionization. The result is an atomic vacancy at its original position, a surplus atom at its final position, and a trail of damage between. While such displacements are generally less than or equal to a few dozen atomic diameters over this distance, the effect is important. Since neutrons, like photons, can penetrate several inches into tissue, atomic displacements can appear at considerable depths.

A nuclear reaction chemically changes an atom. If the neutron is merely absorbed, the atom becomes a different isotope of the same element. However, if the number of nuclear protons is changed as a result of the reaction, the atom becomes a different element. In either event, an atom which was part of a useful biological material often becomes a poison to be eliminated.

Protons, the most important constituent particles of space radiations, produce atomic ionization, atomic displacements and often nuclear radiations as well. For nonrelativistic energies ( $\leqslant 300$ Mev), ionization is the major mechanism [2]. The ionization density is much greater than for electrons of comparable energies, but proton ranges (distance traveled before stopped) are correspondingly less. However, the energetic protons present in space often have ranges of several inches in tissue.

The atomic displacements produced by protons are similar to those produced by neutrons, except that coulomb rather than nuclear forces are involved. The low-energy (less than or equal to a few Mev) proton cannot reach the positively charged nucleus, but can push against it through the electric field. For the same reason the low-energy proton cannot initiate nuclear reactions as the low-energy neutron can.

There are two types of proton interactions which merit special mention [3]. One is the star, which may result from a direct, relativistic collision with a nucleus. The result is a release of nucleons, mesons, and so on, in all directions, producing a nuclear emulsion photograph with a starlike appearance.

Such cascade reaction stars cause considerable radiation damage in a relatively limited region (often a few cubic millimeters).

The other type of interaction is the thin-down hit, the large (factor of $\gtrsim 3$) increase in specific ionization which takes place near the end of the path of a heavy, charged particle. It is important because of the large number of atoms (several thousand) affected in a small region (a few cubic microns).

These are the most important mechanisms by which nuclear radiations produce effects at the atomic and molecular level. How important these effects are depends upon the biological structures of which these atoms and molecules are a part.

## 2. CELL EFFECTS

The subject of cellular radiobiology is an important field by itself, and several comprehensive review articles have been published [5–10]. It is only possible to consider a few of the more important aspects of that field here.

A cell is generally considered to be the smallest living unit of an organism. Consisting essentially of a cell nucleus surrounded by protoplasm, cells vary in diameter from $\sim 10^{-4}$ cm on up. They reproduce by mitosis (cell division) and often live for several weeks (depending upon type and function). Cells are composed of very complex molecules of which DNA and RNA are believed to be the most important.

The effects of nuclear radiation upon cells are many and varied. The most commonly observed effects pertain to mitosis. If lightly irradiated ($\lesssim 1$ rad), cells are apparently unaffected, continuing to divide as before. A heavier dose ($\lesssim 30$ rad) will temporarily halt mitosis, but, after a period of hours, cell division usually resumes. Even heavier doses ($\lesssim 100$ rad) have been observed to produce a temporary halt in mitosis followed by resumption for only a few generations. After these few generations, all cells then usually die. Often the cells produced during such a temporary resumption of mitosis are abnormal in some way. The heaviest doses ($\gtrsim 300$ rad) permanently stop mitosis, and cell death is the result.

The effects of radiation on cells vary according to cell type, with short-lived, rapidly dividing cells (e.g., in embryos) being among the most vulnerable. The cell environment plays an important role also. The presence of oxygen has been observed to increase the radiation damage in cells by about a factor of 2. Other chemicals, principally NO have been observed to have similar effects.

The effects of radiation on a cell are often divided into physical and chemical effects. Physical effects include those due to breaking the DNA molecular bonds. If this takes place before the twin molecule has been formed, part of the pattern is lost, and both parent and offspring cells will be abnormal. Such abnormal cells may be unable to reproduce, or may reproduce other abnormal cells.

Chemical consequences of radiation include the oxygen effect and similar results [11, 12]. These effects are believed to have their origin in free radicals which attack the cell directly or indirectly. Such radicals have been observed by electron spin resonance spectroscopy to live for days under some conditions [13].

Cell radiation damage is rate-dependent within certain limits [9]. If the radiation time is short compared with the time required for oxygen to diffuse into the cell (microseconds) the radiation damage is reduced by about a factor of 2. If the radiation time is long compared to the reproduction cycle for the cell ($\lesssim 1$ hr) corresponding reductions in the effects have been observed. For radiation durations between these two limits, the total amount, not the rate at which it was received, apparently determines the effects.

One undesirable radiation response of cells which sometimes takes place is accelerated mitosis [14]. Such cells are called malignant (cancerous), and constitute a major long-term threat to the organism of which they are a part. Often these cells will revert to normal behavior after a few generations, but those that do not may multiply sufficiently to interfere with the normal functioning of the organism. Fortunately, malignant cells (and rapidly dividing cells) generally are more easily killed by radiation than normal cells. Thus the same radiations that produced the effect can often stop it later.

The concept of fractional cell lethality has been introduced to correlate the biological effects of nuclear radiation [15]. For each type of cell and each energy and type of radiation, an inactivation cross section ($\sigma$) is defined. This is the area within the cell which must be hit for the cell to be killed. This inactivation cross section is usually considered to be a function of the LET (linear energy transfer) varying from $\sim (\text{LET})^1$ to $(\text{LET})^2$ up to $\sim 200$ kev/$\mu$. Above this energy the inactivation cross section tends to become constant.

Inactivation cross sections vary from $\sim 10^{-6}$ cm$^2$ for human kidney cells (for LET $\gtrsim 1000$ kev/$\mu$) down to $\sim 10^{-14}$ cm$^2$ for lysozyme cells (for LET of

$\sim 1$ kev$/\mu$). The cross section is often considered to be composed of a reversible portion and an irreversible portion. The irreversible inactivation cross section increases from essentially zero (low LET) to $\sim 90\ \mu^2$ (the area of the cell nucleus) at high LET. The irreversible portion also becomes less oxygen-dependent as the LET increases.

One advantage of this approach is that it forms an attempt to explain biological effects on the cell level rather than for the organism as a whole. Once the reversible and irreversible portions of the inactivation cross sections are known for all types of cells under all relevant conditions, the number of cells surviving any given radiation field can be readily calculated. Coupling this with the effects of a given fractional cell lethality will result in quantitative estimates of how well given organs can perform their functions following irradiation. In this way the macroscopic effects of radiation on an animal (e.g., man) can be predicted.

## B.  Flux-Dose Relationships

1.   DOSE UNITS

Ionization and atomic displacements may or may not be important depending upon their effects on the molecule(s) involved. Even if the molecule(s) is disrupted, the living cell of which the molecule is a part may live or die. The death of one cell or several cells may or may not be serious. In order to leapfrog such problems, one usually concentrates on the effects of radiation on the entire living organism (e.g., man).

In order to provide a quantitative basis for studying effects of nuclear radiation on man, certain dose units have been established. They are [16–20]:

R (roentgen)—that amount of radiation which will produce esu (electrostatic unit) of electrical charge of either sign in 1 cm$^3$ of STP air. Applied only to charged and electromagnetic radiation, the unit is equivalent to 83 ergs/per gram of tissue.

Rep (roentgen-equivalent-physical)—that amount of nonionizing radiation which produces biological damage equivalent to 1 R. Originally applied to neutrons, it is largely obsolete, having been replaced by the Rem.

Rad—defined to be that amount of any kind of radiation which deposits 100 ergs per gram. It is not limited to any material and is the basic unit for radiation effects in inert materials as well as living organisms.

Rem (roentgen-equivalent-man)—defined as that amount of radiation which produces the same biological effect as 1 rad of X or $\gamma$ rays. It is related to the Rad by the relationship,

$$\text{Rem} = \text{rad} \times \text{RBE}$$

where RBE = relative biological effectiveness.

The flux-to-dose conversion relationships are discussed below.

## 2. RAD DOSE CONVERSION FACTORS

The rad dose effectiveness of nuclear radiation depends upon the energy deposited per gram of material. Due to the dependence of various energy deposition mechanisms upon specific nuclear properties, the flux-to-rad-dose conversion factor is a function of the energy and type of radiation and of the material considered. For biological effects considerations, tissue is used as the reference material.

The flux-to-rad-dose conversion factors have been calculated for protons by Gibson [21], Turner *et al.* [22], Kinney and Zerby [23], and others. Snyder and Neufeld [24], Henderson [25], Gibson [21], and others carried out similar calculations for neutrons, while Halpern and Hall [26] and Crawford [27] investigated flux-to-dose conversion factors for electrons. Photon conversion factors have been published by Ellis and Ellis [28], Henderson [25], Hine and Brownell [16], and others. Alpha particle conversion factors may be inferred from those for protons by multiplying by the ratio of their specific ionization (11.5) at the same energy. The results are only approximate above $\sim 100$ Mev, because nuclear interactions play an increasing role above this energy and alpha particles will interact differently from protons.

The resulting flux-to-rad dose conversion factors for protons, neutrons, electrons, photons, and alpha particles are shown in Fig. 4-1. The proton curve shown is that of Gibson [21], which is believed to be conservative for high energies ($E \gtrsim 300$ Mev), the secondaries being assumed to deposit all of their energy locally. It is seen that on a per-particle basis, alpha particles are by far the most dangerous, with protons in second place. However, protons are the most numerous of the nuclear radiations in space, and they will be the largest source of rad dose for essentially all situations where secondary radiations are unimportant.

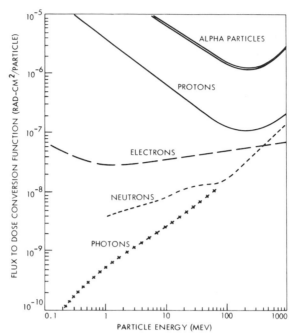

FIG. 4-1.   Flux-Rad dose conversion factors.

TABLE 4-1

CONSTANTS FOR FITS-TO-FLUX-TO-DOSE CONVERSION FACTORS[a]

| Particle (range of validity of fit) | $B_1$ | $C_1$ | $B_2$ | $C_2$ |
|---|---|---|---|---|
| Electron ($\pm$ 3%) (0.1–100 Mev) | $6 \times 10^{-9}$ | $-0.9$ | $2.5 \times 10^{-8}$ | $+0.15$ |
| Proton ($\pm$ 1%) (1–1000 Mev) | $4 \times 10^{-6}$ | $-0.8$ | $6 \times 10^{-10}$ | $+0.85$ |
| Neutron ($\pm$ 30%) (1–1000 Mev) | $5 \times 10^{-9}$ | $0.0$ | $1.5 \times 10^{-10}$ | $+1.0$ |
| Alpha particle ($\pm$ 10%) (1–1000 Mev) | $4.6 \times 10^{-5}$ | $-0.8$ | $7 \times 10^{-9}$ | $+0.85$ |
| Photon (X, $\gamma$ ray) ($\pm$ 20%) (0.01–10 Mev) | $-8 \times 10^{-11}$ | $-2.3$ | $5 \times 10^{-10}$ | $+0.73$ |

[a] $C(E) = B_1 E^{C_1} + B_2 E^{C_2}$; $C(E) = $ Rad–cm$^2$/particle (flux-to-dose conversion function), and $E = $ Mev (particle kinetic energy).

It has been possible to fit the flux-to-rad-dose conversion factors analytically by expressions of the form,

$$C(E) = B_1 E^{C_1} + B_2 E^{C_2} \tag{4.1}$$

where $C(E)$ is the conversion factor (Rad-cm$^2$/particle), and $E$ the particle energy (Mev). The various values of the constants $B_1$, $C_1$, $B_2$, and $C_2$ are listed in Table 4-1. The energy region over which the fit is valid and the approximate error of the fit are also given. The error for the fit to the alpha particle conversion function is estimated.

## 3. RELATIVE BIOLOGICAL EFFECTIVENESS

The concept of relative biological effectiveness (RBE) was introduced because it was found that energy deposition alone was insufficient to account for the biological effects of radiation [29]. It was observed that the biological effects varied for different types of nuclear radiation, or even different energies of the same type. The quality factor (QF) has been introduced as the low dose limit of the RBE [30]. The RBE and the QF may be taken as identical for many practical considerations.

The RBE is essentially based upon the $LD_{50}$ [30] effects on cells and animals [31–34]. This is the amount of radiation required to produce death in 50% of the organisms irradiated within 30 days. X or $\gamma$ radiation is generally used as the comparison standard. The time limit of 30 days is used, because death due to acute radiation exposure after 30 days is unusual.

There are certain limitations to this approach. The first is that different radiations affect the body in different ways. For example X and $\gamma$ rays kill primarily by affecting the blood-forming organs (bone marrow), while protons usually kill by affecting the intestines (gut death). Gut death usually follows irradiation in 4–5 days, while marrow death often requires 10–20 days [35]. Both result in death, but direct comparison has its limitations.

A second limitation is that comparison of sublethal effects is difficult. Some experiments have been carried out with different radiations using white blood cell count, cancer incidence, cataract production, and such, as comparisons [36]. Again the problem is that different radiations act in different ways. The difficulties of equating a blistering of the skin with a given change in white blood cells illustrates this.

A third difficulty is that of extrapolating from mere cells and other animals to man. The lethal dose of radiation is (to some extent) a decreasing function of size [35]. In addition compensation for the self-shielding of the body is difficult. The relative sizes of various organs in the body makes extrapolation difficult, especially for nonuniform or partial body radiation exposure.

In spite of these limitations, recourse to cell and animal experiments affords the only alternative to human exposure for estimating the RBE's of various nuclear radiations.

A considerable amount of evidence suggests that the RBE is a function of the linear energy transfer (LET). For situations in which the radiation damage is by ionization, the LET is equal to the specific ionization (number of ion pairs formed per unit of path length). In particular, Schaefer [37], Snyder [38], Rossi [39], Tobias and Todd [40], and others have extensively investigated this relationship. Qualitatively there seems to be agreement that the RBE is independent of LET below a threshold value. Above this threshold value, the RBE increases approximately linearly with increasing LET, reaching a maximum of approximately 20 at 100–200 kev/$\mu$. For still higher LET values, the RBE decreases, since any energy deposited in a cell beyond that required to kill it, is essentially wasted.

The work of Rossi, based upon lethality effects in mice, is often used for the RBE–LET dependence [39, 41]. This relationship, shown in Fig. 4-2, may be fit by the expression, ($40 \lesssim \text{LET} \lesssim 2000$),

$$\text{RBE} = 2 \times 10^{-2} \, (\text{LET}) - 5 \times 10^{-6} \, (\text{LET})^2 \tag{4.2}$$

where the LET is in units of Mev-cm$^2$/gm. The threshold and limiting values of the LET are 40 Mev-cm$^2$/gm (4 kev/$\mu$) and 2000 Mev-cm$^2$/gm (200 kev/$\mu$), respectively. (Tissue density is taken as unity.) The kinetic energies of charged particles for these LET-values are listed below.

| Particle | Threshold LET (4 kev/$\mu$) | Limiting LET (200 kev/$\mu$) |
|---|---|---|
| Electron | 120    ev | $\sim 0$ ev |
| Proton | 10.8 Mev | 0.077 Mev |
| Alpha particle | 249    Mev | 3.1    Mev |

The RBE values for particles in infinite tissue (i.e., tissue whose thickness exceeds the range of the particle energy considered) may be obtained by evaluating the ratio,

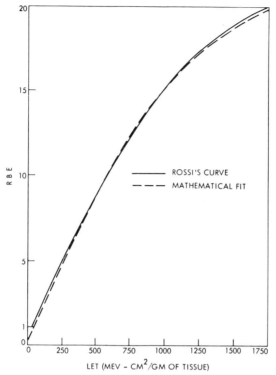

FIG. 4-2. RBE-LET relationship.

$$\text{RBE} = \frac{\text{effective energy lost}}{\text{actual energy lost}} = \frac{\int \text{LET} \cdot \text{RBE (LET)} \cdot dx}{\int \text{LET} \cdot dx} \tag{4.3}$$

By substituting Eq. (4.2) into Eq. (4.3) and making use of the range-energy relation (LET $= dE/dx$), it is possible to obtain RBE as a function of energy for electrons, protons, and alpha particles. For low incident particle energies (LET $\gtrsim 4$ kev/$\mu$), the procedure is straightforward. For high incident particle energies (LET $< 4$ kcv/$\mu$), the RBE is assumed to be unity until the 4 kev/$\mu$ threshold is reached. The overall RBE in this case is

$$\text{RBE} = 1 + \frac{\Delta}{E} \tag{4.4}$$

where $\Delta = 1.1 \times 10.8 = 12$ Mev for protons and $= 1.2 \times 249 = 300$ Mev for alpha particles, and $E =$ particle energy (Mev).

It is seen that the RBE's for the threshold energies (LET $= 4$ kev/$\mu$) are 2.1 for protons and 2.2 for alpha particles. The difference between protons and alpha particles is due to the charge acquisition characteristics of the particles near the ends of their paths. The results of these calculations are shown in Fig. 4-3.

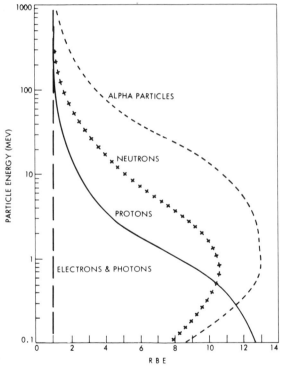

FIG. 4-3.   RBE for various particles as a function of energy.

The RBE for neutrons below 10 Mev has been calculated by Henderson [25], based upon the first collision rate in ethylene. Above 10 Mev the results were obtained from graphical interpolation based upon the RBE of protons. For electrons the RBE as based on Rossi's curve is unity down to 120 ev. For photons the RBE is taken as unity for all energies.

The results presented in Fig. 4-3 are for infinite tissue. For protons below $\sim 200$ Mev in humans, this is a fairly good approximation, since the human body is often considered to be $\sim 30$ gm/cm$^2$ thick. For smaller animals and/or higher energies, the infinite tissue approximation is not valid. In this case, the radiation does not lose all of its energy in tissue, and two definitions of the RBE are possible. These are

(*a*)
$$\text{RBE} = \frac{\text{effective energy lost in tissue}}{\text{actual energy lost in tissue}} \qquad (4.5)$$

or

(*b*)
$$\text{RBE} = \frac{\text{effective energy lost in tissue}}{\text{total particle energy}}$$

In the first convention, the RBE is always $\geqslant 1$, and may be written

(*a*)
$$\text{RBE} = \frac{E_0 \cdot \text{RBE}(E_0) - E' \cdot \text{RBE}(E')}{E_0 - E'} \qquad (4.6)$$

where $\text{RBE}(E_0)$ is the RBE for the particle of incident energy $E_0$ in infinite tissue, and $E'$ is the energy with which the particle emerges from a finite thickness of tissue.

In the second convention, the RBE may be $< 1$, and may be written

(*b*)
$$\text{RBE} = \frac{E_0 \cdot \text{RBE}(E_0) - E' \cdot \text{RBE}(E')}{E_0} \qquad (4.7)$$

While the first convention is theoretically preferred, the second is often used because of its experimental simplicity. This avoids difficulties due to the complex geometries of the animals.

The RBE's of high-energy protons in animals have been investigated by Sondhaus [42, 43], Bonet-Maury *et al.* [44], Saksonov *et al.* [45], Lebedinsky *et al.* [46], and others. A brief list of some of their results is contained in Table 4-2.

Deuteron, alpha particle, and heavy-ion effects have been investigated by Tobias *et al.* [47], Todd [48], Sondhaus [43], and others. Neutron RBE-values have been studied by Upton *et al.* [32], Bond *et al.* [33], and others. While the RBE–LET relationship seems to hold, the use of the second convention makes comparison with the theoretical values of RBE difficult.

Of special interest is the RBE for $E^{-x}$ proton integral energy spectra.

TABLE 4-2

List of Some RBE Experiments

| Group | P-energy | Effect used | Doses | Animal | RBE |
|---|---|---|---|---|---|
| LRL UCRL-11014 Ashikawa et al. [51] | 730 Mev | $LD_{50}$ at 6 and 30 days | 600, 700 and 800 rad | Mouse | 0.8 for $LD_{50}/30$ 1.3 $LD_{50}/30$ (Gut vs marrow effects) |
| French-IAEA Sm-44/48 | 157 Mev | $LD_{50}$ at 8 days | 790 rad | Mouse | 0.77 for $LD_{50}/8$ |
| P. Bonet-Maury [44] | 592 Mev | $LD_{50}/30$ $LD_{50}/10$ | 580 rad 595 rad | | 0.98 for $LD_{50}/30$ 1.06 for $LD_{50}/30$ |
| BNL BNL-7359 Lippincott et al. [52] | 10 Mev | Progressive epithelial dysplasia in mouse skin | 1200 rad 2000 rad | Mouse | |
| LRL UCRL-11015 Sondhaus [42] | 150 Mev | LET calculations | | 30 cm tissue sphere | 1.12 |
| BNL BLN-7343 Jesseph et al. [53] | 2 Bev | $LD_{50}$ at 30 days | $1.2 \times 10^{10}$ to $9.7 \times 10^{11}$ protons | Mouse | |

| Source | Energy | | Animal | Value |
|---|---|---|---|---|
| USSR Saksonov et al. [45] | 120 Mev | $LD_{50}$ | Mouse; rat | 0.7 |
| USSR Saksonov et al. [45] | 660 Mev | $LD_{50}$ | Mouse | 0.7 |
| USSR Lebedinsky et al. [46] USSR Acad. Sci. | 510 Mev | $LD_{50}$ | Rats | 0.8 |
| USSR Lebedinsky et al. [46] USSR Acad. Sci. | 510 Mev | $LD_{50}$ | Dogs | 1.2 |
| USA Zellmer and Allen [54] Aerospace Med. | 730 Mev | Organ injury | Monkey | 2.0 |

After passing through a shield of thickness $X$ (gm/cm$^2$), the differential energy spectrum becomes

$$\phi(E)dE = A\alpha E^{-(\alpha+1)} \left[ 1 + \left(\frac{E'}{E}\right)^n \right]^{-[(\alpha/n)+1]} \tag{4.8}$$

where $E' = (X/\delta)^{1/n}$ = shield cutoff energy (Mev), and $n$, $\delta$ are constants associated with the $R = \delta E^n$ fit to the range $(R)$–energy $(E)$ relationship. This energy spectrum exhibits a peak at

$$E = E' \left(\frac{n-1}{\alpha+1}\right)^{1/n} \tag{4.9}$$

It is not possible to evaluate the RBE for this spectrum in closed form. However, if it is assumed that the spectral shape is unchanged down to the

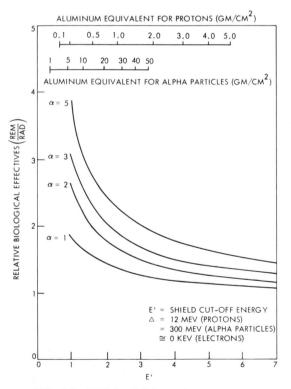

FIG. 4-4.   RBE for $E^{-\alpha}$ integral energy spectra.

peak energy, the RBE can be calculated as [49]

$$\text{RBE} = 1 + \frac{\alpha}{\alpha + 1}\left(\frac{\alpha + 1}{n - 1}\right)^{1/n}\frac{\Delta}{E'} \tag{4.10}$$

where $\Delta = 12$ Mev for protons. This is shown in Fig. 4-4. It is seen that for shields with cutoff energies much above $\Delta$, the RBE is less than two.

A similar analysis has been carried out by Madey and Stephenson [50], who chose to retain the shape of the degraded energy spectrum and deal with the resultant beta functions instead. Their analysis was essentially parallel in other respects, and yielded similar results.

## C. Acute Human Response

### 1. GENERAL EFFECTS

From the standpoint of space travel, interest in extraterrestrial nuclear radiation derives from the effects of this radiation on men and materials. Most of this interest centers on man as the most radiation-sensitive component of the spacecraft [3, 55–57]. In this section some of the effects of acute nuclear radiation exposure of man are considered, with special emphasis on those effects which would tend to interfere with successful completion of the mission.

The current available information has been obtained from several sources. Nuclear radiation exposure data on human beings are limited to essentially three situations. The first involves persons exposed to nuclear weapon radiations during World War II and afterward [58–60]. The second category consists of radiation workers exposed to accidental reactor excursions [61–64]. The third group includes medical patients exposed to X or $\gamma$ radiation for diagnosis or therapy [65, 66]. Unfortunately none of these situations involved exposure to protons, which are the main constituent of all three types of space radiation.

Several experiments using laboratory animals have been carried out with protons as well as with other nuclear radiations. Mice, rats, and monkeys have been studied extensively, although other animals have also been used. While experiments with animals can be carried out which are not feasible in the case of men, the problem of extrapolating the results to men is not straightforward.

For severe radiation exposure, there are apparently four distinct phases

[18, 67, 68]. Phase I begins within an hour or more after acute exposure and lasts for a day or two. This phase is characterized by prostration, vomiting, and nausea, and occasionally diarrhea. Phase II is an interim period during which the patient feels fairly well and generally exhibits no outward effects of illness. For mild exposures, this is the recovery phase and lasts indefinitely; for severe exposures, phase II lasts only a few days at most. It is followed by phase III, which often lasts a week or two. During this phase, the patient develops a progressive fever, hemorrhages of the skin and often internal organs as well, and ulceration of the mouth and throat; loses hair; and often lapses into unconsciousness. This is the final stage for those who do not survive. Those patients who do survive enter phase IV, during which the symptoms gradually decrease, leading to recovery over a period of several months.

For acute whole-body exposure to 0.1–10 Mev (X or $\gamma$ rays), there seems to be general agreement that the macroscopic effects listed in Table 4-3 result. The dose at which the incidence of sickness (as evidenced by vomiting and nausea) occurs varies by a factor of 2–3 from person to person. One person may become sick at $\lesssim 75$ Rem, while another may not become similarly ill at $\sim 200$ Rem (Fig. 4-5). Of course a healthy person can generally

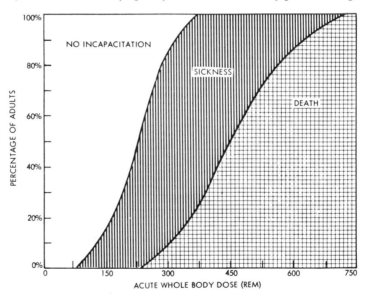

FIG. 4-5.   Incidence of sickness and death from acute radiation.

TABLE 4-3

Expected Effects of Acute Whole-Body Radiation Doses

| Acute Dose (roentgens) | Probable effect |
|---|---|
| 0–50 | No obvious effect, except possibly minor blood changes |
| 80–120 | Vomiting and nausea for about 1 day in 5 to 10 percent of exposed personnel; fatigue, but no serious disability |
| 130–170 | Vomiting and nausea for about 1 day, followed by other symptoms of radiation sickness in about 25 percent of personnel; no deaths anticipated |
| 180–220 | Vomiting and nausea for about 1 day, followed by other symptoms of radiation sickness in about 50 percent of personnel; no deaths anticipated |
| 270–330 | Vomiting and nausea in nearly all personnel on first day, followed by other symptoms of radiation sickness; about 20 percent deaths within 2 to 6 weeks after exposure; survivors convalescent for about 3 months |
| 400–500 | Vomiting and nausea in all personnel on first day, followed by other symptoms of radiation sickness; about 50 percent deaths within 1 month; survivors convalescent for about 6 months |
| 550–750 | Vomiting and nausea in all personnel within 4 hours from exposure, followed by other symptoms of radiation sickness; up to 100 percent deaths; few survivors convalescent for about 6 months |
| 1000 | Vomiting and nausea in all personnel within 1 to 2 hours; probably no survivors from radiation sickness |
| 5000 | Incapacitation almost immediately; all personnel will be fatalities within 1 week |

tolerate more radiation than a sick one (all results quoted are for healthy adults unless otherwise stated).

Death due to whole-body photon exposure will usually follow vomiting within 10–20 days if the dose is 350–550 Rem, leading to the $LD_{50}$ value of ~450 Rem for men. The mechanism of death for photon exposure is damage to the blood-forming organs (bone marrow) [69]. After an acute exposure, the blood cell count falls for a few days, reaching a small percentage of its preirradiation value. If death does not occur, the blood count gradually recovers over a period of several weeks.

Very large photon doses ($\gtrsim 5000$ Rem) appear to act also on the central nervous system, resulting in incapacitation within a matter of minutes [70, 71]. Death within less than about 7 days due to photon exposure is generally attributed to this cause.

The effects of neutron irradiation are qualitatively similar to those for gamma irradiation, except that the lethal mechanism appears to be different. Lethal doses of neutrons often kill in 3–7 days, and the cause of death in many cases is due to damage of the gastrointestinal tract (gut) [35, 36, 72, 73]. Internal bleeding is usually observed as well. The $LD_{50}$ dose for whole-body exposure to fission spectrum neutrons is on the order of 300–400 Rem, somewhat lower than for photons. Neutron exposure has an indirect effect of interest. Due to the $(n, \gamma)$ activation reactions in sodium and phosphorus in the blood, $Na^{24}$ and $P^{32}$ are produced *in vivo*. Measuring the radio-activity of the blood due to these radioisotopes afford a good indicator of the neutron exposure if the neutron energy spectrum is known. Such radioisotopes also will produce a small amount of additional biological damage of their own.

For proton exposure effects, recourse to animal experiments is necessary. At once the question of animal size in relation to the ranges of the protons arises, since proton ranges (unlike photon or neutron mean free paths) are strongly dependent upon particle energy. Thus it is difficult to place the results of different experiments on a comparable basis, and the raw data shows wide variations [36, 42–54]. In general, the proton $LD_{50}$ doses are comparable to those for $\gamma$ rays, and the shorter life expectancy (3–7 days for

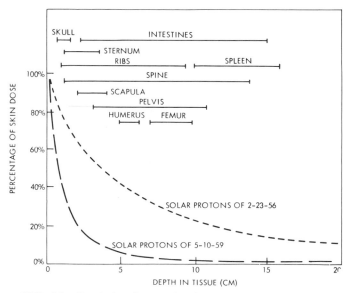

FIG. 4-6.   Depth dose in man showing locations of some organs.

protons versus 10–20 days for $\gamma$ rays) is due to gastrointestinal damage rather than bone marrow damage [74].

One conclusion from the foregoing is that it is not possible to settle upon a single dose limit, even if the effect one wishes to avoid is sickness or death. In the first place the dose as measured in air is not the same as that measured *in vivo* (Fig. 4-6). In addition, the various organs and tissues are not equally susceptible to radiation damage. Radiation exposure is rarely uniform over the whole body, and this must be taken into account. In order to cope with these factors, the critical-organ concept was developed.

## 2. CRITICAL-ORGAN CONCEPT

Uniform whole-body exposure is difficult to achieve when desired, and almost never takes place accidently. By correlating data from partial-body exposure, it has been possible to ascribe certain biological effects to radiation damage of definite organs and tissues. Thus by limiting the doses received by these, the associated effects can be correspondingly limited [75, 76].

The first critical organ is the bone marrow, which is responsible for the formation of blood cells. Located 4–5 cm beneath the skin of an adult human, these blood-forming organs are rather uniformly distributed throughout the body. So long as the functioning ability of these organs is not unduly affected, the precipitous drop in blood cell count which leads to sickness and death can be avoided.

Evidence that these organs are critical in biological radiation damage has resulted in some specialized therapy. One of the more successful treatments for radiation injury has been the use of repeated blood transfusions over a period of a few weeks, until the body can maintain its blood count without them. This works only if blood is not lost due to internal bleeding. Even more spectacular has been the administration of a suspension of bone marrow [77, 78]. This was first performed on five victims of a Yugoslav reactor accident. While all but one of them survived, evidence is inconclusive as to whether survival was due to the administered marrow.

Doses of $\gtrsim 100$ Rem to the blood-forming organs will produce an appreciable decrease in the blood cell count, while $\gtrsim 300$ Rem will often produce death. However, if even a portion of the such organs are shielded, the effects are considerably reduced. If as much as half the said organs are protected, the remaining half can apparently absorb $\gtrsim 1000$ Rem without lethal effects [79, 80].

The skin has been recognized as a critical organ, especially for exposure to radiations of low penetrating ability. The radiation-sensitive portion of the skin is apparently the basal epithelial layer where the skin cells are being formed. While the thickness of the epidermis varies from 0.05 to ~1 mm, a commonly used average is 0.07 mm [81].

The first reactions of skin irradiation are quite similar to sunburn, leading to a redness and itching within approximately 24 hours of exposure. Swelling and blistering may follow. A few days following a moderately severe exposure, the skin will flake and peel, leaving raw flesh. If the damage is not too severe, scabs will form, leading ultimately to fresh (but sensitive) skin. In severe skin damage cases, the scabs will form only to fall off, leading to ulceration. Infection may follow, possibly leading to death [82, 83].

The treatment for radiation damage to the skin is similar to that for burns. Some ointments have been found helpful, but for severe cases resort to skin grafts is often necessary. Recovery often takes several months, and some permanent stiffness of the affected area (especially hands) may result [18].

A dose of $\lesssim 1000$ Rem will produce the described itching and reddening of the skin. Severe radiation burns $\gtrsim 3000$ Rem generally require skin grafts. As with the blood-forming organs, the extent of the irradiated skin plays a role. If only a small area (a few square inches) is irradiated, the results for that area are less severe than if the whole body is similarly irradiated. The unirradiated skin apparently can help the irradiated repair the damage [70].

The gastrointestinal tract is sometimes considered a critical organ. For large doses ($\gtrsim 400$ Rem) of neutrons and/or protons, damage to the gastrointestinal tract is usually the primary cause of death, within 3–7 days. The stomach and intestines lie $\gtrsim 2$ cm below the surface of the skin and can be partially removed by surgery without bringing death. However, they respond to irradiation by clearing themselves (vomiting and diarrhea), and may develop ulcers. The response is similar to that of the skin in some regards. Dead cells are sloughed off, but replacements may not "take," resulting in exposed, bleeding tissues. The bacteria in fecal material constitute an additional hazard [70].

Shielding the trunk of the body reduces the hazard considerably, since even a partial shielding of the gastrointestinal tract increases radiation resistance. Once radiation exposure sufficient to disrupt the entire gastrointestinal tract seriously has taken place, no known practical method of treatment can prevent the consequences [84, 85].

The eye is generally considered a critical organ because of its great importance to normal human functioning. Here the effect of radiation exposure is not sickness or death (as with the bone marrow, gastrointestinal tract, and possibly the skin) but loss of sight due to cataracts. However, the eye is easily shielded, and cataracts generally require at least several weeks to develop. In addition, cataracts can be removed surgically in a relatively routine operation.

For doses $\leqslant 1000$ Rem, complete opacity of the cataract is rare, and cataracts are the main effect observed up to $\sim 3000$ Rem. The rods in the retina may be damaged at $\sim 3000$ Rem, but some of the cones may survive at 10,000 Rem. The optic nerves are apparently more hardy [70].

The reproductive organs are often considered critical, though no more than temporary or permanent sterility is the usual radiation effect. Temporary sterility in the male may result from doses of $\gtrsim 50$ Rem, but the effect usually lasts only about a week. Larger doses extend the period of sterility, but permanent sterility resulting from radiation damage is rare, requiring $\gtrsim 500$ Rem. Irradiation of female reproductive organs may produce sterile offspring, the sensitivity apparently being greater during pregnancy. Permanent sterility may occur at $\gtrsim 100$ Rem under these conditions [70].

The classification of the reproductive organs as critical for astronauts is debatable. Comprising at most a negligible percentage of the population, they will probably have procreated their children prior to undertaking space flights. In any event, local shielding can be used with relative ease to limit doses.

The central nervous system is apparently the least vulnerable of the critical organs. Consisting of the brain and spinal cord, it can function after doses of $\leqslant 10,000$ Rem. Doses of $> 100,000$ Rem to the central nervous system, on the other hand, can probably kill within seconds.

The brain can be shielded relatively easily, and any dose large enough to affect the brain seriously could undoubtedly kill ultimately via other mechanisms. The rapidity with which serious radiation damage to the brain brings death accounts for its inclusion as a critical organ [70, 86].

A few comments concerning the other portions of the body are in order. The limbs (arms, legs) are not considered critical organs *per se*, because they are relatively radio-resistant. Exposure of the limbs affects the associated blood-forming organs and skin, but if the trunk is not irradiated, severity of the results is considerably reduced. Lung tissue appears to be fairly radio-resistant compared to the skin and bone marrow. The liver and pancreas are considered to be quite radio-resistant. These and other organs not discussed are not considered critical.

### 3.  Dose Limits

The selection of dose limits for astronauts is one of the most difficult problems connected with nuclear radiation in space. Nontechnical as well as technical considerations apply. In addition, any dose limits selected must be accompanied by an acceptable probability against their being exceeded, since the major radiation hazard for deep space missions (solar flare particles) can be predicted only on a probability basis.

The first criterion is that acceptable dose limits must be those which will allow successful completion of the mission. These generally include avoidance of vomiting and diarrhea as well as skin inflamation. While temporary discomfort due to these effects may not seem serious on Earth, in the confines of zero-$g$ spacecraft, the results could be serious, especially during critical maneuvers.

On the other hand, space travel is a hazardous undertaking, and reducing the probability of mission failure due to one type of hazard appreciably below that due to other hazards may be undesirable. For example, if the reduction of radiation exposure hazards requires increased shielding, which reduces the safety margin in propulsion, power supply, or life support systems, the overall risk of mission failure may actually be increased. It is, therefore, desirable that the mission dose limits be set as high as possible consistent with crew safety.

Dose limits for radiation workers are currently set at 5 Rem/year, while the doses to the general public are limited to $\leqslant 0.5$ Rem/year. Such limits are unrealistically low for astronauts, even undertaking only a few space missions in a lifetime.

There are two other aspects of human response to nuclear radiation which merit consideration in setting dose limits. The first concerns the effects of such radiation on the ability to perform various tasks. This has been studied in man by Payne [87, 88], Frisby [89], Zellmer [90], and others, and in monkeys by Leary and Ruch [91], Harlow and Moon [92], Brown and McDowell [93], and others. The overall results—which are not conclusive—indicate that radiation exposure may reduce performance indirectly. Direct effects on performance, such as vomiting, and the like, are to be expected.

Another effect which has been observed in animals concerns changes in their food preferences following radiation [94]. It is not known if this effect is important in man. Of negligible importance on Earth, such taste changes could be important to astronauts, whose supply of food is limited.

The overall problem has been studied by Billingham [95], who presents the following dose limits for a typical two-week mission:

|  | Maximum acute exposure (Rem) | Maximum integrated exposure (Rem) |
|---|---|---|
| Skin of whole body | 700 | 1600 |
| Blood-forming organs | 200 | 270 |
| Feet, ankles, hands | 980 | 4000 |
| Eyes | 200 | 270 |

Edgerly [81] carried out a similar analysis for a long-duration (about a year) manned mission to Mars. He concluded that if appropriate local shielding is provided dose limits need be set for only the skin and blood-forming organs. Skin dose limits of $\leqslant 600$ Rem and bone marrow doses of $\leqslant 150$ Rem were recommended.

Kelton [96] considered the hazards of space travel in the context of more common human activities, such as participation in sports, airplane and automobile travel and various types of employment. Considering the wide latitude in human tolerance of nuclear radiation, he argued that a philosophy of risk rather than the establishment of dose limits was the proper starting point. Applying this approach to typical space missions he obtains dose limits in reasonable agreement with those of Billingham [95], Edgerly [81] and others.

Since spacecraft are generally heterogeneous structures, the skin or blood-forming organ dose will vary considerably from one part of the body to another. Rather than use dose limits as average values which might be exceeded by a factor of 2 or more for some parts of the body, Edgerly [81] recommended that dose limits be considered as maximums for any point on the body. Thus the dose at all points on the skin should be $<600$–$700$ Rem, and for much of the skin may be considerably less. Such an interpretation would probably leave a fair margin of reserve while providing the spacecraft designer with a readily applied criteria.

For deep space missions, a 99 % probability is often assigned to dose limits. In other words, the probability of exceeding the chosen dose limit is up to 1 %. This is reasonable, since the overall probability of mission failure is often set at 1 %. The corresponding probability of death due to radiation hazards is then up to 0.1 %.

## D.   Long-Term Human Response

### 1.   DELAYED EFFECTS

Not all of the effects of acute radiation exposure show up within 30 days. Those which make their appearance later are called delayed effects. While these will not be of primary importance except for extended-duration missions, a brief review of some of these effects is included here.

The production of cataracts has already been mentioned. This is a growth on the eye which may result in partial or total loss of sight in that eye. Requiring at least several weeks to progress to the stage where vision is impaired, cataracts are readily removed surgically [59].

As stated, carcinoma (cancer) can be produced in the human body by excessive amounts of radiation. While one or a few cancer cells may be produced at the time the irradiation takes place, they usually require months or years to grow to macroscopic size. Skin cancers are usually detected early, and their surgical removal is often relatively easy. Internal cancer is less readily detected and thus is often allowed to progress further before treated. If not treated in time, death may result. Treatment usually consists of surgical removal or localized irradiation [97].

A related disease is leukemia; it too can probably be caused by nuclear radiation. Characterized by an excessive number of white blood cells, acute leukemia can cause death within a few months. The nonacute variety usually requires at least a few years to be fatal. No satisfactory cure is currently available [98].

Life-shortening is another delayed effect which may possibly result from nonlethal radiation exposure. Studies of animals indicate this effect, but the dependence on total dose and dose rate is conflicting [99].

Another delayed effect concerns the production of mutations in offspring.

While there is agreement that this can result from radiation exposure, the probability is unclear. The number of abnormal offspring from irradiated humans has been surprisingly small ($<0.1\%$), and most of the abnormalities were minor. For astronauts, most of whom will probably have had their families, this is not considered to be an important factor [59].

Quantitative cause-effect relationships for these long-term human responses are not currently known. After they become better defined, these long-term effects may play a role in setting future dose limits for space travel.

## 2. BIOLOGICAL RECOVERY

Living organisms, including human beings, possess the ability to repair biological damage if that damage is not too extensive. In particular the human body has the ability to repair at least some of the damage resulting from a nonlethal exposure to nuclear radiation. The effective residual dose (ERD) concept is usually used to account for the biological recovery from radiation damage.

Most of the experimental work on biological recovery involved observing lethal effects of wholebody X and $\gamma$ radiation on animals, usually mice [100, 101]. The magnitude of the acute lethal dose $D_2$ required a time $t$ after an initial acute dose $D_1$ served to estimate the biological recovery effected during time $t$. While various formulas have been proposed [102] to take this effect into account, Davidson's modification of Blair's empirical relationship [103] is fairly typical. This formula may be written

$$D_0 - D_2 = \text{ERD} = 0.1\,D_1 + 0.9\,D_1 \cdot 10^{-0.023t} \qquad (4.11)$$

where $D_0$ is the dose required to kill in a single exposure (Rem), $D_1$ is the first (nonlethal) exposure (Rem), $D_2$ is the second (lethal) exposure (Rem), and $t$ is the time between $D_1$ and $D_2$ (days). This formula states that $90\%$ of the biological damage caused by a nonlethal exposure to radiation is ultimately repaired. The repair is considered to be exponential with a half-period of 30 days. This relationship is shown in Fig. 4-7. Equation 4.11 applies to the ERD resulting from a single acute dose, $D_1$. If a chronic dose at the rate of $D_1$ per day is received, the ERD after a time $t$ is as exhibited in Fig. 4-8, which shows that a sort of equilibrium is reached on the order of a year. At this time the repair and damage rates are approximately equal.

One limitation of this formula is that it was developed for wholebody radiation, and its application to specific organs is quite uncertain. However,

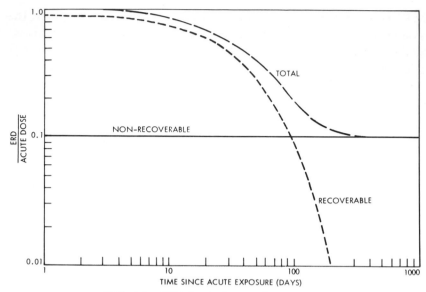

FIG. 4-7.   ERD for single acute dose exposure.

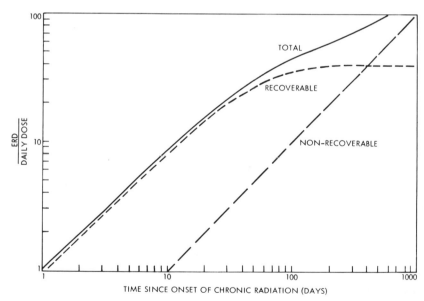

FIG. 4-8.   ERD for chronic dose exposure.

the ERD concept has been applied to individual organs for lack of a suitable alternative [81]. If the maximum doses are kept within limits, so that the lightly irradiated tissue can aid in the recovery of the more heavily irradiated tissue, such application of the ERD concept may be justified.

Another limitation of the ERD concept concerns the relative paucity of information for radiations whose RBE exceeds unity. Schaefer [104] suggested that conservatively the reparable portion is reduced by the factor that the RBE exceeds 1. This leads to the following formula:

$$\text{ERD} = \left(1 - \frac{0.9}{\text{RBE}}\right) D_1 + \frac{0.9}{\text{RBE}} D_1 10^{-0.023t} \tag{4.12}$$

Until more definitive experimental evidence concerning biological recovery becomes available, this equation is suggested as more suitable than Eq. 4.11 for calculating ERD doses for space missions.

Agreement on this or any other recovery formula is not universal, since all of the relevant parameters have not been isolated. Some experiments show little if any biological recovery, and a few even show the opposite effect. Part of the answer may be contained in experiments which show that the white blood cell count drops rapidly for the first 5–7 days after acute irradiation, and remains low for another 10–20 days [105, 106]. A second acute dose within this period may be as effective (or possibly even more so) than if it were administered concurrently with the first acute dose. After about 30 or more days, however, when the white blood cell count has at least partially recovered, the second acute dose would be less effective.

Perhaps the safest approach was proposed by Grahn and Langham [57] who recommended the use of the ERD concept only for single doses $\lesssim 25$ Rem and dose rates $< 2$ Rem/day. These levels are not believed to affect recovery mechanisms seriously. Otherwise, simple addition of the doses is recommended for estimating the effects of space radiation on humans.

## E. Biological Protective Measures

Currently the only satisfactory means of protecting man from the harmful effects of nuclear radiation is to prevent the radiation from reaching man in dangerous quantities. For astronauts this consists of shielding at least a portion of the crew compartment. However, a number of biological measures have been suggested which may ultimately offer a degree of radiation protection.

The most promising approach involves the administration of protective chemicals prior to the radiation exposure. These are essentially useless if administered after the radiation has been received [107]. For mice, survival after exposure to an otherwise lethal dose has been demonstrated by the use of these chemicals [108]. However, in sufficient quantities, such chemicals are toxic themselves, which appears at least to limit their use in man. Chemical protective measures are believed to operate by either reducing the number of free radicals formed by the radiation or by reducing the vulnerability of molecules to the effects of such radicals. Some apparently act by reducing the oxygen present in the cells (a reverse oxygen effect). As the mechanisms by which these chemicals act becomes better understood on the microscopic scale, it is possible that acceptable protective agents will be developed.

The protection afforded by blood transfusions, bone marrow transplants, skin grafts, and so forth, has already been mentioned. While surgery will probably not be performed on astronauts except in extreme cases, a well-shielded supply of blood, lymph, and possibly other body fluids might be included in future spacecraft designed for long duration (more than 30 days) missions. The desirability of this must be weighed against using the space and weight required for extra shielding or for fuel which would facilitate a more rapid accomplishment of the mission.

The possible adaptation of the body to radiation through preexposure has been suggested. While individual cells can apparently adapt to become more radiation-resistant, this has not been demonstrated for mammals [109].

## MATERIALS

A very large amount of work concerning the effects of nuclear radiation on materials has been reported [110–114]. Almost all of this is related to the effects produced by fission reactor neutrons and photons ($\lesssim 10$ Mev). This is due to the very high intensities ($\gtrsim 10^{12}$ particles/cm²/sec) produced in many such reactors. By contrast, the fluxes of nuclear particles in space radiation varies from $\lesssim 10^9$/cm/sec for the solar wind (kev protons) to $\leqslant 4$/cm²/sec for galactic (cosmic) rays (Bev nucleons). Thus material effects due to nuclear radiation in space are of orders of magnitude less than those due to fission reactors. However, they are not necessarily negligible. A brief review of the effects of nuclear radiations on materials is therefore included here.

The Radiation Effects Information Center (REIC) has been established at Batelle Memorial Institute by the U.S. Air Force, NASA (National Aeronautics and Space Administration), and the AEC (Atomic Energy Commission). This center collects and distributes information related to the effects of nuclear radiation on materials. In addition to monthly accession lists, the REIC also issues memorandums from time to time summarizing the current status of work and knowledge in some portion of the field. The major annual publication of the REIC is the *Radiation Effects—State of the Art* [113], issued each June. Each such report includes sections dealing with the effects of radiation on various classes of materials and components (e.g., ceramics, structural metals, electronic equipment, and so on), backed up by a bibliography. In addition, sections on the space radiation environment and on dosimetry are included. Since only a very brief discussion of the field of radiation effects can be included here, the REIC is an excellent source of additional information.

## F. Radiation Damage Thresholds

A rough idea of the radiation susceptibilities of various materials and components is given by Table 4-4. It is seen that the damage thresholds for

TABLE 4-4

RADIATION DAMAGE THRESHOLDS FOR CERTAIN CLASSES OF MATERIALS

| | |
|---|---|
| Electronic components | $10^1$–$10^3$ rad |
| Polymeric materials | $10^7$–$10^9$ rad |
| Lubricants, hydraulic fluids | $10^5$–$10^7$ rad |
| Ceramic, glasses | $10^6$–$10^8$ rad |
| Structural metals, alloys | $10^9$–$10^{11}$ rad |

electronic components are much lower than for the other types of materials listed. Figure 4-9 shows the approximate radiation tolerance of ten classes of electronic components [113]. The wide dose overlapping for each class are due to the materials which are lumped together. For example, while teflon is responsible for the low threshold of organic insulation, polyethylene is found near the top of this class. By careful choice of materials and components, doses to $\sim 10^5$ can be tolerated with little or no effect with the exception of that on semiconductor devices.

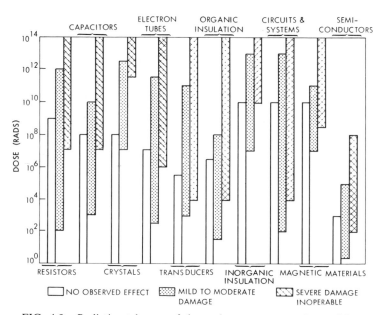

FIG. 4-9.   Radiation tolerance of electronic components and materials.

Organic materials form a class in which radiation effects have been extensively studied [115, 116]. Generally unaffected below $10^3$–$10^4$ rad, they may become a problem if exposed to the combined environment of space on long missions. Organic adhesives often lose their strength if irradiated, especially at cryogenic temperatures. Radiation damage in organic electrical insulation is characterized by decreased resistance and increased dissipation factor. Elastomers lose their elasticity, thermal insulation tends to become conductive, and seals lose strength if sufficiently irradiated. Fluorocarbons are usually inferior to hydrocarbons in radiation resistance in air, but in vacuum, the differences are smaller.

Because of their relative radiation damage sensitivity, semiconductor devices have been the subject of considerable study. Baruch [117], Fan [118], Dearnaley [119, 120], Gandolfo *et al.* [121], Honaker [122], Peck *et al.* [123], Frank and Larin [124], and others have reported that the gain decreases and the leakage current increases as a result of irradiation. The response times are often increased. These changes are attributed to traps which reduce charge carrier lifetime and mobility. Minority carrier semiconductors are especially vulnerable because the fraction of atoms which need be affected to produce macroscopic effects is correspondingly less. Silicon controlled rectifiers are perhaps the most sensitive of semiconductor devices, having a damage threshold of $\sim 10$ rad. Solar cells, integrated circuits, and transistors generally have damage thresholds of $\sim 100$ rad, although some are relatively unaffected to $\sim 1000$ rad. Diodes are generally good for $10^5$ rad, with many (especially microwave and tunnel diodes) usable to $\sim 10^7$ rad.

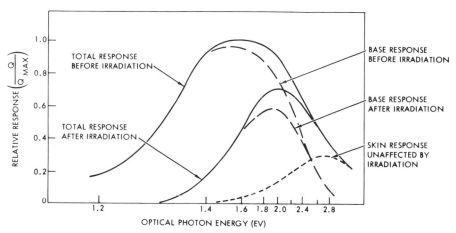

FIG. 4-10.  Spectral effects of charged particle irradiation on solar cells.

Solar cells are a particular class of semiconductor devices often exposed to space radiation by necessity. Various authors [125–127] report that the response of these cells is decreased and shifted toward the blue end of the optical spectrum (Fig. 4-10). This is quite undesirable because the power output of solar cells is proportional to the wavelength integral of this response multiplied by the Sun's output spectrum. Thus while the peak response may be reduced by less than a factor of 2, the shift reduces the output power by over a factor of 5. N–P rather than P–N solar cells are often used because of their greater radiation resistance. For similar reasons, a high-base resistivity (e.g., 10 ohm–cm) is preferred to a low-base resistivity (e.g., 1 ohm–cm). An order-of-magnitude increase in radiation resistance may be obtained by appropriate choice of solar cells. Further increases are possible by using quartz shielding [128].

Photographic film constitutes a special class of radiation-sensitive material. Many of the coarse-grained "fast" films become seriously fogged when exposed to $\gtrsim 10$ rad, while some fine-grained "slow" films are still usable after $\sim 100$ rad. Film must be ranked with man as the most radiation-sensitive components of spacecraft, and shielded containers for both are often advisable, especially for long duration missions.

One radiation effect which deserves mention is activation. Exposure of material to nuclear radiation capable of producing a nuclear transformation may leave the material radioactive. This radioactivity produced by space radiation in a typical $10^4$ lb spacecraft has been investigated by Rusling [129], who concluded that the effects would be minor. The time-integrated gamma-ray dose received by astronauts inside as a result of activation by the average of the six largest observed flares was calculated to be $\sim 0.1$ Rem (Table 4-5).

TABLE 4-5

GAMMA RAY ACTIVATION DOSES

| Element | Weight in spacecraft (lb) | Rem/lb | Rem |
|---------|---------|---------|---------|
| Carbon | 1900 | $1.0 \times 10^{-5}$ | $1.9 \times 10^{-2}$ |
| Nitrogen | 100 | $4.7 \times 10^{-5}$ | $4.7 \times 10^{-3}$ |
| Aluminum | 6000 | $3.3 \times 10^{-6}$ | $1.98 \times 10^{-2}$ |
| Copper | 700 | $2.6 \times 10^{-5}$ | $1.8 \times 10^{-2}$ |
| Silicon | 200 | $7.7 \times 10^{-7}$ | $1.5 \times 10^{-4}$ |
| Iron | 600 | $5.2 \times 10^{-5}$ | $3.1 \times 10^{-2}$ |
| Titanium | 500 | $7.4 \times 10^{-5}$ | $3.7 \times 10^{-2}$ |
| Total | 10,000 | | 0.13 |

## G.  Problems Related to Damage Thresholds

The flux-to-rad dose conversion factors for nuclear radiations in materials are often not well known. Because of the different molecular, atomic, and nuclear properties of materials, the use of tissue flux-to-dose conversion factors is incorrect. However, for lack of suitable alternatives, this is often done. The errors are usually less serious than the uncertainties attached to the damage dose thresholds.

Additional problems are encountered in attempting to apply the available radiation effects information to spacecraft. The relative lack of data for proton- and electron-induced damage have been mentioned. While comparing damage on an energy deposition basis is often the best that can be done, this is dangerous for different types of radiation. For example, photons and electrons (which act primarily by ionization) will not produce the same effects in many materials as neutrons and protons (which can produce atomic displacements) on an energy deposition basis.

TABLE 4-6

COMPARISON OF RADIATION DAMAGE IN SILICON SEMICONDUCTORS
FOR VARIOUS NUCLEAR RADIATIONS

| Radiation | Measured | Ionization | Displacement | Total |
|---|---|---|---|---|
| | | Relative damage/particle | | |
| | | Calculated | | |
| $Co^{60}$ $\gamma$ photon | 1 | 1 | 0 | 1 |
| 1 Mev electron | 2–5 | $\sim 13$ | $\sim 0$ | $\sim 13$ |
| 5 Mev electron | 10–15 | $\sim 10$ | $\sim 0$ | $\sim 10$ |
| Fission neutron | 700–1000 | $\sim 0$ | $\sim 700$ | $\sim 700$ |
| 10 Mev proton | 3000–4000 | $\sim 230$ | $\sim 2500$ | $\sim 2700$ |
| 30 Mev proton | 2000–3000 | $\sim 120$ | $\sim 1400$ | $\sim 1500$ |

There have been a few investigations [130] of the damage equivalence of different nuclear radiations. Based upon two such experimental studies, Table 4-6 has been prepared. It is seen that gamma ray photons are less damaging to silicon semiconductors than particles with a finite rest mass, with protons being the most dangerous on a per-particle basis. It is possible to obtain a rough understanding of Table 4-6 if the following two assumptions are made: (1) electrons and photons produce ionization damage only, and (2) neutrons produce displacement damage only.

On this basis, the relative damage produced by electrons and photons is due to their relative specific ionizations. For electrons, whose range energy relationships can be fit by the formula,

$$R = \delta E^n$$

where $R$ is the range(gm/cm$^2$), $E$ the energy (Mev), and $n$, $\delta$ are constants, the specific ionization is

$$\frac{dE}{dx} = \frac{1}{n\delta}E^{n-1} \tag{4.13}$$

For photons, which are attenuated exponentially, the specific ionization is

$$\frac{dE}{dx} = \mu E \tag{4.14}$$

where $\mu$ is the mass attenuation coefficient (cm$^2$/gm), and $E$ the energy (Mev).

The specific ionization for protons is given by Eq. 4.13, but $n$ and $\delta$ are different for protons and electrons (see Chapter V). The displacement damage produced by protons in silicon appears to be roughly eleven times that produced by ionization. For 10 Mev protons the displacement damage is approximately 3.6 that for fission neutrons, whose average energy is ~ 2.8 Mev. However, the assumption that displacement damage for protons and neutrons is linearly dependent on particle energy alone does not hold for objects with linear dimensions small compared to the particle range.

A more detailed analysis along these lines has been carried out by Van Lint and Wikner [130], who considered three types of radiation effects—transient ionization, atomic displacement, and chemical reactions. In addition to providing an explanation for permanent damage, the approach is useful in studying TREE (transient radiation effects on electronics) effects. Related analysis studies have been carried out by Poblenz [131], Raymond and Willis [132], and others.

These analyses, though oversimplified, do suggest that much of the neutron and gamma ray damage data can be used to estimate electron and proton damage. Until more precise relationships between these different types of radiation damage becomes available, the relative lack of proton- and electron-induced damage data constitutes a limitation in evaluating the effects of space radiations on spacecraft.

Another problem is that the low-energy (kev) protons and electrons are the most numerous in space, but their damage characteristics are less well known than those of the Mev particles. This is of special importance because the radiation damage produced by these kev particles is concentrated in a very thin surface layer. Such spacecraft components as viewing ports, vacuum seals, and thermal control surfaces are undesirably affected if a thin (a few microns) surface layer is damaged [133, 134]. For such a thin layer kev particles are probably more damaging than those of higher energy, and there is little information on radiation damage in this energy range.

A final problem is that nuclear radiation constitutes only one of the environments present in space. Ultrahigh vacuum, optical solar radiation (including ultraviolet), and micrometeoroids are all present. The radiation effects observed in air are often less, but sometimes more severe, than those observed in vacuum. Small surface pits due to micrometeorites may become starting points for radiation damage of the substrate underlying a thermal control surface. Ultraviolet light may assist in the formation of chemical compounds or radicals which decrease nuclear radiation damage thresholds. Thus estimating the effects due to space radiation is difficult even where proton and electron damage data are available.

Temperature is one of the important parameters which affects the extent of radiation damage. In general, the damage thresholds decrease as the temperature drops, increasing the radiation sensitivity in the cryogenic region by an order of magnitude or more. The explanation is believed to lie in the reduced populations of atomic energy levels above the ground state at low temperatures. What would be a transient disturbance within the amplitude of thermal vibrations at high temperature becomes semipermanent damage at low temperatures. Conversely, many of the effects of radiation exposure can be annealed out by heating [113]. This does not work for nuclear transformations of course.

The relative importance of radiation effects in spacecraft materials is minor for many missions. Provided simple precautions are taken, no major problems may be expected to arise from the natural space environment (several dozen operating spacecraft attest to this). However, the introduction of a nuclear power source, either for propulsion or auxiliary power, changes the situation. Space radiation no longer is the major radiation source, at least in the vicinity of such a power plant. For this situation the choice of spacecraft materials and components and the shielding required to protect astronauts is dictated almost completely by the nuclear power source. The problem then becomes a reactor or radioisotope shielding problem, not a space radiation shielding problem.

REFERENCES

1.  H. E. Johns and J. S. Laughlin, Interaction of Radiation with Matter, *in*: "Radiation Dosimetry" (G. J. Hine and G. L. Brownell, eds.), Chap. II. Academic Press, New York, 1956.
2.  R. D. Evans, "The Atomic Nucleus." McGraw-Hill, New York, 1955.
3.  W. P. Saylor, D. E. Winer, C. J. Eiwin, and A. W. Carriker, Space Radiation Guide, Rept. AMRL-TDR-62–86, *Biomedical Lab., USAF* (1962).
4.  H. H. Rossi (ed.), Protection against Neutron Radiation up to 30 Million Electron Volts, *Natl. Bur. Std., U.S., Handbook* **63**, (1957).
5.  A. H. Sparrow and F. Forro, Cellular Radiobiology, *Ann. Rev. Nucl. Sci.* **3**, 339 (1953).
6.  E. L. Powers, Cellular Radiobiology, *Ann. Rev. Nucl. Sci.* **7**, 63 (1957).
7.  P. Howard-Flanders, Physical and Chemical Mechanisms in the Injury of Cells by Ionizing Radiations, *Advan. Biol. Med. Phys.* **6**, 553 (1958).
8.  K. C. Atwood, Cellular Radiobiology, *Ann. Rev. Nucl. Sci.* **9**, 553 (1959).
9.  T. Alper, Cellular Radiobiology, *Ann. Rev. Nucl. Sci.* **10**, 489 (1960).
10. G. F. Whitmore and J. E. Till, Quantitation of Cellular Radiobiological Responses, *Ann. Rev. Nucl. Sci.* **14**, 347 (1964).
11. B. E. Holmes, Biochemical Effects of Ionizing Radiation, *Ann. Rev. Nucl. Sci.* **7**, 89 (1957).
12. M. G. Ord and L. A. Stocker, Biochemical Effects of Ionizing Radiation, *Ann. Rev. Nucl. Sci.* **9**, 523 (1959).
13. D. E. Smith, Free Radicals in Irradiated Biological Materials and Systems, *Ann. Rev. Nucl. Sci.* **12**, 577 (1962).
14. L. D. Hamilton, W. J. Schull, and L. S. Taylor, Radiation Effects on Man, *Nucleonics* **21**, No 3, 45 (1963).
15. S. B. Curtis, D. L. Dye, and W. R. Sheldon, Fractional Cell Lethality Approach to Space Radiation Hazards, p. 219, *Second Symp. Protection against Radiations in Space*, NASA-SP-71 (1964).
16. G. J. Hine and G. L. Brownell (eds.), "Radiation Dosimetry." Academic Press, New York, 1956.
17. L. D. Marinelli, Radiation Dosimetry and Protection, *Ann. Rev. Nucl. Sci.* **3**, 249 (1953).
18. L. H. Hempelmann and J. G. Hoffman, Practical Aspects of Radiation Injury, *Ann. Rev. Nucl. Sci.* **3**, 369 (1953).
19. S. Kinsman, "Radiological Health Handbook." Taft Sanitary Eng. Center, Cincinnati, Ohio, 1954.

20. F. W. Spiers and G. W. Reed (eds.), "Radiation Dosimetry." Academic Press, New York, 1964.
21. W. A. Gibson, Energy Removed from Primary Proton and Neutron Beams by Tissue, Rept. ORNL-3260, *Oak Ridge Natl. Lab. Oak Ridge, Tenessee* (1962).
22. J. E. Turner, C. D. Zerby, R. L. Woodyard, H. A. Wright, W. E. Kinney, W. S. Snyder, and J. Neufeld, Calculations of Radiation Dose to 400 MeV, *Health Phys.* **10,** 783 (1964).
23. W. E. Kinney and C. D. Zerby, Calculated Tissue Current to Dose Conversion Factors for Nucleons of Energy Below 400 MeV, p. 161, *Second Symp. Protection against Radiations in Space*, NASA-SP-71 (1964).
24. W. S. Synder and J. Neufeld, Calculated Depth Dose Curves in Tissue for Broad Beams of Fast Neutrons, *Brit. J. Radiol.* **28,** 343 (1955).
25. B. J. Henderson, Conversion of Neutron or Gamma Ray Flux to Absorbed Dose Rate, Rept. XDC-59-8-179, *General Electric Co., Cincinnati, Ohio* (1959).
26. O. Halpern and H. Hall, The Ionization Loss of Energy of Fast Charged Particles in Gases and Condensed Bodies, *Phys. Rev.* **73,** 477 (1948).
27. G. W. Crawford, Space Dosimetry, *in*: "Space Physics" (D. P. LeGalley and A. Rosen, eds.). Wiley, New York, 1964.
28. S. Ellis and R. Ellis, Dosimetry Conversion Factors, *Nucleonics* **9,** No 11, 210 (1960).
29. J. B. Storer, P. S. Harris, J. E. Furchner, and W. H. Langham, The Relative Biological Effectiveness of Various Ionizing Radiations in Mammalian Systems, *Radiation Res.* **6,** 188 (1957).
30. H. H. Rossi, Correlation of Radiation Quality and Biological Effect, *Ann. N.Y. Acad. Sci.* **114,** 4 (1964).
31. D. Grahn, G. A. Sacher, and H. A. Walton, Comparative Effectiveness of Several X-Ray Qualities for Acute Lethality in Mice and Rabbits, *Radiation Res.* **4,** 228 (1956).
32. A. C. Upton, F. P. Conte, G. S. Hurst, and W. A. Mills, The Relative Biological Effectiveness of Fast Neutrons, X-Rays, and Gamma Rays for Acute Lethality in Mice, *Radiation Res.* **3,** 355 (1955).
33. V. P. Bond, O. D. Easterday, E. E. Stickley, and J. S. Robertson, The Relative Biological Effectiveness of Thermal Neutrons and of Heavy Particles from the $B^{10}$ $(n, \alpha)$ $Li^7$ Reaction for Acute Effects in the Mouse, *Radiology* **67,** 650 (1956).
34. C. C. Wang, J. Lyman, and C. A. Tobias, Relative Biological Effectiveness of 730 MeV Proton Particles for Acute Lethality in Mice, Rept. UCRL-10211, *Univ. California, Berkeley, California* (1962).
35. V. P. Bond and J. S. Robertson, Vertebrate Radiobiology (Lethal Actions and Associated Effects), *Ann. Rev. Nucl. Sci.* **7,** 135 (1957).
36. S. T. Taketa, Biological Effects of Protons and Neutrons in Large Animals, p. 73, *Second Symp. Protection against Radiations in Space*, NASA-SP-71 (1964).
37. H. J. Schaefer, LET Spectrum and RBE of High Energy Protons, p. 393, *Proc. Symp. Protection against Radiation Hazards in Space*, TID-7652 (1962).
38. W. S. Snyder, Some Data on the Relationship of RBE and LET, p. 402, *Proc. Symp. Protection against Radiation Hazards in Space*, TID-7652 (1962).
39. H. H. Rossi, RBE of Ionizing Radiation, p. 150, *Conf. Shielding of High Energy Accelerators*, Rept. TID-7545 (1957).

40. C. A. Tobias and P. W. Todd, Analysis of the Effects of High LET Radiation on Various Biological Test Objects, p. 25, Rept. UCRL-11387, *Univ. California, Berkeley, California,* (1964).

41. S. J. Lindenbaum, Shielding of High Energy Accelerators, *Ann. Rev. Nucl. Sci.* **11,** 213 (1961).

42. C. A. Sondhaus, Biological Effects of High Energy Protons, p. 309 *Proc. Symp. Protection against Radiation Hazards in Space,* TID-7652 (1962).

43. C. A. Sondhaus, Effect of High Energy Protons and Alpha Particles on Small Mammals, p. 97, *Second Symp. Protection against Radiations in Space,* NASA-SP-71 (1964).

44. P. Bonet-Maury, A. Deysine, M. Frilley, and C. Stefan, Relative Effectiveness of 151 MeV Protons, *Compt Rend.* **251,** 3087 (1960).

45. P. P. Saksonov, V. V. Antipov, V. S. Shashkov, B. L. Razgovorov, G. F. Murin, and V. S. Morozov, On the Biological Effect of High Energy Protons, *Proc. 14th Intern. Astro. Congr., Paris* (1963).

46. A. V. Lebedinsky, Y. G. Nefedov and N. I. Ryhov, Abstracts of Repute, *USSR Acad. Sci.,* 13 (1962).

47. C. A. Tobias, H. O. Anger, and J. H. Lawrence, Radiological Use of High Energy Deuterons and Alpha Particles, *Am. J. Roentgen Radiol., Theory Nucl. Med.* **67,** 1 (1952).

48. P. Todd, Biological Effects of Heavy Ions, p. 105, *Second Symp. Protection against Radiations in Space,* NASA-SP-71 (1964).

49. J. W. Haffner, RBE of Protons and Alpha Particles, p. 513, *Proc. Second Symp. Protection against Radiation Hazards in Space,* NASA-SP-71 (1964).

50. R. Madey and T. E. Stephenson, Quality Factors for Degraded Proton Spectra, p. 229, *Second Symp. Protection against Radiations in Space,* NASA- SP-71 (1964).

51. J. K. Ashikawa, C. A. Sondhaus, C. A. Tobias, A. G. Greenfield, and V. Paschkes, Difference in Injury Mode, Dose Rate Dependence, and RBE of 730 MeV Protons, 100 kVp X-Rays and 250 kVp X-Rays, Rept. UCRL-11014, *Univ. California, Berkeley, California* (1963).

52. S. W. Lippincott, J. E. Jesseph, W. G. Calvo, and C. P. Baker, Progressive Epithelial Dysplasia in Mouse Skin Irradiated with 10 MeV Protons, Rept. BNL-7359, *Brookhaven Natl. Lab., Upton,* New York (1962).

53. J. E. Jesseph, W. H. Moore, V. P. Bond, and S. W. Lippincott, Effects of 2 BeV Protons in Mice, Rept. BNL-7343, *Brookhaven Natl. Lab., Upton,* New York (1962).

54. R. W. Zellmer and R. G. Allen, Cosmic Radiation—Laboratory Observations, *Aerospace Med.* **32,** 942 (1961).

55. H. J. Schaefer, Exposure Hazards from Cosmic Radiation beyond the Stratosphere and in Free Space, *J. Aviation Med.* **23,** 334 (1952).

56. H. J. Curtis, Some Specific Considerations of the Potential Hazards of Heavy Primary Cosmic Rays, p. 291, *Proc. Symp. Protection against Radiation Hazards in Space,* TID-7652 (1962).

57. D. Grahn and W. L. Langham, Methods in the Evaluation of Radiation Hazards in Manned Space Flight, p. 59, *Second Symp. Protection against Radiations in Space,* NASA-SP-71 (1964).

58. A. W. Oughterson and S. Warren, Medical Effects of the Atomic Bomb in Japan, *Natl. Nucl. Energy Ser. (Div. VIII* **8** (1956).

59. S. Glasstone (ed.), The Effects of Nuclear Weapons, *U.S. At. Energy Comm.* (1962).

60. P. D. Keller, A Clinical Syndrome Following Exposure to Atomic Bomb Explosions, *J. Am. Med. Assoc.* **131,** 504 (1946).

61. R. J. Hasterlik and L. D. Marinelli, Physical Dosimetry and Clinical Observations on Four Human Beings Involved in an Accidental Critical Assembly Excursion, *Proc. First Intern. Conf. Peaceful Uses At. Energy, Geneva* **11,** 25 (1955).

62. N. Wald and G. E. Thoma, Radiation Accidents: Medical Aspects of Neutron and Gamma Ray Exposures, Rept. ORNL-2748, *Oak Ridge Natl. Lab. Oak Ridge, Tenessee* (1961).

63. D. F. Hayes, A Summary of Accidents and Incidents Involving Radiation in Atomic Energy Activities, Rept. TID-5360, *U.S. At. Energy Comm.* (1956), *Suppl.* (1957, 1959).

64. B. Pendic, "The Zero-Energy Reactor Accident at Vinca, Diagnosis and Treatment of Acute Radiation Injury," p. 67. Columbia Univ. Press, (Intern. Document Service), 1961.

65. L. S. Miller, G. H. Fletcher, and H. B. Gerstner, Radiological Observations on Cancer Patients Treated with Whole-Body Irradiation, *Radiation Res.* **8,** 150 (1961).

66. L. S. Miller, G. H. Fletcher, and H. B. Gerstner, Systemic and Clinical Effects Induced in 263 Cancer Patients by Whole-Body X-Irradiation with Nominal Air Doses of 15 to 200 R, Rept. 57–92, *U.S. School Aviation Med.* (1957).

67. H. B. Gerstner, Acute Radiation Syndrome in Man, *U.S. Armed Forces Med. J.* **9,** 313 (1958).

68. V. P. Bond, T. M. Fliedner, and E. P. Cronkite, Evaluation and Management of the Heavily Irradiated Individual, *J. Nucl. Med.* **1,** 221 (1960).

69. L. O. Jacobson, The Hematologic Effects of Ionizing Radiation, *in*: "Radiation Biology" (A. Hollaender, ed.), Chap. 16. McGraw-Hill, New York, 1954.

70. C. C. Lushbaugh, Vertebrate Radiobiology (The Pathology of Radiation Exposure), *Ann. Rev. Nucl. Sci.* **7,** 163 (1957).

71. W. Langham, K. T. Woodward, S. M. Rothermel, P. S. Harris, C. C. Lushbaugh, and J. B. Storer, Studies of the Effect of Rapidly Delivered Massive Doses of Gamma Rays on Mammals, *Radiation Res.* **5,** 404 (1956).

72. E. L. Alpen, O. S. Shill, and E. Tochilin, The Effects of Total Body Irradiation on Dogs with Simulated Fission Neutrons, *Radiation Res.* **12,** 237 (1960).

73. V. P. Bond, R. E. Carter, J. S. Robertson, P. H. Seymour, and H. H. Hechter, The Effects of Total Body Fast Neutron Irradiation in Dogs, *Radiation Res.* **4,** 139 (1956).

74. J. E. Pickering, Biological Effects of Whole Body Proton Irradiation, *Aerospace Med.* **34,** 942 (1963).

75. W. Bloom and M. A. Bloom, Histological Changes after Irradiation, *in*: "Radiation Biology" (A. Hollaender, ed.), Chap. 17. McGraw-Hill, New York, 1954.

76. J. Furth and A. C. Upton, Vertebrate Radiobiology: Histopathology and Carcinogenesis, *Ann. Rev. Nucl. Sci.* **3,** 303 (1953).

77. E. L. Alpen and S. J. Baum, Modification of X-Radiation Lethality by Autologous Marrow Infusion in Dogs, *Blood* **13,** 1168 (1958).

78. C. C. Congdon, Radiation Injury—Bone Marrow Transplantation, *Ann. Rev. Med.* **13**, 203 (1962).

79. J. C. Crook, E. V. Hulse, J. H. Mulvey, and G. J. Neary, The Acute Effects of Partial Body Irradiation of Mice, *Brit. J. Radiol.* **31**, 477 (1958).

80. M. N. Swift and S. T. Taketa, Modification of Acute Intestinal Radiation Syndrome through Shielding, *Am. J. Physiol.* **185**, 85 (1956).

81. R. H. Edgerly, Single Mission Limits, Sections 2.1 and 3.1 *in*: "Manned Mars Landing and Return Mission Study" (A. L. Jones and W. V. McRae, eds.) Rept. SID 64-619-3, North American Aviation Inc., Los Angeles, California (1964).

82. E. L. Alpen, Radiological Hazard Evaluation—A Critical Review of Present Concepts and a New Approach Thereto, *Hearings before Special Subcommittee on Radiation of the J.C.A.E., Congr. of the U.S.* (June 22–26, 1959).

83. C. C. Burkell, T. A. Watson, H. E. Johns and R. J. Horsley, Skin Effects of $Co^{60}$ Telecurie Therapy, *Brit. J. Radiol.* **27**, 171 (1954).

84. H. Quastler, E. F. Lanzl, M. E. Keller, and J. E. Osborne, Acute Intestinal Radiation Death, *Am. J. Physiol.* **164**, 546 (1951).

85. S. Lesher and H. H. Vogel, A Comparative Histological Study of Duodenal Damage Produced by Fission Neutrons and $Co^{60}$ $\gamma$-rays, *Radiation Res.* **9**, 560 (1958).

86. W. Zeman, H. J. Curtis, K. L. Gebhard, and W. Haymaker, Tolerance of Mouse Brain Tissue to High Energy Deuterons, *Science* **130**, 1760 (1959).

87. R. B. Payne, Effects of Acute Radiation Exposure on Human Performance, p. 343, *Proc. Symp. Protection against Radiation Hazards in Space*, TID-7652 (1962).

88. R. B. Payne, Effects of Ionizing Radiation on Human Psychomotor Skills, Rept. 59–29, *U.S. School Aviation Med.* (1959).

89. C. B. Frisby, A Note on Radiation Treatment in Relation to Performance on Certain Tests, *Brit. J. Med. Psychol.* **52**, 65 (1961).

90. R. W. Zellmer, Human Ability to Perform after Acute Sub-Lethal Radiation, *Military Med.* **126**, 681 (1961).

91. R. W. Leary and T. C. Ruch, Activity, Manipulation, Drive, and Strength in Monkeys Subjected to Low-Level Irradiation, *J. Comp. Physiol. Psychol.* **48**, 336 (1955).

92. H. F. Harlow and L. E. Moon, The Effects of Repeated Doses of Total Body X-Radiation on Motivation and Learning of Rhesus Monkeys, *J. Comp. Physiol. Psychol.* **49**, 60 (1956).

93. W. L. Brown and A. A. McDowell, Visual Acuity, Performance of Normal and Chronic Irradiated Monkeys, *J. Genetic Psychol.* **96**, 133 (1960).

94. R. T. Davis, Latent Changes in Food Preferences of Irradiated Monkeys, *J. Genetic Psychol.* **92**, 53 (1958).

95. J. Billingham, Apollo Dose Limits, p. 139, *Second Symp. Protection against Radiations in Space*, NASA-SP-71 (1964).

96. A. A. Kelton, Radiation Guidelines for Manned Space Vehicles—A Review With Recommendations, Rept. SM-47749, *Douglas Aircraft Co.*, Santa Monica, California (1965).

97. D. Grahn, Late Effects in Man Following Exposure to Ionizing Radiations, p. 275, *Proc. Symp. Protection against Radiation Hazards in Space*, TID-7652 (1962).

98. A. B. Brill, M. Tomonaga, and R. M. Heyssel, Leukemia in Man Following Exposure to Ionizing Radiation, *Ann. Internal Med.* **56**, 590 (1962).

99. J. B. Storer and D. Grahn, Vertebrate Radiobiology Late Effects, *Ann. Rev. Nucl. Sci.* **10**, 561 (1960).

100. D. Grahn and G. A. Sacher, Chronic Radiation Mortality in Mice after Single Whole-Body Exposure to 250, 135, and 80 kVp X-Rays, *Radiation Res.* **8**, 187 (1958).

101. D. Grahn and G. A. Sacher, The Measurement of Residual Acute Injury from Single Exposures by Survival Following Daily Irradiation, *Ann. N. Y. Acad. Sci.* **114**, 158 (1964).

102. E. Shapiro, Operational Significance of Biological Recovery from Chronic Irradiation— A Comparison of General Recovery Theories, Rept. USNRDL-TR-42, *Radiolog. Defense Lab., U.S. Navy*, San Francisco, California (1960).

103. H. O. Davidson, Biological Effects of Whole Body Gamma Radiation on Human Beings, *Tech. Memo* ORO-T-357, *Johns Hopkins Univ.*, Baltimore, Maryland (1956).

104. H. J. Schaefer, LET Spectrum and RBE of High Energy Protons, p. 393, *Proc. Symp. Protection against Radiation Hazards in Space*, TID-7652 (1962).

105. H. G. Chase and J. S. Post, Damage and Repair in Mammalian Tissues Exposed to Cosmic Ray Heavy Nuclei, *J. Aviation Med.* **29**, 533 (1956).

106. W. W. Smith, I. M. Alderman, C. A. Schneider, and J. Cornfield, Radiation Dose Response Characteristics of Leucocyte Recovery in the Mouse, *Proc. Soc. Exptl. Biol. Med.* **113**, 1016 (1963).

107. D. G. Doherty, Modification of the Biological Response of Mammals to Whole Body Radiation, *in*: "Radiation Biology and Medicine" (W. D. Claus, ed.), Addison-Wesley, Reading, Massachusetts (1958).

108. A. W. Kimball *et al.*, Chemical Protection Against Ionizing Radiation, *Radiation Res.* **7**, 1 (1957).

109. A. T. Krebs and J. B. Storer, Adaption to Ionizing Radiation, Rept. 175, *Med. Res. Lab., U.S. Army* (1955).

110. J. D. Pinson, C. A. Schmidheiser, and G. W. Zumwalt, Space Environmental Effects on Materials—A State of the Art. Survey, Rept. AECD-TR-66-12, *Arnold Eng. Develop. Center*, Arnold, Tennessee (1965).

111. H. Brooks, Nuclear Radiation Effects in Solids, *Ann. Rev. Nucl. Sci.* **6**, 215 (1956).

112. D. J. Hamman, A Summary of Radiation Effects Thresholds, p. 117, *Second Symp. Protection against Radiations in Space*, NASA-SP-71 (1964).

113. D. J. Hamman *et al.*, Radiation Effects—State of the Art, Rept. REIC 38, *Batelle Memorial Inst., Columbus, Ohio* (1965).

114. E. R. Beever, Study to Reduce and Compile USAF NAP Radiation Effects Data, Rept. WL-TDR-64-1, *Weapons Lab., U.S. Air Force* Albuquerque, New Mexico, (1964).

115. R. O. Bolt and J. G. Carroll, "Radiation Effects on Organic Materials." Academic Press, New York, 1963.

116. S. E. Harrison and E. A. Szymkowiak, Radiation Induced Electrical Property Changes in Polymeric Solids, p. 131, *Second Symp. Protection against Radiations in Space*, NASA-SP-71 (1964).

117. P. Baruch, Radiation Damage in Semiconductors, *Intern. Conf. Phys. Semiconductors*, (Academic Press, New York) **3**, (1964).

118. H. Y. Fan, Radiation Effects on Semiconducting Materials, p. 121, *Second Symp. Protection against Radiations in Space*, NASA-SP-71 (1964).

119. G. Dearnaley, Radiation Damage by Charged Particles in Silicon Junction Detectors, *IEEE Trans.* **NS–10**, No 1, 106 (1963).

120. G. Dearnaley, Radiation Damage Effects in Semiconductor Detectors, *Nucleonics* **22**, No 7, 78 (1964).

121. D. A. Gandolfo, D. M. Arnold, J. A. Baicker, H. Flicker, J. R. Parker, J. Vilms, and J. Vollmer, Proton Radiation Damage in Semiconductor Devices, p. 230, *Proc. Symp. Protection against Radiation Hazards in Space*, TID-7652 (1962).

122. W. C. Honaker, The Effects of Protons on Semiconductor Devices, p. 220, *Proc. Symp. Protection against Radiation Hazards in Space*, TID-7652 (1962).

123. D. S. Peck, R. R. Blair, W. L. Brown, and F. M. Smits, Surface Effects of Radiation on Transistors, p. 136, *Proc. Symp. Protection against Radiation Hazards in Space*, TID-7652 (1962).

124. M. Frank and F. Larin, Effects of Operating Conditions and Transistor Parameters in Gain Degradation, *IEEE Trans.* **NS–12**, No 5, 126 (1965).

125. J. A. Baiker and P. Rappaport, Radiation Damage to Solar Cells, p. 118, *Proc. Symp. Protection against Radiation Hazards in Space*, TID-7652 (1962).

126. R. Madey, Solar Cell Degradation by Protons in Space, p. 243, *Proc. Symp. Protection against Radiation Hazards in Space*, TID-7652 (1962).

127. F. M. Smits, The Degradation of Solar Cells Under Van Allen Radiation, *IEEE Trans.* **NS–10**, No 1, 88 (1963).

128. H. Weiner, Optimum Solar Cell Shielding for the Advanced Orbiting Solar Observatory, p. 377, *Second Symp. Protection against Radiations in Space*, NASA-SP-71 (1964).

129. D. H. Rusling, Spacecraft Activation by Solar Flare Protons, *Trans. Am. Nucl. Soc.* **8**, 196 (1965).

130. V. A. J. Van Lint and E. G. Wikner, Correlation of Radiation Types with Radiation Effects, *IEEE Trans.* **NS–10**, No. 1, 80 (1961).

131. F. W. Poblenz, Analysis of Transistor Failure in a Nuclear Environment, *IEEE Trans.* **NS–10**, No. 1, 74 (1963).

132. J. P. Raymond and J. P. Willis, Generalized Model Analysis of Ionizing Radiation Effects in Semiconductor Devices, *IEEE Trans.* **NS–12**, No. 5, 55 (1965).

133. T. G. James, Effect of Electron Irradiation on the Mechanical Properties of a Composite Foil for Inflatable Satellites, p. 260, *Proc. Symp. Protection against Radiation Hazards in Space*, TID-7652 (1962).

134. W. E. Spicer, Radiation Effects in Optical Materials, p. 123, *Second Symp. Protection against Radiations in Space*, NASA-SP-71 (1964).

# V

# ATTENUATION OF CHARGED PARTICLES

## A. Differential Interactions

The primary radiation encountered in space (trapped radiation, solar events, and galactic radiation) consists of charged particles. These particles interact in matter in basically three ways:

> Ionization
> Radiation
> Nuclear Interactions

### 1. IONIZATION BY CHARGED PARTICLES

As a moving charged particle passes an atom, its associated electric and magnetic fields disturb the electronic structure of the atom. This disturbance may excite one or more electrons to a higher energy state, and may even remove one or more electrons from the atom, ionizing it. The removed electron(s) may have received sufficient energy to be projected through matter itself, creating secondary ionization.

Ionization interactions are divided into classes by particle mass (light or heavy) and by particle velocity (relativistic or nonrelativistic). A convenient starting point for consideration of such ionization interactions is the Rutherford cross section. This nonrelativistic relationship for the transfer of energy of amount $Q$ to $Q+dQ$ is [1]

$$\sigma_{\text{Rutherford}} = \frac{2\pi Z^2 z^2 e^4}{\mu V^2} \frac{dQ}{Q^2} \text{ cm}^2 \qquad (5.1)$$

where $Ze$ is the charge of incident particle, $ze$ the charge of struck particle, $\mu$ the reduced mass of the system $mM/(m + M)$ (where $m$ and $M$ are the

151

masses of the two interacting particles), $V$ the velocity of the incident particle, and $Q$ the energy transferred to the struck electron.

It will be noticed that small energy transfers are favored by the $Q^{-2}$ relationship. For two identical particles, $Q_{max}$ is taken as $E/2$ ($E$ = incident particle kinetic energy), since the more energetic of the outgoing particles is considered to be the incident one.

The simple Rutherford approximation is valid only for two free, spinless, nonrelativistic particles. If the incident particle energy is sufficiently high compared with the electron binding energy, and the impact parameter (distance of closest approach if the two particles did not interact) is sufficiently small, the atomic electron may be considered free. The W. Pauli exclusion principle prevents two identical particles with half integral angular momentums (e.g., electrons, protons) from approaching too closely unless their spins are antiparallel. As the particle velocity approaches $c$ ($3 \times 10^{10}$ cm/sec), the changing mass, time, and magnetic effects play a role. These complications lead to involved expressions for the energy transfer cross sections [2, 3].

The formula for the energy transfer cross section between two electrons is [4]:

$$\sigma = \frac{2\pi e^4}{m_0 V^2} \frac{dQ}{Q^2} \left(\frac{E}{E-Q}\right)^2 \left[1 - 2\left(\frac{Q}{E}\right) + 2\left(\frac{Q}{E}\right)^2\right] \text{cm}^2/\text{electron} \quad (5.2)$$

where $E$ is the incident electron kinetic energy, $Q$ the energy transferred to struck electron ($Q \leqslant E/2$), $V$ the velocity of incident electron, and $m_0$ the rest mass of electron.

This formula shows that for electrons the cross sections remain approximately at their classical value for all but the largest energy transfers ($E/2$). For electrons below $\sim 5$ Mev, the cross sections for large energy transfers are decreased $\lesssim 50\%$, while for electrons above $\sim 5$ Mev increases $\lesssim 15\%$ are observed. In some treatments the classical energy transfer cross section has been used.

For protons the large difference between the masses of the two particles is important. The protons are nonrelativistic for all energies where atomic ionization is the major energy loss mechanism, and the exclusion principle does not operate because the particles are not identical. The resulting energy transfer cross section for heavy particles of spin 1/2 with atomic electrons is [4]

$$\sigma_{\text{proton}} = \frac{2\pi z^2 e^4}{m_0 V^2} \frac{1}{Q^2} \left[ 1 - \beta^2 \frac{Q}{Q_{\text{max}}} + \tfrac{1}{2} \left( \frac{Q}{E + Mc^2} \right)^2 \right] \text{cm}^2/\text{electron}$$

(5.3)

where $Q_{\text{max}} = (2m_0 V^2)/(1 - \beta^2)$, $m_0$ is the electron rest mass, $M$ the proton rest mass, and $\beta$ the $V/c$. All other symbols are as previously defined. The final term is due to quantum-mechanical spin effects. It vanishes for particles with zero spin (e.g., alpha particles).

In order to obtain the specific ionization $(dE/dx)$, it is necessary to integrate the atomic cross section over all possible energy transfers. For protons various approaches have been used, of which that of Bethe and Bloch is generally accepted as the standard. The Bethe–Bloch formula is [5, 6]

$$-\left(\frac{dE}{dx}\right)_{p+\text{ion}} = \frac{2\pi n e^4}{mv^2} \left[ \ln \frac{2mv^2 W_{\text{max}}}{I^2 (1 - \beta^2)} - 2\beta^2 - \delta - U \right]$$

(5.4)

where $n$ is the electron density in material considered (electrons/cm$^3$), $m$ the mass of electron (gm), $e$ the electron charge, $v$ the velocity of incident particle (cm/sec), $\beta$ the $v/c$ (where $c =$ free space velocity of light), $W_{\text{max}}$ the maximum energy transfer to a free electron from incident particle (ergs), $I$ the mean excitation potential (ergs) of material, $\delta$ the correction for the density effect, and $U$ the correction for electron shell structure.

The evaluation of the Bethe–Bloch equation depends especially upon the parameters $I$, $W_{\text{max}}$, $\delta$, and $U$, each of which is dependent upon the atomic model used. Bloch based his work on the Thomas-Fermi atomic model, which yields a linear relationship between $I$ and the atomic number $(I = kZ)$. Early work was based upon $k = 11$ ev [7], but more recent studies have shown $k = 13$ ev [6].

The shell correction is required because near the end of the incident particle's range its velocity becomes comparable to and less than the velocity of the bound atomic electrons in their orbits. This correction has the form:

$$U \cong \frac{2C_K}{Z} + \frac{2C_L}{Z}$$

(5.5)

where $C_K$ and $C_L$ are constants associated with the K and L electronic shells, respectively. $C_K$ is appreciably larger than $C_L$, and additional terms are not required for Mev protons.

$W_{max}$ has been evaluated by Bhabha [8], who obtained

$$W_{max} = \frac{E^2 - \mu^2 c^4}{\mu c^2 \left[ \dfrac{\mu}{2m} + \dfrac{m}{2\mu} + \dfrac{E}{\mu c^2} \right]} \tag{5.6}$$

where $E$ is the total (rest plus kinetic) energy of the incident particle (rest energy of a proton = 931 Mev), $\mu$ the reduced mass of the electron-incident particle system = $(mM)/(M + m)$, and $M$ the mass of incident particle.

The density-effect correction $\delta$ can be expressed as a power series in $\log_{10} P$, where $P$ is the momentum of the incident particle. This function varies slowly, accounting for the small increase in particle range (gm/cm²) as the density increases [9].

TABLE 5-1

SOME VALUES OF PROTON IONIZATION LOSS IN VARIOUS
MATERIALS OBTAINED BY STERNHEIMER

| Proton energy (Mev) $E_p$ | Specific ionization (Mev–cm²/gm) | | | |
|---|---|---|---|---|
| | C | Al | Cu | Pb |
| 2 | 140.6 | 110.8 | 78.93 | 41.14 |
| 5 | 70.74 | 57.19 | 44.08 | 26.36 |
| 10 | 40.87 | 33.80 | 26.77 | 17.18 |
| 20 | 23.34 | 19.70 | 15.91 | 10.73 |
| 50 | 11.14 | 9.584 | 7.925 | 5.581 |
| 100 | 6.526 | 5.674 | 4.760 | 3.424 |
| 200 | 4.016 | 3.522 | 2.989 | 2.189 |
| 500 | 2.448 | 2.169 | 1.863 | 1.390 |
| 1000 | 1.960 | 1.754 | 1.522 | 1.153 |

The net result of evaluating the preceding equations is the specific ionization Mev–cm²/gm as a function of particle type, particle energy, and material. A few of the over 500 values obtained by Sternheimer [6] are listed in Table 5-1. While Sternheimer lists values of specific ionization to 100 Bev, above ~300, Mev nuclear interactions become increasingly important. Above this energy, calculations of $dE/dx$ based only upon atomic ionization become progressively too low.

For electrons the integration of the energy transfer cross section by Bethe and Ashkin [10] yielded:

$$-\left(\frac{dE}{dx}\right)_{e\text{-ion}} = \frac{2\pi e^4}{m_0 V^2} NZ \left\{\ln\left[\frac{m_0 V^2 E}{I^2(1-\beta^2)}\right] - \beta^2\right\}\qquad(5.7)$$

where all symbols are as previously identified. $I$ is $\sim 13\,Z$ ev, where $Z$ is the atomic number of the material, based upon the Fermi–Thomas model of the atom.

This expression yields the specific ionization for electrons in matter. Below a few million electric volts ionization is the main energy loss mechanism in many materials, and electron ranges can be obtained by integrating this

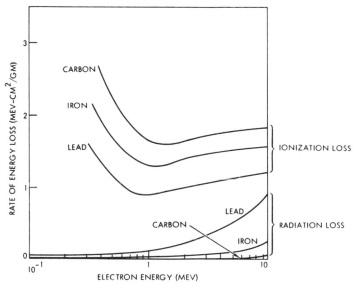

FIG. 5-1. Specific energy loss for electrons in various materials.

expression. Above $\sim 1$ Mev, radiation plays an increasing role in electron energy loss, and hence must be taken into account. (See Fig. 5-1.)

It will be noted that while protons have specific ionizations (Mcv–cm²/gm) on the order of 10–100 (Table 5-1), electrons have specific ionizations on the order of 1. Therefore, a proton produces a more heavily ionized trail of atoms than an electron. As a result a proton expends its energy more rapidly, and (for equal energy) cannot penetrate as far as an electron. However, in space the energies are not equal, so that the protons encountered can produce a greater ionization density and still penetrate further than the electrons encountered [11]. It is this combination of high specific ionization and relatively great penetrating power that makes protons in space dangerous.

## 2. RADIATION BY CHARGED PARTICLES

As a charged particle passes through matter its trajectory is not necessarily a straight line. Departures from a straight line trajectory take place because of collisions with electrons and nuclei comprising the matter being traversed. These collisions may be mechanical or electric. In any event the moving charged particle is subjected to accelerations due to these collisions, and therefore may emit electromagnetic radiation (bremsstrahlung).

If a moving charged particle of mass $m$ and charge $ze$ interacts with an initially stationary charged particle of mass $M$ and charge $Ze$, the intensity of the bremsstrahlung is proportional to [12, 13]:

$$I_{rad} \sim \frac{Z^2 z^2}{\mu^2}$$

where $\mu$ = the reduced mass of the system.

Thus the total bremsstrahlung per atom varies as the square of the charge-to-mass ratio of the moving charged particle. Therefore bremsstrahlung is important for electrons but negligible for protons. For the remainder of this discussion the charged particles considered will be electrons.

Bremsstrahlung has an energy distribution which varies continuously from zero up to the maximum energy of the moving charged particle (Duane and Hunt's law) [14]. Thus some charged particles are brought to rest in a single radiative collision, others only lose a portion of their energy. For thin targets, the intensity between $hv$ and $h(v + dv)$ decreases as $1/\Delta E$ where $\Delta E$ is the energy lost in the radiative encounter.

Bremsstrahlung is emitted with a polar angular distribution which is a function of the initial energy of the moving charged particle. At low energies the intensity is a maximum at 90 deg to the direction of motion of the charged particle becoming peaked more forward as particle energy increases. The tangent of the angle is approximately inversely proportional to the initial energy in units of $m_0 c^2$.

The cross section for electron bremsstrahlung production in the field of a nucleus at low energies ($E \lesssim 0.1$ Mev) is [12]:

$$\sigma_{rad} = \left(\frac{8}{3\pi}\right)\left(\frac{1}{137}\right)\left(\frac{Z}{\beta}\right)^2 \text{ barn/atom (1 barn } = 10^{-24} \text{ cm}^2) \quad (5.8)$$

where $1/137$ is the fine structure constant $= 2\pi e^2/hc$, $Z$ the atomic number of atom involved, and $\beta = v/c$.

At relativistic energies the formula (with screening included) becomes [12]:

$$\sigma_{rad} = 4\sigma_0 Z^2 \left[\ln\left(\frac{183}{Z^{\frac{1}{3}}}\right) + \frac{1}{18}\right] \quad (5.9)$$

where $\sigma_0 = 5.8 \times 10^{-28} \text{ cm}^2/\text{nucleus}$.

The majority of the electron-nuclear encounters which result in radiation have impact parameters on the order of the Compton wavelength $\lambda$ ($\sim 4 \times 10^{-11}$ cm). For larger impact parameters, the electron deflections are too small to produce appreciable radiation, but the probability for smaller impact parameters decreases with the size of area through which the electron must pass. Atomic electron screening also reduces the effective charge of the nucleus for producing electron bremsstrahlung.

The integral of the bremsstrahlung cross section yields the specific radiation loss in material. For thin targets, this energy loss per unit path length is [12]

$$-\left(\frac{dE}{dx}\right)_{e^- rad} = \sigma_0 N Z^2 (E + m_0 c^2) \int_0^1 Bd\left(\frac{h\nu}{E}\right) \text{ ergs/cm} \quad (5.10)$$

where $N$ is the atomic density (atoms/cm$^3$), $h\nu$ is the bremsstrahlung photon energy, $E$ is the electron kinetic energy, $B$ is a parameter which varies from 20 for $h\nu/E = 0$ to 0 for $h\nu/E = 1$.

The specific radiation loss due to bremsstrahlung for electrons in carbon ($Z = 6$), iron ($Z = 26$), and lead ($Z = 82$) is shown in Fig. 5-1. It will be noted that the radiation loss rate increases more rapidly with electron energy than ionization loss rate, becoming predominant at high energies.

Another form of radiation by electrons passing through matter is Cerenkov radiation [15]. Cerenkov radiation is emitted when a charged particle has a velocity in matter greater than photons of some energy in that matter. When this occurs photons in that energy range are emitted in a cone about the direction of particle motion of half-angle $\cos^{-1}(c/vn) = \cos^{-1}(1/\beta n)$, where $n$ is the index of refraction and $v$ is the particle velocity.

The average number of Cerenkov photons emitted per centimeter of particle travel is [4]

$$I = \frac{2\pi z^2}{137} \left( \frac{1}{\lambda_2} - \frac{1}{\lambda_1} \right) \left( 1 - \frac{1}{\beta^2 n^2} \right) \tag{5.11}$$

These photons are generally in the blue end of the visible spectrum, having a $1/\lambda^2$ distribution. Since the Cerenkov effect is strictly relativistic, it does not show up for electron energies much less than $\sim 1.0$ Mev. It is also observed for Bev protons.

### 3.  NUCLEAR INTERACTIONS BY CHARGED PARTICLES

Nuclear interactions between moving charged particles and the matter they are traversing are a complex class by themselves. Essentially we are dealing with protons and heavy ions, since electrons interact only weakly with nuclei.

At high energies the de Broglie wavelength of the moving charged particle becomes sufficiently short that the interaction takes place primarily with one or a few nucleons in a nucleus. The collision is somewhat like breaking a rack of pool balls. The nucleons immediately affected fly off (cascade), often leaving the residual nucleus with several tens of millions of electron

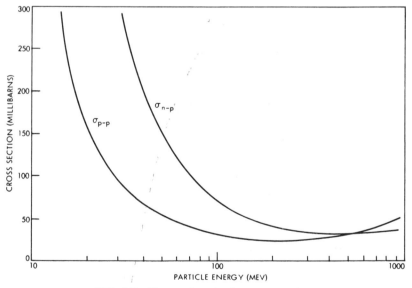

FIG. 5-2.   Free nucleon-nucleon cross section.

volts in excitation energy. The residual nucleus then emits particles (evaporation protons and neutrons) and radiation (gamma rays) to return to its ground state. If the ground state is not stable, beta (and possibly gamma) decay follows until a stable ground state is reached.

The free nucleon cross sections between incident protons and protons or neutrons is shown in Fig. 5-2 [16, 17]. The actual cross sections are somewhat modified from these, because the free particle assumption is only partially valid [18–20].

Nuclear interaction experiments especially directed toward space shielding applications have been reported by Strauch [16], Maienschein *et al.* [21], Peele *et al.* [22], Shen [23], Cohen [24], Jarmie and Seagrave [25], and others. These experiments, using particle accelerators, have been concerned with measuring the types, energies, and directions of secondaries produced by high-energy protons. The data has been supplemented by theoretical work of Bertini [27–29], Metropolis *et al.* [26], and others.

A comprehensive summary of proton and neutron cross-sectional data applicable for space radiation shielding studies has been compiled by Alter [18]. (In addition to collecting cross-sectional data over the energy range of 10–5000 Mev, a bibliography of nearly 500 references is included.)

The nuclear inelastic cross sections for both protons and neutrons are approximately constant above $\sim 100$ Mev. In this energy range,

$$\sigma_{\text{nuclear}} \cong 0.05 Z^{0.8} \text{ barns} \tag{5.12}$$

Hydrogen is an exception, and the formula is most accurate for $Z \geqslant 6$. Below $\sim 100$ Mev, nuclear interactions are much less important than atomic ionization for stopping protons and bare nuclei.

While both cascade neutrons and protons are emitted, neutron emission is somewhat more probable because the coulomb field inhibits proton emission. Both proton and neutron cascade emission increase with incident proton energy. Cascade neutron emission probability increases with the atomic number of the struck nucleus, but in cascade proton emission the coulomb field of the nucleus favors low atomic numbers except at extreme energies ($\gtrsim 1$ Bev). This behavior is shown in Fig. 5-3 [28, 30].

The detailed behavior of proton-initiated cascade processes in aluminum is shown in Fig. 5-4 [31]. It is seen that the number of secondary particles tends to level off somewhat with increasing incident proton energy, while the energies of these cascade secondaries increase almost linearly. This is due

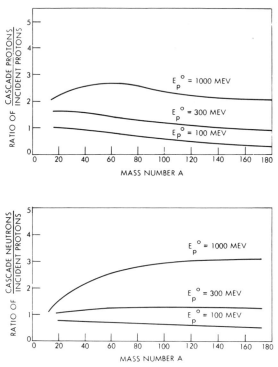

FIG. 5-3.   Number of cascade protons and neutrons per incident proton as a function of
mass number.

to the limited number of nucleons present. It is also noted that proton cascade emission is somewhat more probable than neutron emission in the low-Z range ($Z \lesssim 13$). However, indications are that for slightly higher atomic numbers and incident proton energies, neutron cascade emission will predominate.

Cascade particles are emitted preferentially forward in order to conserve linear momentum [29]. The greater the energy of the primary particle, the more sharply peaked forward the polar angular distribution of the cascade secondaries will be. Unless the incident primary particles are polarized (i.e., their spins are all pointing in the same direction with respect to their directions of travel), there will be no azimuth angular dependence to the cascade secondaries. As far as is known, there is no such polarization present in any of the radiations in space.

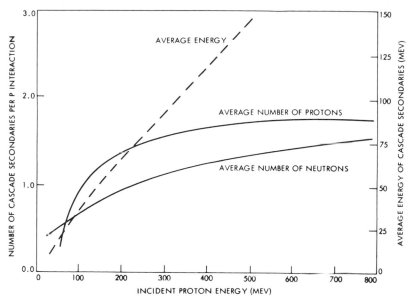

FIG. 5-4. Numbers and energies of cascade secondaries in Al$^{27}$.

Evaporation or "boil-off" nucleons may be visualized by recourse to the liquid drop nuclear model. The remaining excitation energy corresponds to a certain nuclear "temperature." Just as in a heated liquid certain molecules will receive sufficient energy to evaporate, lowering the temperature of the remaining liquid, so the evaporation of nucleons lowers the temperature of the remaining nucleus. Because the evaporation process is slower than the cascade process, it follows the latter. Also the number and energies of protons and neutrons evaporated is almost independent of the incident proton energy. In other words, the cascade process leaves a residual nucleus with a certain amount of energy which approximates a constant depending on the nucleus. This residual (evaporation) energy is removed by neutrons and protons until it is essentially all used up.

Reviews of the evaporation process have been written by Skyrme [32], Dostrovsky *et al.* [33], and others. In the evaporation process even more than in the cascade process, the nuclear coulomb field plays a role. The energy distributions of evaporation nucleons, as predicted by the statistical model of the nucleus, are shown in Fig. 5-5 [33, 34]. The level density of

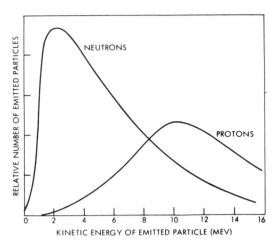

FIG. 5-5.   General energy spectra of evaporated nucleons.

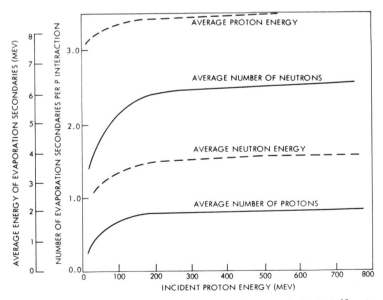

FIG. 5-6.   Numbers and energies of evaporation secondaries in Al$^{27}$.

residual nuclear states is responsible for the decreases at high particle energies, and the coulomb field inhibits low-energy evaporation proton emission. Nuclear edge effects are responsible for the decreased emission probability of low-energy evaporation neutrons.

Again aluminum is examined in detail, showing the expected behavior as a function of incident proton energy (Fig. 5-6) [31]. Note that below $\sim 100$ Mev, where the cascade process becomes appreciably less probable, the evaporation probabilities and energies decrease. This is due to the fact that there is not enough energy to go around. Above $\sim 100$ Mev, the excess energy is carried off by the cascade process, leaving $\sim 100$ Mev for the evaporation process. Evaporation particles are emitted isotropically since their time of emission ($10^{-12}$–$10^{-15}$ sec) is long compared with the characteristic nuclear time of $\sim 10^{-23}$ sec.

## B.  Integral Relationships

### 1.  PROTONS AND HEAVY PARTICLES

As has been seen, the stopping power (energy lost per unit path length in material) increases as the proton loses energy (slows down). This is entirely

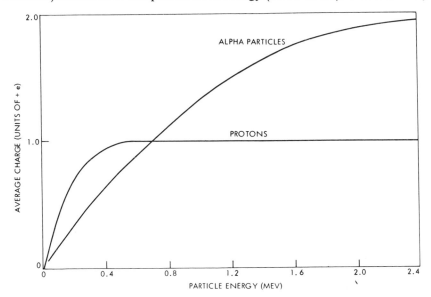

FIG. 5-7.   Residual charge on protons and alpha particles as their energies approach zero.

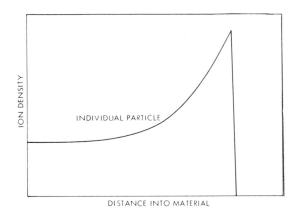

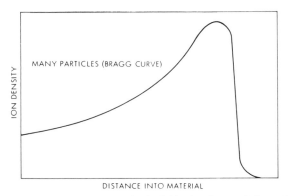

FIG. 5-8.  Bragg ionization curves for individual and several charged particles.

due to the increase in specific ionization, because nuclear interactions play a minor role in attenuation below $\sim 100$ Mev. However, as the proton velocity drops below $\sim 10^9$ cm/sec, it has a tendency to acquire an electron. The same effect is observed for alpha particles and other bare nuclei (Fig. 5-7). The result is that an individual proton will exhibit an energy loss (essentially all ionization) curve in matter; it is rather sharply peaked just before it acquires an electron (Bragg curve). A large number of protons of the same energy will exhibit a somewhat more rounded peak due to statistical differences as to where the electron is acquired. The difference in these energy deposition curves is shown in Fig. 5-8.

Because of this statistical fluctuation, there are three slightly different ranges which can be associated with monoenergetic protons. First, there is the range of an individual particle ($R$). Unless only one particle is involved or a permanent record is made (e.g., on a nuclear track plate), this range is difficult to observe. Secondly, there is the extrapolated Bragg ionization (energy deposition) range ($R_i$). Since the Bragg curve bends and approaches the axis asymptotically, determination of the actual Bragg range reflects the maximum range of any of the protons. Instead the steep slope of the Bragg curve is continued to obtain the $x$-axis intercept. This range, which represents a sort of average of the individual proton ranges, is called the extrapolated Bragg range. The third range is the extrapolated number range ($R_n$). This corresponds to the extrapolated Bragg range, except that the number versus distance, rather than the specific energy loss versus distance, relationship is used. Due to the acquisition of electrons, the extrapolated number range is the longest of the three. These three ranges are illustrated in Fig. 5-9.

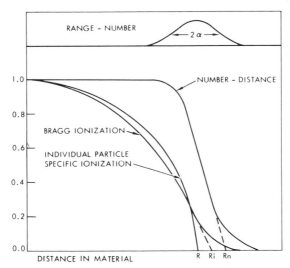

FIG. 5-9.  Schematic showing various types of proton ranges.

It will be noted that the distribution of ranges is approximately Gaussian, with a half-width at $1/e$ max ($\alpha$) which is defined as the range-straggling parameter. It is typically $1.5\%$ of the proton range for incident energies

$\lesssim 100$ Mev [35]. This gives an idea of the uncertainties attached to the various "ranges." It is the mean range $R$ which is usually dealt with, where such range is

$$R = R_n - 0.866\,\alpha$$

where $\alpha$ is the range-straggling parameter discussed. Typical range-energy curves for protons in various materials are shown in Fig. 5-10 [31]. As would

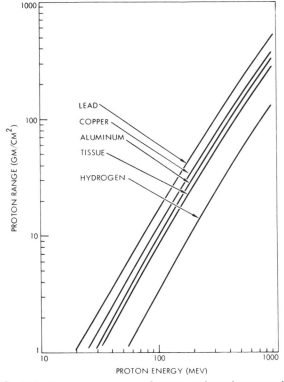

FIG. 5-10.   Range-energy curves for protons in various materials.

be expected, protons in low $Z$ elements have shorter ranges than in high $Z$ ones. For alpha particles the energy scale is multiplied by a factor of 4.

An analytical expression for the range of a proton in matter as a function of its energy may be obtained by integrating the formula for proton stopping power. The atomic stopping power ($B$) for the nonrelativistic case in which proton spin and electron screening are ignored becomes [36]

$$B = Z \ln \left( \frac{2m_0 V^2}{I} \right) \tag{5.13}$$

where $Z$ is the atomic number of the material, $m_0$ the rest mass of an electron, $V$ the proton velocity in the material, and $I$ the geometric mean excitation and ionization potential of the atoms comprising the material and $= kZ$ for Fermi–Thomas model of the atom.

The result of integrating this is [36]

$$R = \frac{M}{z^2} \frac{1}{32\pi e^4 m_0} \frac{I^2}{NZ} (Y_2 - Y_1) + R_0 \tag{5.14}$$

where $R$ is the range of protons in matter, $M$ the mass of the proton, $e$ the charge of an electron, $N$ the atomic density of the material (atoms/cm$^3$), $R_0$ the residual range below which the integration is not valid and which therefore must be added, and $Y_1 = \int_0^y dy/\ln y$—where $y = (2m_0 V^2/I)$.

The more general proton range-energy relationship has been extensively investigated by Sternheimer [6], Aron *et al.* [37], Uehling [38], Rich and Madey [39], and others. Sternheimer's work is often taken as the standard for shielding studies. He calculated the ranges in various materials, using the formula,

$$R(E) = R(E_0) + \int_{E_0}^{E} \frac{dE}{- (1/\rho)(dE/dx)} \tag{5.15}$$

where $R(E)$ is the range (gm/cm$^2$) of proton of energy $E$ (Mev), $\rho$ the material density (gm/cm$^3$), and $dE/dx$ the specific ionization as given by the Bethe–Bloch formula.

It was necessary to evaluate the integral from some lower limit $E_0$ to the proton energy, because the Bethe–Bloch formula introduces errors below $\sim 2$ Mev. This is attributed to the neglect of electron acquisition by the proton in this energy region.

Some of the results of Sternheimer's calculations are presented in Table 5-2. A convenient fact to remember is that a 100-Mev proton has a range of 10 gm/cm$^2$ in aluminum. The concept of a definite range becomes less accurate for protons above $\sim 1$ Bev, where the exponential attenuation of nuclear interactions becomes predominant.

TABLE 5-2

PROTON RANGES IN VARIOUS MATERIALS CALCULATED BY STERNHEIMER

| Proton energy (Mev) | Ranges (gm/cm²) | | | |
|---|---|---|---|---|
| | C | Al | Cu | Pb |
| 2 | 0.0084 | 0.0115 | 0.0190 | 0.0410 |
| 5 | 0.0406 | 0.0517 | 0.0724 | 0.1345 |
| 10 | 0.1376 | 0.1700 | 0.2234 | 0.3761 |
| 20 | 0.4759 | 0.5742 | 0.7276 | 1.138 |
| 50 | 2.488 | 2.928 | 3.599 | 5.275 |
| 100 | 8.623 | 10.01 | 12.09 | 17.17 |
| 200 | 29.02 | 33.34 | 39.71 | 55.14 |

TABLE 5-3

CONSTANTS FOR $R = \delta E^n$ FITS TO RANGE-ENERGY CURVES

| Material | Protons | | Alpha Particles | | Electrons | |
|---|---|---|---|---|---|---|
| | $n$ | $\delta$ | $n$ | $\delta$ | $n$ | $\delta$ |
| Hydrogen | 1.817 | $8.21 \times 10^{-4}$ | 1.817 | $6.62 \times 10^{-5}$ | 1.32 | 0.155 |
| Beryllium | 1.788 | $2.35 \times 10^{-3}$ | 1.788 | $1.98 \times 10^{-4}$ | 1.32 | 0.390 |
| Carbon | 1.787 | $2.22 \times 10^{-3}$ | 1.787 | $1.86 \times 10^{-4}$ | 1.32 | 0.356 |
| Aluminum | 1.730 | $3.47 \times 10^{-3}$ | 1.730 | $3.15 \times 10^{-4}$ | 1.32 | 0.400 |
| Copper | 1.728 | $4.07 \times 10^{-3}$ | 1.728 | $3.71 \times 10^{-4}$ | 1.32 | 0.464 |
| Cadmium | 1.708 | $4.97 \times 10^{-3}$ | 1.708 | $4.70 \times 10^{-4}$ | 1.32 | 0.516 |
| Lead | 1.680 | $7.18 \times 10^{-3}$ | 1.680 | $7.00 \times 10^{-4}$ | 1.32 | 0.640 |
| Air | 1.777 | $2.39 \times 10^{-3}$ | 1.777 | $2.04 \times 10^{-4}$ | 1.32 | 0.364 |
| Water | 1.793 | $1.95 \times 10^{-3}$ | 1.793 | $1.62 \times 10^{-4}$ | 1.32 | 0.356 |
| Tissue | 1.783 | $2.17 \times 10^{-3}$ | 1.783 | $1.83 \times 10^{-4}$ | 1.32 | 0.353 |

In a later article Sternheimer [40] presents a somewhat different method for calculating proton ranges. The basic formula used for the range is

$$R(E) = R(2 \text{ Mev}) + \frac{A}{2Z} \, \Phi_{al}(E) \left[ 1 + \sum_{1}^{3} GX^n \right] \qquad (5.16)$$

where $X = \log_{10} (I/166)$, $A$ is the atomic weight, $Z$ the atomic number, and $\Phi_{al}$ and $G_i$ are constants.

Sternheimer presented values of $\Phi_{al}$ and the $G_i$'s in tables. The main value of this method is that it facilitates obtaining ranges for any element. For the elements for which range-energy tables are available, their use is by far the fastest and most accurate.

A somewhat simpler expression which is often used is of the form [41–43]:

$$R = \delta E^n \qquad (5.17)$$

where $R$ is the range of particle $(gm/cm^2)$, $E$ the energy of particle in material (Mev), and $\delta$ and $n$ are constants depending on material and particle.

Values of $\delta$ and $n$ for protons and alpha particles in various materials are listed in Table 5-3 [43].

The corresponding ionization stopping powers may be represented by an expression of the form:

$$\frac{1}{\rho}\frac{dE}{dx} = BE^{-\beta} \qquad (5.18)$$

where $(1/\rho)(dE/dx)$ is the stopping power of the material $(Mev–cm^2/gm)$, $E$ the particle energy (Mev), and $B$ and $\beta$ are constants depending upon the material and the particle.

It can be seen that $B$ and $\beta$ depend upon $n$ and $\delta$.

The relationships obtained by differentiating Eq. (5.17) are

$$B = \frac{1}{n\delta} \qquad \beta = n - 1$$

If the thickness of material $(X_1)$ is known, and one desires to obtain the corresponding thickness $(X_2)$ of another material (based upon proton attenuation) the readily derived formula is

$$X_2 = \delta_2 \left(\frac{X_1}{\delta_1}\right)^{n_2/n_1} \qquad (5.19)$$

where $n_i$ and $\delta_i$ are the constants for the range-energy fit in material $i$. Of course the same relationship is valid for any charged particle for which Eq. (5.17) holds.

If the constants $n$ and $\delta$ are not known, it is possible to estimate the proton ranges $(R_i)$ in different materials by using the Bragg-Kleeman rule. This rule states that

$$\frac{R_2}{R_1} = \frac{\rho_1}{\rho_2}\frac{\sqrt{A_2}}{\sqrt{A_1}} \qquad (5.20)$$

where $\rho$ = density, and $A$ = atomic number, of the materials. This relationship is accurate to within $\sim \pm 15\%$ in estimating proton ranges.

The apparent simplicity of the proton range-energy relationships tends to conceal the fact that protons do not lose energy linearly. While the Bragg curve illustrates this to some extent, another insight may be gained by examining the energy of the proton along its path.

Based upon Eq. (5.17), the energy ($E'$) of a proton after penetrating any depth $X$ (gm/cm²) is

$$E' = \left[ E_0^n - \frac{x}{\delta} \right]^{1/n} \tag{5.21}$$

where $E_0$ is the incident energy at $X = 0$. This equation is presented graphically in Fig. 5-11.

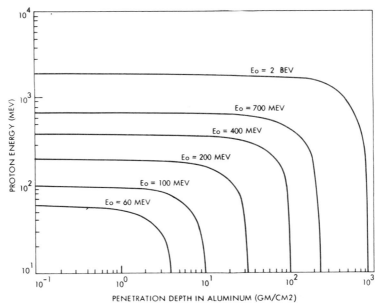

FIG. 5-11.  Residual energies for protons in aluminum.

As Fig. 5-11 shows, a proton of a given energy loses that energy relatively slowly until near the end of its path when it loses it rapidly. This is important in dose calculations, since the product of the proton energy distribution and the flux-to-dose conversion factor determines the dose behind a shield.

While ionization is by far the most important energy loss mechanism for low-energy ($\lesssim 100$ Mev) protons, nuclear interactions become increasingly important above this point. These nuclear interactions may be taken into account approximately by an exponential attenuation factor,

$$e^{-x/\rho\lambda}$$

where $x$ is the material thickness (gm/cm$^2$), $\lambda$ the nuclear mean free path for protons in material (cm), and $\rho$ the material density (gm/cm$^3$).

However, $\lambda$ is not a constant for different proton energies, since

$$\frac{1}{\lambda} = N\sigma$$

where $N$ is the nuclear density (nuclei/cm$^3$), and $\sigma$ the total nuclear interaction cross section (cm$^2$/nucleus).

Above $\sim 100$ Mev, $\sigma$ may be approximated by Eq. (5.12).

Measurements and calculations have been carried out for the dose-distance relationships of monoenergetic protons [44–46]. For low energies the curves follow the Bragg curve, rising to a peak and falling to zero at the end of the proton range. For protons of energies above $\sim 100$ Mev, the situation is changed because the protons can produce secondaries (principally neutrons) which can penetrate beyond the protons. Thus the concept of range, when speaking of heavy charged particles, becomes less meaningful as incident energy increases [47].

Since there is increasing evidence for the presence of alpha particles in the radiation from the sun, and it is known that heavy ($Z \geqslant 2$) nuclei are present in galactic radiation, the behavior of alpha particles and other heavy nuclei in matter deserves attention. To a very good approximation (nonrelativistically),

$$\frac{dE}{dx} \sim \frac{Z^2}{m_0 v^2}$$

where $Z$ is the atomic number of moving charged particle, $m_0$ the rest mass of electron, and $v$ the velocity of moving charged particle.

Thus for particles with the same initial velocity,

$$\frac{\text{Range}_1}{\text{Range}_2} = \frac{\text{Mass}_1 \, (Z_2)^2}{\text{Mass}_2 \, (Z_1)^2}$$

Using this relationship it is possible to obtain the approximate range-energy curves for any heavy charged particle from those for protons.

## 2.   ELECTRONS

Electrons, like protons, tend to lose their energy continually as they pass through matter. Thus electrons tend to exhibit definite ranges, although the concept of range becomes less meaningful as incident electron energy increases. The first difference between electrons and protons is that for protons the path length and range are essentially the same, while for electrons the path length is longer than the range (i.e., the straggling parameter is often $\gtrsim 10\%$ of the range). This is due to the much lighter mass of the electron, which allows it to be deflected in its path much more easily. It is also responsible for the bremsstrahlung the electrons radiate as they pass through matter.

The variations of $R$ and $S$ with electron energy $(E)$ have been investigated in some detail by Williams [48], Katz and Penfold [49], Berger and Seltzer [50], Magnuson and McReynolds [51], and others. The range varies approximately as $E$ in the high-energy $(\gtrsim 1 \text{ Mev})$ region and as $\sim E^2$ in the low-energy region $(\lesssim 0.1 \text{ Mev})$. In the latter the path length is given approximately by the Thompson-Whiddington law, which states that electron range is proportional to the fourth power of initial velocity. In this energy region $(E \lesssim 0.1 \text{ Mev})$ electrons are nonrelativistic, and the electron range is approximately $80\%$ of the path length. Here the path length is given approximately by

$$S = \text{const}(E^2/NZ)$$

At higher energies the behavior of $S$ is complicated, increasing somewhat more rapidly than the above relationship would indicate.

It is possible to fit the range-energy relationships for electrons approximately by the same relationship as used for protons, namely,

$$R \text{ (gm/cm}^2) = \delta E^n \text{(Mev)} \tag{5.22}$$

Approximate values of $\delta$ and $n$ for electrons were listed in Table 5-3.

Katz and Penfold [49] obtained a somewhat more accurate fit to the range-energy relationship for electrons in aluminum by using the formula,

$$R \text{ (gm/cm}^2) = 0.412 \, E^{1.265 - 0.0954 \ln E} \qquad E \lesssim 2.5 \text{ Mev}$$
$$= 0.53 \, E - 0.106 \qquad E \gtrsim 2.5 \text{ Mev} \tag{5.23}$$

where $E$ is in Mev. Corresponding formulas for other materials are expected to be quite similar.

The relationship between path length and range depends upon the bremsstrahlung. The greater the fraction of energy lost through bremsstrahlung, the greater the difference between path length and range, since bremsstrahlung depends upon the direction changes of the electron path. The fraction of electron energy ($E$) converted to bremsstrahlung ($I$) in a thick target is [52, 53]

$$\frac{I}{E} \cong 7 \times 10^{-3} ZE \qquad (E \text{ in Mev}) \qquad (5.24)$$

Thus bremsstrahlung is responsible for a greater fraction of electron energy loss as atomic number ($Z$) and electron energy ($E$) increase. As the product $ZE$ approaches $\sim 1.4 \times 10^2$, the relationship fails, because the bremsstrahlung energy cannot exceed the energy of the electron that produced it.

Thus, electrons lose energy by radiation at high energies in high-$Z$ materials and by ionization at low energies in low-$Z$ materials. The so-called "critical energy" is that in a given material at which ionization losses and

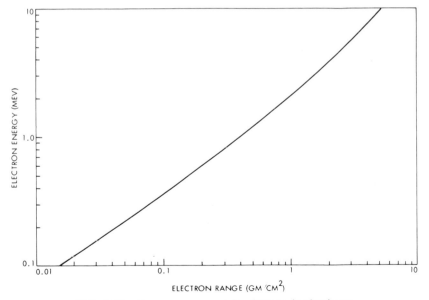

FIG. 5-12.   Range-energy curve for electrons in aluminum.

radiation losses are equal. At high energies another significant parameter is the radiation length, which is the distance an electron travels in a given material while having its energy reduced by a factor of $e$ due to bremsstrahlung. In the extreme relativistic energy region, where the energy loss is almost completely due to bremsstrahlung, the radiation length can be read directly from the range-energy curves.

It is the extrapolated range $(\bar{R})$ which is the basis of range-energy graphs. The range-energy curve up to 10 Mev for electrons in aluminum is shown in Fig. 5-12. For other materials the range-energy relationship is essentially the same on a gm/cm² basis, because the saturation effects present for protons (shell and density effects) are unimportant. This same curve may also be used for the continuous beta spectra emitted by nuclei, except that the end-point energy of the beta spectrum is used. However, in this case, the values of the range-energy curve are for the range $(R)$ rather than for the extrapolated range $(\bar{R})$ [54].

Because of the continuous energy distribution of beta particles emitted by nuclei, the number-distance relationship for these beta particles is approximately exponential. For these polyenergetic spectra, the relationship is

$$I = I_0 e^{-\mu x}$$

where $I$ and $I_0$ are the readings obtained by an ionization chamber, $\mu$ is the linear attenuation coefficient, and $x$ is the distance in the material considered. While $\mu$ varies considerably from element to element, $\mu/\rho$ is very nearly a constant dependent upon maximum beta energy (but not material). An approximate relationship is [49, 55]

$$\frac{\mu}{\rho} = \frac{17}{E_m^{1.14}} \tag{5.25}$$

where $\rho$ is the material density (gm/cm³), and $E_m$ the beta end-point (max) energy (Mev).

Methods based upon similar relationships were used at one time to measure the end-points of unknown beta spectra.

## REFERENCES

1. R. D. Evans, "The Atomic Nucleus," Appendix B. McGraw-Hill, New York, 1955.
2. C. Moller, On the Theory of the Penetration of Fast Electrons through Matter, *Ann. Physik* **14**, 531 (1932).
3. H. J. Bhabha, The Scattering of Positrons by Electrons with Exchange on Dirac's Theory of the Positron, *Proc. Roy. Soc. (London)* **A154**, 195 (1936).
4. R. D. Evans, "The Atomic Nucleus," Chap. 18. McGraw-Hill, New York, 1955.
5. U. Fano, Penetration of Protons, Alpha Particles, and Mesons, *Ann. Rev. Nucl. Sci.* **13**, 1 (1963).
6. R. M. Sternheimer, Range-Energy Relations for Protons in Be, C, Al, Cu, Pb, and Air, *Phys. Rev.* **115**, 137 (1959).
7. J. A. Wheeler and R. Landenberg, Mass of the Meson by the Method of Momentum Loss, *Phys. Rev.* **60**, 754 (1941).
8. H. J. Bhabha, On the Penetrating Component of Cosmic Radiation, *Proc. Roy. Soc. (London)* **A164**, 257 (1937).
9. R. M. Sternheimer, Density Effect for the Ionization Loss in Various Materials, *Phys. Rev.* **103**, 511 (1956).
10. H. A. Bethe and J. Ashkin, "Passage of Radiation through Matter," *Exp. Nucl. Phys.*, (*E. Segre, ed., Wiley, New York*) **1** (1953).
11. W. P. Saylor, D. E. Winer, C. J. Eiwen and A. W. Carriker, Space Radiation Guide, Rept. AMRL-TDR-62-86, *Biomed. Lab., U.S. Air Force, Dayton, Ohio* (1962).
12. R. D. Evans, "The Atomic Nucleus," Chap. 20. McGraw-Hill, New York, 1955.
13. H. W. Koch and J. W. Motz, Bremsstrahlung Formulas and Experimental Data, Rept. 6104, *Natl. Bur. Std., Washington, D.C.* (1958).
14. W. Duane and F. L. Hunt, On X-Ray Wavelengths, *Phys. Rev.* **6**, 166 (1915).
15. P. A. Cerenkov, Visible Radiation Produced by Electrons Moving in a Medium with Velocities Exceeding That of Light, *Phys. Rev.* **52**, 378 (1937).
16. K. Strauch, Measurements of Secondary Spectra from High-Energy Nuclear Reactions, p. 409 ff., *Proc. Symp. on Protection against Radiation Hazards in Space*, TID 7652 (1962).
17. W. Rarita, P-P Scattering in the BeV Range, *Phys. Rev.* **104**, 221 (1956).
18. H. Alter, Basic Microscopic Data for Space Shielding Analysis, Rept. AMTD-240, *Atomics Intern. Canoga Park, California* (1963).
19. R. Jastrow and I. Harris, Nuclear Cross Sections of Neutrons and Protons, *Nucl. Phys.* **9**, No 11, 437 (1958).
20. H. W. Bertini, A Literature Survey of Nonelastic Reactions for Nucleons and Pions Incident on Complex Nuclei at Energies between 20 MeV and 33 BeV, Rept. ORNL-3383, *Oak Ridge Natl. Lab.*, Oak Ridge, Tennessee (1963).
21. F. C. Maienschein *et al.*, Experimental Techniques for the Measurement of Nuclear Secondaries from the Interactions of Protons of a Few Hundred MeV, p. 523, *Proc. Symp. Protection against Radiation Hazards in Space*, TID-7652 (1962).
22. R. W. Peele, T. A. Love, N. W. Hill, and R. T. Santoro, Differential Cross Sections by Flight-Time Spectroscopy for Proton Production in Reactions of 160 MeV Protons on Nuclei, p. 331, *Second Symp. Protection against Radiations in Space*, NASA-SP-71 (1964).

23. B. S. P. Shen, Some Experimental Data on the Nuclear Cascade in Thick Absorbers, *p.* 351 ff., *Second Symp. Protection against Radiations in Space*, NASA-SP-71 (1964).

24. B. L. Cohen, Angular Distributions and Yields of Neutrons from $(p, n)$ Reactions, *Phys. Rev.* **98**, 49 (1955).

25. N. Jarmie and J. D. Seagrave, Charged Particle Cross Sections, Repts. LA-2014 and LA-2424, *Los Alamos Scientific Lab.*, Los Alamos, New Mexico (1956 and 1960).

26. N. Metropolis, R. Bivins, M. Storm, A. Turkevich, J. Miller, and G. Friedlander, Monte Carlo Calculations of Intranuclear Cascades, I and II, *Phys. Rev.* **110**, 185, 204 (1958).

27. H. W. Bertini, Monte Carlo Calculations for Intranuclear Cascades, p. 433, *Proc. Symp. Protection against Radiation Hazards in Space*, TID-7652 (1962).

28. H. W. Bertini, Parametric Study of Calculated Cascade and Evaporation Reactions for 25 to 400 MeV Nucleons Incident on Complex Nuclei, *Oak Ridge Natl. Lab. Rept. ORNL*-3499 **2**, 31 (1963).

29. H. W. Bertini, Particles Emitted in the Forward Directions from High Energy Nucleon-Nucleus Knock-on Reactions, p. 157, *Second Symp. Protection against Radiations in Space*, NASA-SP-71 (1964).

30. R. Wallace and C. Sondhaus, Techniques Used in Shielding Calculations for High Energy Accelerators: Applications to Space Shielding, p. 829, *Proc. Symp. Protection against Radiation Hazards in Space*, TID-7652 (1962).

31. J. W. Keller, A Study of Shielding Requirements for Manned Space Missions, Rept. FZK-124, *Convair Div. General Dynamics Corp.*, *Ft. Worth, Texas* (1960).

32. D. M. Skyrme, The Evaporation of Neutrons from Nuclei Bombarded with High Energy Protons, *Nucl. Phys.* **35**, 177 (1962).

33. I. Dostrovsky, P. Rabinowitz, R. Bivins, Z. Fraenkel, and G. Friedlander, Monte Carlo Calculations of High Energy Nuclear Interactions—I, Systematics of Nuclear Evaporation, *Phys. Rev.* **111**, 1659 (1958); and III, Applications to Low Energy Reactions, *Phys. Rev.* **116**, 683 (1959).

34. R. D. Evans, "The Atomic Nucleus," Chap. 11, McGraw-Hill, New York, 1955.

35. R. R. Wilson, Range, Straggling, and Multiple Scattering of East Protons, *Phys. Rev.* **71**, 385L (1947).

36. R. D. Evans, "The Atomic Nucleus," Chap. 22, McGraw-Hill, New York, 1955.

37. W. A. Aron, B. G. Hoffman and F. C. Williams, Range vs Energy and Rate of Energy Loss vs Energy for Particles in Various Media, Rept. UCRL-121, *Univ. Calif. Berkeley, California* (1949).

38. E. A. Uehling, Penetration of Heavy Charged Particles in Matter, *Ann. Rev. Nucl. Sci.* **4**, 315 (1954).

39. M. Rich and R. Madey, Range-Energy Tables, Rept. UCRL-2301, *Univ. Calif., Berkeley, California* (1954).

40. R. M. Sternheimer, Range-Energy Relations for Protons in Various Substances, *Phys. Rev.* **118**, 1045 (1960).

41. S. K. Allison and S. D. Warshaw, Passage of Heavy Particles through Matter, *Rev. Mod. Phys.* **25**, 779 (1953).

42. Do In Seb, Remark on the Range-Energy Relationship, *Soviet Phys. English Transl. JETP,* **16,** 87 (1963).
43. R. A. Weagant, Nomogram for Heavy Charged Particle Shielding Calculations, Rept. SID 64–10, *North Am. Aviation, Downey, California* (1964).
44. J. E. Turner *et al.,* The Calculations of Radiation Dose in Tissue from High Energy Protons, p. 619, *Proc. Symp. Protection against Radiation Hazards in Space,* TID-7652 (1962).
45. R. Wallace, P. G. Steward, and C. Sondhaus, Primary and Secondary Proton Dose Rates in Spheres and Slabs of Tissue, p. 301, *Second Symp. Protection against Radiations in Space,* NASA-SP-71 (1964).
46. II. J. Schaefer, Local Dose from Proton and Alpha Particle Enders behind Complex Shield Systems, p. 507, *Second Symp. Protection against Radiations in Space,* NASA-SP-71 (1964).
47. R. G. Alsmiller and J. E. Murphy, Space Vehicle Shielding Studies—Calculations of the Attenuation of a Model Flare and Monoenergetic Proton Beams by Aluminum Shields, Rept. ORNL-3317, *Oak Ridge Natl. Lab.* Oak Ridge, Tennessee (1963).
48. E. J. Williams, The Rate of Loss of Energy by Beta-Particles in Passing through Matter, *Proc. Roy. Soc. (London)* **A130,** 310 (1931).
49. I. Katz and A. S. Penfold, Range-Energy Relations for Electrons and the Determination of Beta-Ray End Point Energies by Absorption, *Rev. Mod. Phys.* **24,** 28 (1952).
50. M. J. Berger and S. M. Seltzer, Tables of Energy Losses and Ranges of Electrons and Positrons, NASA Rept. SP-3012 (1964).
51. G. D. Magnuson and A. W. McReynolds, Space Electron Radiation Shielding—Bremsstrahlung and Electron Transmission, p. 455, *Second Symp. Protection against Radiations in Space,* NASA-SP-71 (1964).
52. H. W. Koch and J. W. Motz, Bremsstrahlung Cross Section Formulas and Related Data, *Rev. Mod. Phys.* **31,** 920 (1959).
53. L. L. Baggerly, W. E. Dance, B. J. Farmer, and J. H. Johnson, Bremsstrahlung Production in Thick Aluminum and Iron Targets by 0.5 to 3.0 MeV Electrons, p. 449, *Second Symp. Protection against Radiations in Space,* NASA-SP-71 (1964).
54. S. Kinsman, "Radiological Health Handbook," Taft Sanitary Eng. Center, Cincinnati, Ohio, 1954.
55. M. Curie *et al.,* The Radioactive Constants as of 1930—Report of the International Radium Standards Commission, *Rev. Mod. Phys.* **3,** 427 (1931).

# VI

# UNCHARGED RADIATION

# ATTENUATION

Uncharged nuclear radiation is important in space radiation shielding because such radiation (neutrons and photons) is produced when the primary charged radiations (electrons, protons, heavy ions) in space interact with matter. Under certain conditions this uncharged secondary radiation may be more dangerous to occupants of a spacecraft (because of its relatively great penetrating ability) than the charged primary radiation which produced it.

The calculation of the effects of secondary radiation must begin with the secondary radiation sources. The secondary radiation source strength $(S')$ is

$$S'(E', r) = \int v(E, E')n(r)\sigma(E)\phi(E, r)dE$$

where $n$ is the density of centers interacting with the primary radiation (e.g., atoms/cm$^3$, nuclei/cm$^3$), $\sigma$ the interaction cross section per interaction center (e.g., barns/nucleus, cm$^2$/atom), $\phi$ the flux of primary radiation (e.g., protons/cm$^2$–sec), $v$ = number of secondary particles or quanta released per interaction of the primary radiation, $E$ the energy of the primary radiation, and $E'$ the energy of the secondary radiation.

The units of $S'$ are secondary particles (or quanta) per unit volume (cubic centimeter) per unit time (second). Obviously $S'$ will be a function of position $(r)$ as well as of incident particle energy $(E)$. The secondary source strength $(S')$ will also be a function of direction for some processes (bremsstrahlung production; cascade reactions), since the direction of the initial particle plays a role.

Once the secondary radiation sources are known, they are treated as any primary source, and the transport of their radiations is handled accordingly. The attenuation of such uncharged secondary radiations is discussed in the following sections.


## DIFFERENTIAL INTERACTIONS

### A. Neutron Interactions with Matter

Neutrons, because of their zero charge and nonzero mass, have a behavior all their own in matter. Basically, they undergo the following three types of interaction:

> Elastic scattering
> Inelastic scattering
> Absorption

### 1. ELASTIC SCATTERING
Elastic neutron scattering may be visualized as the collision between two hard spheres. The neutron hits the nucleus, and both come off with the total kinetic energy and momentum being shared between them. In a barely grazing collision, the neutron keeps virtually all of its energy; in a head-on collision, the neutron may lose all of its energy (in hydrogen). The neutron energy $(E)$ after an elastic collision with a nucleus of mass number $A$ initially at rest is

$$E = E_0 \left[ \frac{A^2 + 2A \cos \theta + 1}{(A + 1)^2} \right] \tag{6.1}$$

where $E_0$ is the neutron energy before the collision and $\theta$ is the angle through which the neutron is scattered.

If the preceding expression is averaged over all angles, one obtains as the average energy after scattering [1]:

$$E = E_0 e^{-\xi} \tag{6.2}$$

where $\xi = 1 + \left( \frac{A - 1}{2A} \right)^2 \ln \left( \frac{A - 1}{A + 1} \right) \cong \frac{2}{A + \frac{2}{3}}$ = average logarithmic energy decrement per collision.

Thus the number of collisions for a neutron to lose a certain amount of energy varies almost inversely with the mass number of the atoms in the medium.

As a neutron bounces from atom to atom, losing energy by elastic collisions, it tends to lose any sense of direction. However, from random walk considerations, the neutron will migrate a given distance from its starting point. This crow flight distance is $\sqrt{6}$ times the slowing down length, which depends upon the initial and terminal energies considered. Most of the calculations carried out have been for fission neutrons slowing down to the indium capture resonance (1.45 ev) or to thermal energies (0.025 ev at 20°C). Neutron slowing down parameters have been reported by Glasstone and Edlund [1], Templin *et al.* [2], Amster [3], Moller and Sjostrand [4], Ghatak and Krieger [5], and others. In Table 6-1 the distances and times for the slowing down of fission neutrons (moderation) in a few materials are given. The steady progression toward longer slowing down lengths and times as $A$ increases will be noted. The slowing down lengths for a few

TABLE 6-1

List of Some Neutron Slowing Down Parameters[a]

| Material | Age (cm$^2$) | Slowing down length (cm) | Crow flight distance (cm) | Slowing down time (sec) |
|---|---|---|---|---|
| Water ($H_2O$)   (18)[b] | 33 | 5.7 | 14 | $1 \times 10^{-5}$ |
| Heavy water ($D_2O$)   (38) | 130 | 11.4 | 28 | $4.8 \times 10^{-5}$ |
| Beryllium (Be)   (86) | 97 | 9.9 | 24.2 | $6.6 \times 10^{-5}$ |
| Graphite (C)   (114) | 350 | 18.7 | 45.8 | $1.5 \times 10^{-4}$ |

[a] For fission (evaporation) neutron sources to thermal energies (0.025 ev).
[b] Number of collisions to thermalize.

materials as a function of neutron energy are shown in Fig. 6-1. The compounds must be considered as mixtures of H (or D) and O atoms, with the oxygen not taking much energy from the neutron.

As the neutron slows down it approaches the energies of molecular binding of atoms. As these energies are approached, nuclei, which before acted as if they were isolated, begin to exhibit an effective mass representative of the molecule in which they are bound. Thus neutrons lose energy more slowly than they would if this effect were absent.

In the preceding, it was assumed that the nuclei were at rest. Since room temperature thermal energy is 0.025 ev, a room temperature nucleus is essentially at rest as far as a neutron in the Mev or kev energy range is concerned. However, as the neutron slows down into the ev energy range and below, this thermal motion of the nuclei becomes more important. Once a neutron reaches thermal energies, its energy tends to stabilize, since it is as likely to gain as to lose energy by an elastic collision with a nucleus. Consequently the slowing down and diffusion parameters are temperature-dependent [6, 7].

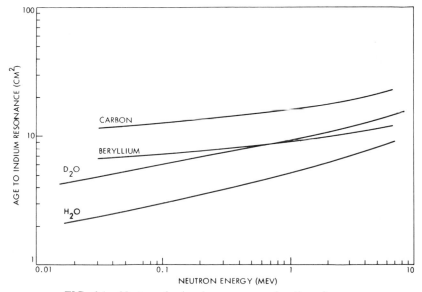

FIG. 6-1.   Neutron slowing down ages as a function of energy.

Thus a neutron cannot lose energy on the average once it has reached thermal energies. However, it can still elastically scatter, except that no net energy transfer takes place. Under these conditions the neutron merely diffuses in matter until it is captured. During the diffusion process it will migrate a crow flight distance equal to $\sqrt{6}$ times the diffusion length. Diffusion parameters have been reported by Glasstone and Edlund [1], Templin *et al.* [2], Lloyd *et al.* [7], Antonov [8], Cohen [9], McInerney [10], and others. A few diffusion and crow flight lengths and the survival times for a neutron in thermal equilibrium at room temperature before being captured are listed in Table 6-2.

TABLE 6-2

LIST OF SOME NEUTRON DIFFUSION PARAMETERS[a]

| Material | Diffusion length (cm) | Crow flight travel (cm) | Diffusion time (sec) |
| --- | --- | --- | --- |
| Water ($H_2O$) | 2.7 | 6.6 | $2 \times 10^{-4}$ |
| Heavy water ($D_2O$) | 100 | 245 | $1.5 \times 10^{-1}$ |
| Beryllium (Be) | 21 | 51.4 | $4.2 \times 10^{-3}$ |
| Graphite (C) | 54 | 132 | $1.3 \times 10^{-2}$ |

[a] All data for 20°C.

## 2. INELASTIC SCATTERING

In addition to being scattered elastically by a nucleus, a neutron can scatter inelastically. In this type of interaction the nucleus is left in an excited state, and the neutron loses an energy equal to this excitation energy over and above what it would have lost in an elastic collision. The struck nucleus thus acquires two types of energy-translational kinetic energy as in elastic scattering and excitation (potential) energy.

The nucleus can only absorb excitation energy when the potential energy absorbed equals that of one of its energy levels. Each nucleus has energy levels for its constituent nucleons [11, 12]. These may be bound, in which case the nucleus usually emits a gamma ray and returns to its ground state [13, 14]. Or they may be unbound, in which case one or more particles leave the nucleus [15, 16]. All stable nuclei heavier than He have bound energy levels. Neutrons whose energies are less than the first excited level of the nucleus cannot be inelastically scattered. Among light nuclei, $Be^9$ has its first excited nuclear level at 1.75 Mev, $C^{12}$ at 4.43 Mev, and $Al^{27}$ at 1.78 Mev. Since the density of energy levels increases as excitation energy and mass number increase [17], inelastic neutron scattering is most probable for energetic neutrons in heavy nuclei.

The neutron tends to be emitted in the forward direction in an inelastic scattering collision. The resulting gamma rays are isotropically emitted to a first approximation. Inelastic neutron scattering cross sections are measured by observation of the gamma rays emitted. The cross sections typically are in the mb ($10^{-27}$ cm$^2$/atom) to barn ($10^{-24}$ cm$^2$/atom) region (Fig. 6-2).

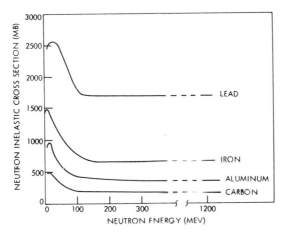

FIG. 6-2.   Neutron inelastic cross sections as a function of energy.

3.   ABSORPTION

The third nuclear process for neutrons is absorption. In this case the neutron becomes incorporated into the capturing nucleus. Of course, this gives the capturing nucleus an excitation energy equal to the binding energy of the captured neutron in the residual nucleus. Usually the nucleus emits one or more gamma rays to return to its new ground state, but it may emit a particle instead of, or in addition to, the gamma rays.

The probability of neutron capture generally increases directly with the time the neutron spends in the vicinity of the nucleus (the $1/v$ cross section). However, at intermediate neutron energies there exist nuclear resonances, some of which are absorption resonances. In the vicinity of an absorption resonance, the cross section varies according to the Breit-Wigner relationship [18]:

$$\sigma(n, \gamma) = \pi \lambdabar^2 \frac{(2I_c + 1)}{(2I_n + 1)(2I_t + 1)} \frac{\Gamma_n \Gamma_\gamma}{(E - E_0)^2 + (\Gamma/2)^2} \tag{6.3}$$

where $\lambdabar = \lambda/2\pi$ ($\lambda$ is the Broglie wavelength of the incoming neutron), $I_n = 1/2$ is the neutron spin, $I_t$ the spin of the target nucleus, $I_c$ the spin of

TABLE 6-3

LIST OF SOME THERMAL NEUTRON CAPTURE
AND ACTIVATION CROSS SECTIONS

| Element | Cross sections (mb) | |
| --- | --- | --- |
| | Capture | Activation |
| H   (Z = 1) | 332 | — |
| Li  (Z = 3) | 71,000 | 34 |
| C   (Z = 6) | 3.4 | — |
| O   (Z = 8) | 0.2 | — |
| Mg  (Z = 12) | 63 | 3 |
| Al  (Z = 13) | 220 | 220 |
| Ti  (Z = 22) | 5,800 | 7 |
| Fe  (Z = 26) | 2,600 | 150 |
| Cu  (Z = 29) | 3,800 | 3,800 |
| W   (Z = 74) | 18,000 | 10,000 |
| Pb  (Z = 82) | 170 | 0.3 |

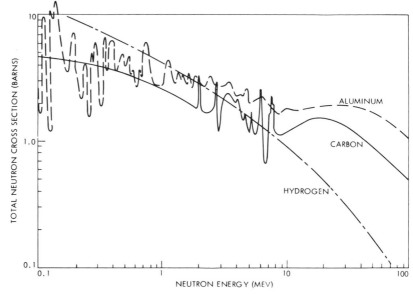

FIG. 6-3.  Total neutron cross sections in the Mev region.

the compound nucleus, $E$ the neutron energy, $E_0$ the resonance peak energy, $\Gamma_\gamma$ the partial level width for $\gamma$ emission, $\Gamma_n$ the partial level width for neutron emission, and $\Gamma = \Gamma_\gamma + \Gamma_n + \Gamma_{\text{reaction}}$ the total level width of the nucleus.

For completeness, it should be mentioned that there are elastic scattering resonances. They occur in the same energy region (ev–kev) and exhibit a similar relationship. The only change in the preceding formula is the replacement of $\Gamma_\gamma$ by $\Gamma_n$ in the numerator of the last term.

As was pointed out in the discussion of neutron elastic scattering, a neutron can only drift (diffuse) after it reaches thermal equilibrium and until it is captured.

It will be noted that the survival time of a thermal neutron is a function of the density of the medium and the neutron absorption cross section of the nucleus. This cross section does vary with neutron energy, and hence temperature, of the medium. A neutron will generally survive longer and migrate farther in a warm medium than in a cold one of the same density and composition because of the $1/v$ absorption cross section [6, 7].

Thermal neutron absorption cross sections are usually classed as total and activation. If the nucleus that has just captured a neutron is not stable after gamma emission it may emit a beta particle (and possibly other gamma rays) in order to achieve stability. Beta emission is a slow process, and hence such a capturing nucleus is said to have been activated. Often a nucleus may decay two ways to achieve stability. Tables of capture and activation cross sections for thermal [19, 20] and 14 Mev [20, 21] neutrons have been prepared. A list of a few thermal absorption and activation neutron cross sections is given in Table 6-3.

Thus, the life history of a neutron in matter depends upon the cross sections of the three processes: elastic scattering, inelastic scattering, and absorption. Generally, elastic and inelastic scattering predominate at high (Mev) energies, while absorption predominates at low (ev) energies. Typical behavior of the neutron cross section for light nuclei as a function of neutron energy is shown in Fig. 6-3 for hydrogen, carbon, and aluminum. The absence of resonances in hydrogen will be noted, while those of carbon (in the Mev region) and of aluminum (in the 100 kev region) are quite evident.

It should be pointed out that protons also exhibit behavior somewhat similar to that of neutrons—elastic and inelastic scattering in particular, as well as a small amount of nonthermal absorption. However, these effects are masked at low energies by the large amounts of ionization they produce, so that in bulk shielding they play only a minor role. At high energies ($\gtrsim 150$ Mev) these interactions become important for protons. For neutrons they are the important interaction mechanisms at all energies.

## B.   Gamma Ray Interactions with Matter

Gamma rays have their own unique set of interactions with matter. While twelve interaction mechanisms exist, only three are important in almost all cases. These three are

Photoelectric effect

Compton effect

Pair production

### 1.   THE PHOTOELECTRIC EFFECT

In the case of the photoelectric effect, a gamma ray photon is, in effect, absorbed by an atomic electron (usually in the K shell). The electron leaves its atom with an energy equal to the difference between that of the absorbed photon and the electron binding energy in the atom. The ejected electron acts like any other moving electron, losing energy by ionization and radiation until it is brought to rest.

For low gamma ray energies, the photoelectron tends to be ejected at right angles with respect to the incident photon direction. At high gamma ray energies the photoelectron will leave the atom in approximately the same direction as the incident photon. The similarity to bremsstrahlung production by electrons is apparent, and may be considered in many respects to be the inverse process [22, 23].

The photoelectric process is quite dependent upon the atomic number of the material and the gamma ray energy. To a first approximation, the cross section varies as [22]

$$\sigma_{\text{photo}} \sim \frac{Z^4}{(h\nu)^3} \tag{6.4}$$

where $h\nu$ is the gamma ray energy. Actually the $Z$ dependence varies from 4.0 (for low-energy photons of $\sim 0.1$ Mev) to 4.6 (for medium-energy photons of $\sim 3$ Mev). Also the exponent in the denominator varies from one for medium-energy photons to three for low-energy photons. Since the photoelectric effect is most important for low-energy photons, its low energy behavior was given.

### 2.   THE COMPTON EFFECT

The Compton effect is basically the scattering of gamma ray photons by electrons. The electron can for most practical purposes be considered free. The energy of the scattered photon ($E'$) is [24]

$$E' = \frac{E_0}{1 + E_0/(m_0 c^2)(1 - \cos\theta)} \tag{6.5}$$

where $E_0$ is the initial energy of the gamma ray photon and $\theta$ is the angle through which the photon is scattered. A large angle of scatter transfers much of the photon energy to the electron, and the scattered photon energy is almost independent of the initial photon energy for scattering angles > 90 deg. The remaining energy is transferred to the electron.

The cross section for Compton scattering is given by the Klein–Nishina formula [25]. For unpolarized radiation the formula may be written:

$$\sigma_{\text{Compton}} = \frac{r_0^2}{2}\left(\frac{v'}{v_0}\right)\left[\frac{v_0}{v'} + \frac{v'}{v_0} - 2\cos^2\theta\right]d\Omega \tag{6.6}$$

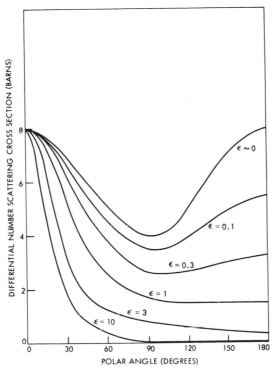

FIG. 6-4.  Differential number scattering cross section for photons ($\varepsilon = E/m_0 c^2$).

where $r_0$ is the classical electron radius $= e^2/m_0c^2 = 2.8 \times 10^{-13}$ cm, $v_0$ the initial frequency $= E_0/h$, $v'$ the scattered frequency $= E'/h$, and $d\Omega$ the solid angle element.

At low energies, the cross section is that of the classical Thompson scattering formula $(r_0^2 \sin^2 \theta)$, while at high energies the scattering is strongly peaked forward [26]. At 0 deg the cross section is $10^{-26}$ cm²/electron for all energies. The differential number scattering cross sections for various energies are shown in Fig. 6-4. It will be noted that the Compton effect is a function of the number of electrons only. Thus, lead is a better gamma ray shield in the energy range where the Compton effect predominates (0.3–3.0 Mev) only because it has more electrons.

### 3. PAIR PRODUCTION

Pair production is a process in which a gamma ray photon creates an electron-positron pair in the vicinity of a nucleus. The photon disappears in the process. The energy of each of the created particles is essentially one-half the difference between the initial photon energy and 1.02 Mev (the rest energy of the pair). Photons with energies $<1.02$ Mev cannot take part in this process.

The electron created in the pair-production process loses energy by ionization and radiation as it traverses matter, until it is brought to rest. The positron does likewise, except that as its energy decreases to a few electron volts, it forms an unstable positronium "atom" with an electron. The electron and the positron quickly annihilate each other, resulting in two 0.51 Mev photons emitted back to back. These photons undergo Compton scattering until finally absorbed via the photoelectric effect.

The cross section for pair production as a function of energy $E^+$ may be written [22]:

$$\sigma_{\text{pair}} = \frac{Z^2 P \sigma_0}{hv - 2m_0c^2} dE^+ \tag{6.7}$$

where $\sigma_0 = 5.8 \times 10^{-28}$ cm²/nucleus, and $P$ is a dimensionless quantity which varies from

$$0 \ (hv \leqslant 2m_0c^2) \text{ to } \sim 20 \ (hv = \infty).$$

Integrating the foregoing expressions over all positron energies to obtain the total cross section per nucleus is analytically possible only in the extreme relativistic case. Electron screening corrections add to the difficulty. Tables and graphs of the atomic pair-production cross sections have been prepared [27, 28]. In order to conserve linear and angular momentum, the electron-positron pair is projected forward, the two particles being separated by an angle on the order of $m_0 c^2/E$ except at lower energies ($m_0 c^2 \sim E$), where the strongly peaked forward behavior largely disappears.

The theory of pair production, according to Dirac, presupposes an infinite density of electrons in negative (and therefore unobservable) energy states. When an electron is removed from this negative energy "sea," the electron and its hole (positron) both become observable. The annihilation process is just the reverse of this, whereby the positive energy electron falls into a negative energy hole to make both of them unobservable again. The creation and decay of the $\pi^0$ meson is apparently quite similar [29].

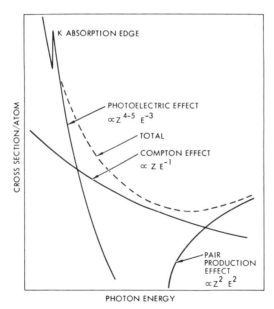

FIG. 6-5.  Behavior of three effects of matter on photons.

The overall behavior of gamma ray photons in matter is affected by all three processes. The cross sectional behavior as a function of gamma ray energy is shown in Fig. 6-5. The energy regions of dominance for lead are approximately:

| Photoelectric effect | 0.3 Mev |
| Compton effect | 0.3–3.0 Mev |
| Pair production | $\gtrsim 3.0$ Mev |

These boundaries spread apart for lower $Z$ atoms, reaching $\sim 0.05$ Mev and $\sim 50$ Mev for carbon. The approximate $Z$ versus $E$ behavior is indicated in Fig. 6-5.

The microscopic total cross section is obviously the sum of the individual interaction processes. The macroscopic cross section is the microscopic one multiplied by the nuclear density (nuclei/cm³). When dealing with compounds and for many other purposes, the macroscopic cross section (linear attenuation coefficient) divided by the density to yield the mass attenuation coefficient is more useful. Linear and/or mass attenuation coefficients for photons have been compiled by Kinsman [30], Stainer [31], Rose [32], Grodstein [33], and others. The mass attenuation coefficients for a few

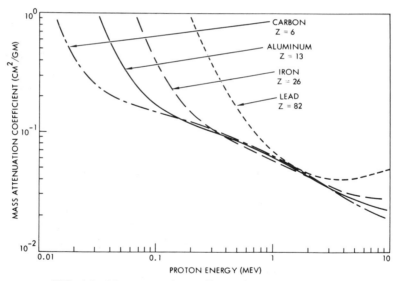

FIG. 6-6.　Mass attenuation coefficients for photons in matter.

elements are shown in Fig. 6-6. The curves correspond to the envelope of those shown in Fig. 6-5.

It is possible to fit the curves of Fig. 6-6 approximately by an expression of the form:

$$\sigma = 4.2 \times 10^{-23}\left(\frac{Z^4}{E^3}\right) + 2.3 \times 10^{-25}\left(\frac{Z}{E^{\frac{1}{3}}}\right)$$

$$+ 3.4 \times 10^{-27} Z^2 \log\left(\frac{E+2}{3.5}\right)$$

(6.8)

The three terms in this expression are the respective contributions due to the photoelectric effect, the Compton effect, and pair production. Cross sections tabulated by Grodstein [33] were used in the fit.

It is obvious that, since gamma rays are photons, they always travel with the velocity $c/n$. Since the structure of matter is too loose to make the real part of the index of refraction ($n$) for gamma rays depart appreciably from unity this velocity is essentially constant independent of whether matter is present or not. Thus, the life history of a gamma ray photon in matter is on the order of a few nanoseconds ($10^{-9}$ sec).

The life history of a gamma ray photon is controlled by the three processes—pair production, Compton scattering, and photoelectric absorption, in that order. If absorbed in a pair-production event, it is in effect reemitted (twice) at lower energy when the positronium atom destroys itself. In this sense, it continues losing energy by pushing electrons around until it is captured by a photoelectron.

## INTEGRAL RELATIONSHIPS

The basis of essentially all attenuation calculations of nuclear radiation is the Boltzmann transport equation. For charged particle radiation the range-energy relations have been sufficiently convenient that calculational techniques based upon the Boltzmann equation have not been developed. For uncharged nuclear radiation, which does not exhibit definite ranges, the Boltzmann equation has been the basis of several calculational techniques. The Boltzmann equation and its solutions (especially for fission neutrons) are discussed by Marshak [34], Davison [35], Weinberg and Wigner [36], Soodak [37], and others.

The Boltzmann equation is a mathematical relationship between the particles entering and leaving a unit volume of phase space (three spatial dimensions; three momentum dimensions). The equation is linear because the radiation is assumed not to interact with itself.

Radiation can enter a volume element of phase space by being born in it, being scattered into it (changing momentum coordinates), or migrating into it (changing spatial coordinates). Radiation can leave a volume of phase space by being absorbed, being scattered out of it, or migrating out of it. In differential form the Boltzmann equation may be written:

$$\nabla \cdot \boldsymbol{\Omega} \phi(\omega, r, p) + \phi(\omega, r, p) \cdot \sum_T (\omega, r, p)$$

$$= \int_0^\infty \phi(\omega, r, p) \cdot \sum_S (r, p'|p)(p')^2 \frac{dp'}{4\pi} \tag{6.9}$$

$$+ \int_0^\infty \phi(\omega, r, p')v \sum_F (\omega, r, p')(p')^2 \frac{dp'}{4\pi}$$

where $\nabla \cdot \boldsymbol{\Omega}\phi$ represents the net loss by particles due to migration across the geometrical boundaries, $\phi\Sigma_T$ represents the loss of particles due to scattering or absorption (crossing momentum boundaries), $\int \phi\Sigma_S(p')^2 dp'/4\pi$ represents the gain of particles due to scattering from other phase space volume elements, and $\int \phi v\Sigma_F(p')^2 dp'/4\pi$ represents the gain of particles due to interactions which produce them in the volume elements.

The Boltzmann equation can also be written in integral form, thus:

$$\phi(\omega, r, p) = \int \frac{\exp\left[-\int \Sigma_T(\omega, r'', p)dr''\right]}{4\pi(r - r')^2} \delta(r - r')Q(\omega, r, p)dV(r') \tag{6.10}$$

where

$$Q(\omega, r, p) = \int \phi(\omega, r, p) \Sigma_S (r, p'|p)(p')^2 dp'/4\pi$$
$$+ \int \phi(\omega, r, p)v \Sigma_F(\omega, r, p')(p')^2 dp'/4\pi,$$

and where $\delta$ is the usual mathematical delta function, $Q$ is the source function, including the source due to scattering into the volume element (first term) and the source due to production in the volume element (second term).

In these equations the time dependence has been eliminated. From the standpoint of shielding calculations this is unimportant. When these same equations are used in the calculation of fluxes in multiplying systems (nuclear reactors; nuclear bombs), the time dependence often plays a major role.

The remainder of this section is concerned with the attenuations of neutrons and gamma rays through matter. These are, as has been seen, among the most important types of secondary radiation resulting from the interactions of primary radiations present in space (protons and electrons) with matter.

It should be pointed out that most approaches for solving the Boltzmann equation are based upon digital techniques using high-speed electronic computers (e.g., IBM 7090). For this approach, differential equations become difference equations and integrals become summations. In the remainder of this section such changes have often been made with no explanation.

## C. Neutron Attenuation in Matter

### 1. *P* AND *S* APPROXIMATIONS

Neutron calculations based upon the Boltzmann transport equation have been used extensively in dealing with nuclear reactors and weapons. The usual practice has been to expand the neutron flux ($\phi$) in a series of terms based upon the angular dependence of the neutrons [35–38]. In this way only a few terms are usually required to achieve a satisfactory degree of accuracy. The usual expansion is based upon the Legendre polynomials, thus (for the one-dimensional situation):

$$\phi(r, p) = \sum_l A_l P_l(\cos \theta)\phi(E, r) \tag{6.11}$$

If only the first term is used, the $P_0$ (diffusion) approximation results [39, 40]. Substituting this into the differential form of the Boltzmann equation results in

$$-D\frac{d^2 \phi(E)}{dx^2} + \sum_T (E)\phi(E) = 2S(E)\int v \sum_F (E')\phi(E')\,dE'$$

$$+ \quad \xi\sum_S (E')\phi(E')\,dE' \tag{6.12}$$

where $D$ is the diffusion coefficient ($cm^{-1}$):

$$D = \frac{1}{3\Sigma_T (1 - \bar{\mu}_0)(1 - 4\Sigma_a/5\Sigma_T...)}$$

$\bar{\mu}_0$ = average of the cosine of the scattering angle = $\sim 2/(3A)$.

Therefore $D \sim 1/[(3\Sigma_T(1 - 2/3A)]$, and $\xi$ is the average of the logarithm of the ratio $E'/E_0$, $E_0$ the neutron energy before scattering, and $E'$ the neutron energy after scattering.

This equation is called the one-dimensional diffusion equation. Usually it is solved by considering the energy spectrum to be broken up into several divisions or groups. The flux is considered to be constant within each group, and neutrons scattered out of one group appear in another group of lower energy. The slowing down parameter controls this, and various approximate formulations for $\xi$ have been developed. These formulations, called slowing down models, differ in the type and degree of approximation that they apply to the rigorous transport formalism. Modifications of the Fermi continuous slowing down model work fine especially for heavy nuclei, while the Coveyou–McCauley model has certain advantages for light nuclei with small neutron absorption cross sections. Other models (Wigner, Greuling–Goertzel, Selengut–Goertzel) exist which are somewhat more complicated but have some advantages under specialized conditions [41, 42].

The diffusion equation has the advantage of being readily applied to complex geometries (slabs, ducts, and so on). The solutions obtained from the diffusion equation become more accurate as the neutron energy decreases, and are often more accurate as to their energy dependence than their spatial dependence. In particular the uncollided flux obtained decreases with distance according to

$$\phi(E) = \frac{S(E) \exp[-\Sigma_T(E)r]}{4\pi r}$$

where $S$ is the source strength in $n/\text{sec}$, and where $r$ is the distance in a material.

It will be noted that the geometrical attenuation $(1/4\pi r)$ falls off as $1/r$ rather than $1/r^2$. This is a serious limitation and has been responsible for errors when the diffusion equation has been used in deep-penetration shielding calculations.

If higher-order terms are retained in the Legendre expansion of the flux, the equations and the corresponding solutions obtained are called $P_1$ approximations, and so on. The even-numbered $P$ approximations are almost as much work as the next higher odd $P$ approximations, but are not as accurate under many conditions [43]. If the scattering cross sections $\Sigma_S$ are also expanded in Legendre polynomials, double-$P$ approximations are obtained. Double $P_1$ approximations solutions have been obtained, but the higher-order double-$P$ approximations are seldom used because they involve difficulty.

Carlson and others have obtained a slightly different angular approximation to the flux by expanding the flux in a digital representation called the $S$ approximation [43–46]. Graphically the flux angular distribution is drawn by an even number of straight line segments. Thus the $S_2$ approximation is approximately equivalent to the $P_1$ approximation, $S_4$ is equivalent to the $P_3$, and so forth. While offering no advantage for hand calculations, the $S_n$ approach is somewhat more general and adaptable to solution with digital electronic computers.

### 2. POINT KERNEL APPROXIMATIONS

An almost opposite approach is that of the point kernel based upon the integral formulation of the Boltzmann transport equation. If only the uncollided neutron flux is desired, the integral formulation reduces to

$$\phi(E) = \frac{S(E)e^{-\mu(E)r}}{4\pi r^2} \tag{6.13}$$

Note that this is essentially the same expression as obtained from the diffusion equation, except that the denominator is $4\pi r^2$. This is the correct expression for the geometrical attenuation in a three-dimensional system. The material attenuation is given by $e^{-\mu r}$, where $\mu$ is the linear attenuation coefficient.

While quite satisfactory regarding the spatial dependence of the flux, the given expression yields little information concerning the energy spectra at any point. For many materials the energy spectrum becomes approximately constant beyond several centimeters, and this spectrum is used for all $r$. According this assumption the total neutron flux is

$$\phi = \sum_E \frac{S(E)\, B(E, \mu r)e^{-\mu(E)r}}{4\pi r^2} \tag{6.14}$$

where $B$ is the number "build-up" factor. This build-up factor is the ratio of the total (collided plus uncollided) flux to the uncollided flux. However, the number build-up factor is seldom used. Rather, the dose build-up factor is usually employed, since it is often the dose one wishes to obtain. The dose due to uncollided neutrons may be written:

$$D_n^0 = \sum_E \frac{S(E)\,C_n(E)e^{-\mu(E)r}}{4\pi r^2} \tag{6.15}$$

where $C_n(E)$ is the neutron flux-to-dose conversion factor as a function of neutron energy ($E$). The neutron dose due to both collided and uncollided neutrons then may be written:

$$D_n = \sum_E \frac{S(E)B'(E,\mu r)C_n(E)e^{-\mu(E)r}}{4\pi r^2} \tag{6.16}$$

where $B'(E,\mu r)$ is the neutron dose build-up factor. The neutron dose build-up

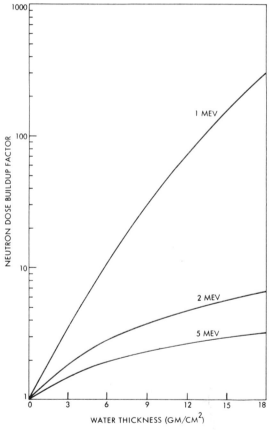

FIG. 6-7.   Some neutron dose build up factors for point isotropic source in water.

factor $(B')$ will be smaller than the neutron number build-up factor, because the neutron flux-to-dose conversion factor increases as neutron energy increases. Since scattering can only reduce neutron energy, the scattered neutrons are less effective at producing dose than the corresponding un-scattered neutrons. Neutron dose build-up factors in water are shown in Fig. 6-7. All build-up factors equal unity at zero thickness and generally increase as the neutron energy decreases. This behavior is due to neutron scattering cross sections which generally increase as the neutron energy decreases.

Such an approach is discussed in detail for neutrons and/or photons by Blizard and Abbott [47], Price *et al.* [48], Goldstein [49], Rockwell [50], and others. The advantage of this simple approach using neutron build-up factors is the ease and generality with which it may be applied. In particular it may be used for any neutron source energy spectrum and for any material. Unfortunately, relatively few of the neutron build-up factors have been obtained and published [51].

A particular neutron point attenuation kernel has been developed for use with fission sources [52]. This kernel (the Albert-Welton) is based upon the number of neutrons arriving at a point due to a fission source a distance away in a hydrogenous material. The neutron dose at the receiver point is given by

$$D = \frac{P_1(E)P_2(E, r)P_3(E, r)}{4\pi r^2} \tag{6.17}$$

where $P_1(E)$ is the probability of a neutron being emitted at the source with an energy $E \cong Ae^{-0.72E}$ for a fission (evaporation) source, $P_2$ the probability that the neutron penetrates a distance $r$ without being scattered through an angle $\gtrsim 25$ deg by hydrogen $= e^{-\sigma_H \Theta_H r}$, and $P_3$ the probability that the neutron penetrates a distance $r$ without being removed from the beam by any other nuclei present $= e^{-\Sigma_i n_i \sigma_i' r}$.

The function $P_2$ is an approximate fit to 80% of the hydrogen scattering cross section. This corresponds to neutron scatterings through angles $\gtrsim 25$ deg. Neutrons scattered $\lesssim 25$ deg are assumed to be unaffected. The hydrogen cross section thus can be represented by the expression,

$$\sigma_H \cong 0.281E^{-0.725} \quad \text{(barns/atom)}$$

The function $P_3$ is simply exponential attenuation due to all nonhydrogenous nuclei, except that an energy-independent neutron cross section is used. This cross section ($\sigma'$) is called the neutron effective removal cross section and includes all the absorption plus a fraction of the scattering cross section averaged over the equilibrium spectrum of the neutrons.

Substituting the foregoing expressions into the equation for $D$ yields (after simplifying):

$$D = \frac{A'(\Theta r)^{0.29} \exp[-0.83(\Theta r)^{0.58}] \exp[-\Sigma_i n_i \sigma_i \Theta_i r]}{4\pi r^2} \qquad (6.18)$$

where $\Theta$ is the volume fraction of the hydrogenous material present as compared to that of water and the $\Theta_i$'s are the volume fractions of the nonhydrogenous materials present.

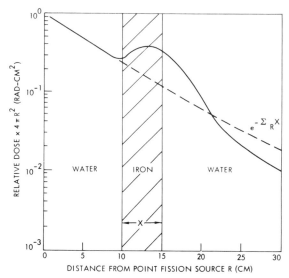

FIG. 6-8.   Behavior of neutron dose in an iron-water shield, showing the effective neutron removal concept.

The validity of the effective removal concept depends upon the reestablishment of the equilibrium neutron energy spectrum after passing through nonhydrogenous material. The dose-distance curve thus becomes parallel to that observed if the nonhydrogenous material were absent (Fig. 6–8). In other words, a homogeneous mixture of hydrogenous and nonhydrogenous material is assumed. This assumption is clearly invalid $\lesssim 20$ cm behind the nonhydrogenous material and also requires that all non-hydrogenous material be backed by hydrogenous.

Under such conditions the effective removal concept is reasonably valid for neutron fission sources. However, the energy spectra of evaporation neutrons is very similar to that of fission neutrons, and to a first approximation the Albert–Welton kernel and the effective removal concept may be used in the attenuation of evaporation neutrons in hydrogenous material.

Neutron effective removal cross sections have been measured for several materials when backed by hydrogenous material (e.g., water, oil) [53]. The results are exhibited graphically in Fig. 6-9 and several values are listed in Table 6-4. The effective removal cross sections would be smaller for a non-

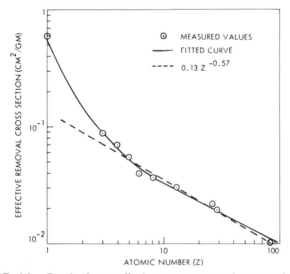

FIG. 6-9. Graph of some effective neutron removal cross sections.

hydrogenous backing material. This is because the energy-degraded neutrons from the nonhydrogenous slab will not be as rapidly slowed down (reducing their dose effectiveness) by a nonhydrogenous backing as by a hydrogenous one.

The Albert–Welton point attenuation kernel has been shown to be

TABLE  6-4

<small>List of Some Effective Removal Cross Sections
for Fission (Evaporation) Neutrons</small>

| Element | Cross section (barns/atom) |
|---|---|
| Li   $(Z = 3)$ | 0.9 |
| Be   $(Z = 4)$ | 1.07 |
| B    $(Z = 5)$ | 0.97 |
| C    $(Z = 6)$ | 0.81 |
| O    $(Z = 8)$ | 0.92 |
| F    $(Z = 9)$ | 1.29 |
| Al   $(Z = 13)$ | 1.31 |
| Cl   $(Z = 17)$ | 1.2 |
| Fe   $(Z = 26)$ | 1.98 |
| Cu   $(Z = 29)$ | 2.04 |
| W    $(Z = 74)$ | 3.36 |
| Pb   $(Z = 82)$ | 3.53 |
| U    $(Z = 92)$ | 3.6 |

quite accurate for fission sources in water. The moments method calculations can be fitted almost exactly for distances of 10–120 cm (Fig. 6-10) [54]. It is possible by differentiating the Albert–Welton kernel to obtain the neutron energy spectra as a function of position in a hydrogenous material. The result is that an approximately Gaussian uncollided spectrum is obtained, whose peak energy increases with penetration (spectrum hardening), as experimental evidence indicates is the case. This largely explains the excellent fits to the data which have been obtained using the Albert-Welton kernel.

The advantages of that kernel and the effective removal concept are their accuracy and ease of application when conditions under which they were derived are present. Unfortunately, these conditions occur rather seldom in space shielding. Even when they do, the neutron energy spectra in the vicinity of slabs of nonhydrogenous materials are not obtained.

3.   Combination and Monte Carlo Techniques

A particularly useful approach in neutron shielding is to combine solutions obtained from $P$ or $S$ approximations to the differential Boltzmann transport equation with point kernel approximations to the integral Boltzmann transport equation [55, 56]. The former are generally satisfactory for cal-

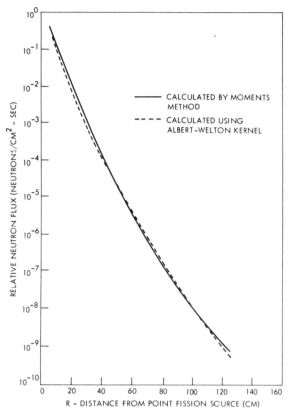

FIG. 6-10. Comparison of neutron flux calculations in water from point isotropic source.

culating the energy dependence of the neutron flux but are poor for calculating the spatial dependence of the flux. For the latter (point kernel) the opposite is true. By spatially normalizing the fluxes from $P$ or $S$ approximations to the results of point kernel calculations, a solution is obtained which is generally satisfactory for both the neutron energy and spatial dependences.

This point-by-point normalization is most easily accomplished by using the neutron flux-to-dose conversion factor. The dose due to a neutron energy spectrum obtained from $P$ or $S$ approximations is

$$D_n = \Sigma \, C_n(E)\phi(E, r)$$

If this is compared with the results of a point kernel calculation, a ratio is obtained. Multiplying the *P* or *S* approximate neutron energy spectrum by this ratio on a spatial point-by-point basis yields the normalized neutron spectrum at each point. Thermal (subcadmium) neutron fluxes calculated by this technique are as accurate as those obtained by any other (Fig. 6-11) and much easier to obtain than by some techniques.

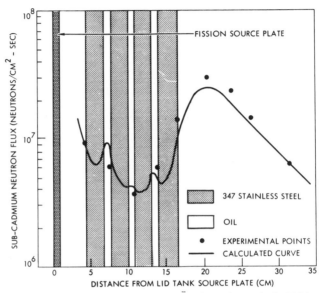

FIG. 6-11. Calculated and measured sub-cadmium fluxes in steel-oil shield configuration.

Another approach to radiation transport problems generally and neutron transport specifically is a statistical technique known as Monte Carlo. In this approach a number of "roulette wheels" are presumed available, each weighted according to some differential aspect of the shielding calculation to be performed. One roulette wheel may determine the initial particle energy, the second the initial particle direction, and so forth. Other wheels are weighted according to the scattering and absorption laws of the material involved. By spinning the wheels in succession the "history" of a particle is followed until it either penetrates the shield or is absorbed within it. Successive particles are treated the same way to build up meaningful statistics. The application of the Monte Carlo technique to neutron shielding problems has been discussed by Kalos [57], Wells [58], Hungerford [59], Loechler and MacDonald [60], and many others [61, 62].

The Monte Carlo technique is invaluable when the differential behavior of a phenomenon is known but its integral behavior is not. It is also able to handle very complicated geometries and material compositions quite readily [61]. However, it is a time-consuming process and must be run on a digital electronic computer. Even so, running times measured in hours are common for many shielding calculations.

The difficulty with using straightforward Monte Carlo on shielding calculations is that only a small fraction of the particles may penetrate the shield. Thus, a great deal of time is spent following particle histories which do not contribute to the final answer (assuming the final answer is the flux or dose behind the shield; if the answer desired is the energy deposition within the shield, all particle histories contribute). Straightforward Monte Carlo is seen to be more efficient the larger the fraction of the particles which contribute to the phenomenon investigated. In order to increase this fraction various weighting techniques are employed (doubling, Russian roulette, statistical elimination, and so on). These consist, in effect, of biasing the roulette wheels to yield the desired answers more frequently than they otherwise would. In order to compensate for this the answers obtained must be divided by exactly the same ratio that such answers were increased by biasing the roulette wheels. In practice this is sometimes difficult, with the result that unsuspected errors can creep into Monte Carlo calculations. Nevertheless, some of the most valuable data used in shielding calculations have been obtained by the use of this technique [47–50, 62]. These data have the advantage of showing the fraction of the dose deposited by the various mechanisms. Instruments to obtain this sort of data do not exist, and if they did their presence would produce errors in measurement.

## D.   X- and Gamma Ray Attenuation in Matter

### 1.   THE MOMENTS METHOD

The Boltzmann transport equation is also the basis of techniques for calculating gamma ray attenuation. However, there is one important difference. Because gamma rays fluxes are scattered according to different relationships from those for neutron fluxes, the gamma ray angular distributions at a given point are more sharply peaked in direction than the fluxes.

Therefore, if the flux is to be described in terms of angular moments, many more terms are required. While gamma ray transport has been treated by $P$ and $S$ approximations [63], the resulting complications in solving even a simple problem are formidable.

The customary procedure, pioneered by Spencer and Fano [64], and developed for shielding calculations by Goldstein and Wilkins [65], is to expand the gamma ray flux in a series of spatial moments instead. Usually the approximate spatial behavior of the gamma rays is factored out first, so fewer spatial moments are required. Thus one has

$$\phi = \frac{Se^{-\mu r}}{4\pi r^2} \sum_i A_i X^i \tag{6.19}$$

The coefficients $A_i$ are evaluated by substituting the above expression in the integral formulation of the Boltzmann equation. The result is a series of linked equations which can be solved by straightforward (if somewhat laborious) techniques. The greater the penetration depth desired, the greater the number of spatial moments which must be employed. Often eight spatial moments are used, which is sufficient for up to about twenty mean free paths for the uncollided flux.

The original moments method technique was strictly applicable to infinite homogenous media only, but modifications have been introduced to allow its use for multiregion shields. The results have been used to calculate energy spectra in various materials for different monoenergetic sources. Such energy spectra for water are shown in Fig. 6-12. It will be noted that the spatial moments are essentially a polynomial expansion for the gamma ray build-up factor. In fact one of the most common ways of presenting the results of moments method calculations is to plot these factors. As discussed in the section dealing with neutron attenuation, such factors depend upon the quantity ultimately desired (viz., number, dose, or energy absorption). The corresponding factors are different, and the correct one must be chosen in any calculation. The same situation holds even more strongly for gamma rays because materials differ much more in their gamma ray attenuating properties than they do in their fast neutron attenuating properties. Usually the gamma ray dose build-up factors are desired. Thus, the spatial moments set up are

$$D = \frac{S(E_0)\,\exp[-\mu(E_0)r]}{4\pi r^2} \sum_j \sum_i A_{ij}(E_j)C_j X^i$$

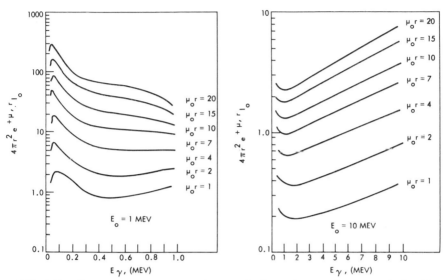

FIG. 6-12.   Gamma ray energy spectra due to point isotropic source in water, calculated by the moments method.

where $j$ is the scattered energy group, $i$ is the spatial moment index, and $C_j$ is the gamma ray flux-to-dose conversion factor for energy $E_j$.

Replacing the double sum by the ratio of the gamma ray dose build-up factor to the flux-to-dose conversion factor at $E_0$ yields the well-known expression,

$$D_\gamma = \frac{S_\gamma(E_0)\, C_\gamma(E_0)\, B_\gamma(E_0,\, \mu r)}{4\pi r^2} \exp\left[-\mu(E_0)r\right] \qquad (6.20)$$

This expression has been the basis of many, if not most, gamma ray shielding calculations. The dose build-up factors for water obtained from the moments method for use in the above expression are shown in Fig. 6-13.

As pointed out previously, the moments method is at its best in homogenous infinite media. The build-up factors obtained from it apply strictly only to this situation. However, various techniques dealing with multiregion shields using build-up factors have been devised. Since the build-up is basically due to the scattered gamma ray flux, it is of lower energy than the primary (unscattered) flux. Due to the behavior of the scattering process (Compton effect), this scattered flux is largely below 1 Mev in energy. This is the energy region where the photoelectric effect begins to make itself felt.

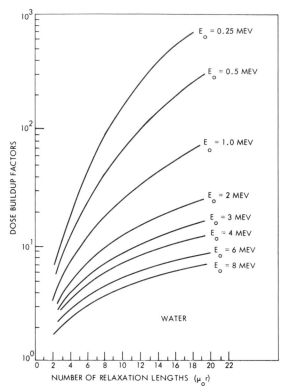

FIG. 6-13. Calculated gamma ray dose build up factors for point isotropic source in water.

Therefore, if a low-$Z$ material (low photoelectric cross section) is present, the build-up factor will be large, and conversely it will be small for a high-$Z$ material (large photoelectric cross section). Therefore, if a slab of high-$Z$ material is followed by a slab of low-$Z$ material, the build-up in the former will not be attenuated appreciably by the latter. Therefore, the product of the two build-up factors is usually used. For this case the dose is

$$D_\gamma = \frac{S_\gamma(E_0)\, C_\gamma(E_0)\, B_1(E_0, \mu_1 r_1)\, B_2(E_0, \mu_2 r_2)\, \exp-\left[\mu_1(E_0)r_1 + \mu_2(E_0)r_2\right]}{4\pi r^2}$$

(6.21)

where $r_1$ is the thickness of material 1 (higher $Z$), $r_2$ is the thickness of material 2 (lower $Z$), and $B_1$ and $B_2$ are the dose build-up factors for materials 1 and 2, respectively.

However, if the same two materials are reversed, the gamma ray attenuation is changed. This is because the build-up in the low-$Z$ material (which now comes first) will be rapidly attenuated by the high-$Z$ type (which follows it). Rather than use the product of the build-up factors in this situation, a much more accurate result is obtained by using the lower build-up factor of the high-$Z$ material for the entire assembly. For this case the dose is

$$D_\gamma = \frac{S_\gamma(E_0)\, C_\gamma(E_0)\, B_2(E_0,\, \mu_1 r_1 + \mu_2 r_2) \exp - [\mu_1(E_0)r_1 + \mu_2(E_0)r_2]}{4\pi r^2}$$

(6.22)

where $r_1$ is the thickness of material 1 (lower $Z$), $r_2$ is the thickness of material 2 (higher $Z$), $\mu_1$ and $\mu_2$ are the linear attenuation coefficients of materials 1 and 2, respectively, and $B_2$ is the build-up factor characteristic of material 2, but for the total (material 1 plus material 2) number of mean free paths.

The system can be extended to three or more materials. By starting at the back (inside) of the shield the build-up factor of the last material is used until a material of higher $Z$ is encountered. The build-up factor of the higher-$Z$ material is used from that point forward through the shield, until an even-higher-$Z$ material is encountered. The final build-up factor will be the product of the factor obtained by the process just described, each factor being for the total number of relaxation lengths (mean free paths) to which that factor applies.

It should be pointed out that the moments method has been applied to neutron attenuation calculations as well [51]. The resulting neutron energy spectra agree well with those obtained by the point-kernel-normalized diffusion calculations. While the latter are more easily obtained for multilayer shields, the former approach is more general in that hydrogenous material need not be present.

## E.  Radiation Scattering

Up to now radiation has been treated as though it were attenuated in a straight line (the so-called line-of-sight approach). This is not strictly correct, especially for uncharged nuclear radiation. The path lengths of neutrons and gamma rays are usually appreciably longer than their crow flight penetration distances in matter.

So long as one is dealing with infinite homogenous media, this erratic behavior of radiation has little effect other than to decrease the distance it

can penetrate from its source. However, in most cases of physical interest
geometrical factors play a role. In these situations the ability of radiation to
go "around a corner" must be considered. If the line-of-sight path is sufficiently shielded over and above that encountered along another path (not
line-of-sight) a nonnegligible fraction of the radiation may penetrate the
shield along the nonline-of-sight path [66, 67].

As an example, consider a point source and a unit sphere detector em-
bedded a distance apart in a homogenous isotropic infinite medium (Fig.
6-14). Now suppose an infinite attenuation is present in the line-of-sight

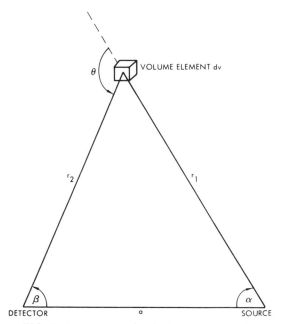

FIG. 6-14.   Geometry for single scattering model.

path between the source and the detector. It is still possible for radiation to
reach the detector from the source by being scattered in the medium. The
contribution due to radiation, which scatters only once in going from the
source to the detector, can be obtained analytically in closed form.

Using the geometry of Fig. 6-14, the radiation arriving at the detector
after being emitted at an angle $\alpha$ and being scattered in volume element is
(neglecting attenuation along the legs, $r_1$ and $r_2$):

$$\phi = \frac{S(\alpha)}{4\pi(r_1)^2} \, ndV \left(\frac{d\sigma}{d\Omega}\right) \frac{1}{(r_2)^2}$$

where $S(\alpha)$ is the probability of particles being emitted at an angle $\alpha$ by the source, $ndV$ the number of scattering centers in the volume element $dV$, and $(d\sigma/d\Omega)_\theta$ the differential scattering cross section.

The total number of particles arriving at the detector after being single-scattered is the integral of the above equation. By making use of the relations,

$$r_1 = \frac{a \sin \beta}{\sin \theta} \qquad r_2 = \frac{a \sin \alpha}{\sin \theta} \qquad \theta = \alpha + \beta$$

the result obtained (for cylindrically symmetric sources) is

$$\phi = \frac{2\pi n}{a} \int_{\alpha=0}^{\alpha=\pi} \int_{\beta=0}^{\beta=\pi-\alpha} S(\alpha) \left(\frac{d\sigma}{d\Omega}\right)_\theta d\alpha \, d\beta$$

For isotropic scattering (applicable for low-energy neutrons but not for high-energy neutrons or photons) one can substitute

$$\frac{d\sigma}{d\Omega} = \frac{\sigma}{4\pi}$$

The result is

$$\phi = \frac{n\sigma}{2a} \int_0^\pi \int_0^{\pi-\alpha} S(\alpha) \, d\alpha \, d\beta \qquad (6.23)$$

This formula is especially useful in calculating the radiation scattered around shadow shields (e.g., in an air or water medium). To the extent that a space vehicle can be considered to be a homogenous medium, this formula could also be used to estimate the structure scattering.

Experiments have been carried out with aircraftborne nuclear reactors to measure structure scattering. The results appear to be unique to the structure investigated, and recipes or generalizations useful for other situations have not resulted [68].

One particular geometry which has received considerable attention is the bent opening or duct through a shield [69 72]. Various radiations have the ability to "follow" the duct opening through the shield to produce appreciably higher radiation levels beyond the shield than a line-of-sight model would predict. Thermal or epithermal neutrons "follow" ducts with the least attenuation, with the fast neutrons losing this "ability" as their energies increase. Gamma rays are less able to "follow" ducts than neutrons because of their strongly forward peaked scattering probabilities. Electrons and charged particles exhibit essentially no ability to follow ducts. An extension of the single scattering model just discussed has been used for rough estimates of neutron duct leakage. This is the Simon-Clifford model, which is based upon the reflection coefficient (albedo) of the radiation (neutrons usually) at the duct walls.

As a first approximation, the attenuation of fast neutrons through a cylindrical duct composed of straight sections each of length $l_i$ making angles $\theta_i$ with the previous section is [50]

$$\phi_i = \phi_0 \left[ \frac{1}{8} \left( \frac{d}{l_i} \right) \frac{\alpha}{\sin \theta_i} \right]^n \tag{6.24}$$

where $\phi_0$ is the flux entering a section, $\phi_i$ the flux leaving that section, $d$ the duct diameter, $\alpha$ the reflection coefficient of the duct walls at the elbows, and $n$ the number of sections.

Thus the quantity in the brackets must be evaluated for each duct segment and the product obtained for a multisegment duct. If the duct is filled with a poor shielding material (rather than being empty), the result must be multiplied by the attenuation along the duct centerline.

For an annular duct, the formula becomes

$$\phi_i = 10\phi_0 \left[ (2R^2 - r^2) \cos^{-1} \left( \frac{r}{R} \right) - r\sqrt{R^2 - r^2} \right]^n \Pi \left( \frac{1}{l_i} \right)^2$$

where $R$ is the outer diameter of the duct segment, $r$ is the inner diameter of segment, and $l_i$ the length of the $i$th segment of the duct.

The annular duct is less leaky than the circular duct because only a fraction of the area at a duct bend can be "seen" from a point at the adjacent bend. This formula reduces to that of the circular duct when $r$ goes to zero.

In both formulas presented above, the attenuation is more rapid than $e^{-\mu l}/l^2$, but still is less than $l^{-2}$ for values of $\mu$ normally encountered ($\sim 0.1$ cm$^{-1}$).

For gamma rays the situation is complicated by the fact that the angular distribution of the photons can vary considerably depending upon the situation. The three commonly treated angular distributions are spherical, cosine, and Fermi. For cylindrical ducts without bends the corresponding flux transmission factors are

Spherical source angular distribution
(negligible self-absorption), $\phi = (\phi_0/8)(d/l)^2$
Cosine source angular distribution
(self-absorbing homogenous source), $\phi = (\phi_0/4)(d/l)^2$
Fermi source angular distribution, $\phi = (\phi_0/3)(d/l)^2$

For straight annular sections, the leakage becomes

$$\text{spherical } \phi = \frac{\phi_0}{2\pi l^2}\left[\left(\cos^{-1}\frac{r}{R}\right)(2R^2 - r^2) - r\sqrt{R^2 - r^2}\right]$$

$$\text{cosine } \phi = \frac{\phi_0}{\pi l^2}\left[\left(\cos^{-1}\frac{r}{R}\right)(2R^2 - r^2) - r\sqrt{R^2 - r^2}\right]$$

$$\text{Fermi } \phi = \frac{1.27\phi}{\pi l^2}\left[\left(\cos^{-1}\frac{r}{R}\right)(2R^2 - r^2) - r\sqrt{R^2 - r^2}\right]$$

In this case, $R^2 - r^2$, is assumed to be $\ll l^2$. For secondary gamma rays produced from space radiations, the angular distributions vary from spherical (produced by secondary neutron capture) to rather sharply peaked (produced in electron-photon showers).

## REFERENCES

1.  S. Glasstone and M. C. Edlund, "The Elements of Nuclear Reactor Theory," Chap. 5, 6. Van Nostrand, Princeton, New Jersey, 1954.
2.  L. J. Templin (ed.), Reactor Physics Constants Rept. ANL-5800, 2nd ed., *Argonne Natl. Lab.*, Lemont, Illinois (1963).
3.  H. Amster, The Slowing Down of Neutrons in Hydrogenous Mixtures, *Nucl. Sci. Eng.* **21**, 206 (1965).
4.  E. Moller and N. G. Sjostrand, The Time Scale of Neutron Slowing Down in Water, *Nucl. Sci. Eng.* **15**, 221 (1963).
5.  A. K. Ghatak and T. J. Krieger, Neutron Slowing Down Times and Chemical Binding in Water, *Nucl. Sci. Eng.* **21**, 304 (1965).
6.  R. W. Deutsch, Temperature Dependence of the Thermal Diffusion Length in Water, *Nucl. Sci. Eng.* **1**, 252 (1956).
7.  R. C. Lloyd, E. D. Clayton, and C. R. Ritchie, Variation of Graphite Diffusion Length with Temperature, *Nucl. Sci. Eng.* **4**, 690 (1958).
8.  A. V. Antonov, A Study of Neutron Diffusion in Beryllium, Graphite, and Water by the Impulse Method, *Proc. First Intern. Conf. Peaceful Uses of Atomic Energy* **5**, 3 (1955).
9.  E. R. Cohen, Transport Mean Free Path and Diffusion Length of Neutrons Calculated from Markov Chain Statistics, *Nucl. Sci. Eng.* **12**, 309 (1962).

10.  J. J. McInerney, Some Exact Expressions for the Monoenergetic Neutron Diffusion Length, *Nucl. Sci. Eng.* **19,** 458 (1964).

11.  F. Ajzenberg-Selove and T. Lauritsen, Energy Levels of Light Nuclei, *Ann. Rev. Nucl. Sci.* **10,** 409 (1960).

12.  D. Strominger, J. M. Hollander and G. T. Seaborg, Table of Isotopes, *Rev. Mod. Phys.* **30,** 585 (1958).

13.  E. Troubetzkoy and H. Goldstein, Gamma Rays from Thermal Neutron Capture, *Nucleonics* **18,** No 11, 171 (1960).

14.  G. A. Bartholomew, Neutron Capture Gamma Rays, *Ann. Rev. Nucl. Sci.* **11,** 259 (1961).

15.  D. H. Templeton, Nuclear Reactions Induced by High Energy Particles, *Ann. Rev. Nucl. Sci.* **2,** 93 (1953).

16.  R. Wallace and C. Sondhaus, Techniques Used in Shielding Calculations for High Energy Accelerators: Applications to Space Shielding, Rept. UCRL-10439, *Univ. Calif.,* Berkeley, California (1962).

17.  R. D. Evans, "The Atomic Nucleus," Chap. 11. McGraw-Hill, New York, 1955.

18.  G. Breit and E. Wigner, Capture of Slow Neutrons, *Phys. Rev.* **49,** 519 (1936).

19.  D. J. Hughes and R. B. Schwartz, Neutrons Cross Sections, Rept. BNL-325, *Brookhaven Natl. Lab.,* Upton, New York (1958).

20.  R. C. Koch, Activation Analysis Handbook, *Nucl. Sci. Eng. Corp., Pittsburgh,* Pennsylvania (1958).

21.  S. C. Mathur, J. B. Ashe, and I. L. Morgan, Compilation of Neutron Reaction and Total Cross Sections at 14 MeV, Rept. ASD-TDR-62-1038, *Materials Lab., Wright-Patterson* AFB, Dayton, Ohio (1964).

22.  R. D. Evans, "The Atomic Nucleus," Chap. 24, McGraw-Hill, New York, 1955.

23.  D. R. Corson and A. O. Hanson, Extranuclear Interactions of Electrons and Gamma Rays, *Ann. Rev. Nucl. Sci.* **3,** 67 (1953).

24.  R. D. Evans, "The Atomic Nucleus," Chap. 23, McGraw-Hill, New York, 1955.

25.  O. Klein and Y. Nishina, On the Scattering of Radiation by Free Electrons According to the Relativistic Quantum Mechanics of Dirac, *Z. Physik* **52,** 853 (1928).

26.  A. T. Nelms, Graphs of the Compton Energy-Angle Relationship and the Klein-Nishia Formula from 10 keV to 500 MeV, *Circular* **542,** *Natl. Bur. Std.,* (1952).

27.  W. Heitler, "The Quantum Theory of Radiation," Chap. 23. Oxford Univ. Press, London and New York, 1944.

28.  C. M. Davisson and R. D. Evans, Gamma Ray Absorption Coefficients, *Rev. Mod. Phys.* **24,** 79 (1952).

29.  J. W. Haffner, A Proposed Elementary Particle Model, *Bull. Am. Phys. Soc.* **5,** 64 (1960).

30.  S. Kinsman, Radiological Health Handbook, *Taft Sanitary Eng. Center, Cincinnati, Ohio* (1954).

31.  H. M. Stainer, X-Ray Mass Absorption Coefficients—A Literature Survey, *Circular* IC-8166, *U.S. Bur. Mines* (1963).

32.  R. G. Rose, Gamma Ray Attenuation Coefficients, *Nucleonics* **22,** No. 8, 120 (1964).

33.  G. W. Grodstein, X-Ray Attenuation Coefficients from 10 keV to 100 MeV, *Circular* **583,** *Natl. Bur. Std.* (1957).

34. R. E. Marshak, Theory of the Slowing Down of Neutrons by Elastic Collisions with Atomic Nuclei, *Rev. Mod. Phys.* **19,** 185 (1947).

35. B. Davison, "Neutron Transport Theory." Oxford Univ. Press, London and New York, 1957.

36. A. M. Weinberg and E. P. Wigner, The Physical Theory of Neutron Chain Reactors, *Univ. Chicago* Press, Chicago, Illinois, 1958.

37. H. Soodak, The Theory of Neutron Transport, Chap. 3 of vol. 3, Part A of "Reactor Handbook." Wiley (Interscience), New York, 1962.

38. W. R. Conkie, An Improved Spherical Harmonics Method, *Nucl. Sci. Eng.* **18,** 370 (1964).

39. M. Tobias and T. B. Fowler, The Equipoise Method—A Simple Procedure for Group Diffusion Calculations in Two and Three Dimensions, *Nucl. Sci. Eng.* **12,** 513 (1962).

40. K. F. Hanson, Multi-Group Diffusion Methods, Rept. NYO-10206, *U.S. At. Energy Comm.* (1962).

41. A. H. Barnett and J. R. Terrall, Calculation of Neutron Spectra from Slowing Down Models, Rept. XDC-60-6-70, *General Electric Co., Cincinnati, Ohio* (1959).

42. G. Goertzel and E. Greuling, An Approximate Method for Treating Neutron Slowing Down, *Nucl. Sci. Eng.* **7,** 69 (1960).

43. J. O. Mingle, The Even Order Spherical Harmonics Methods in Cylindrical Geometry, *Nucl. Sci. Eng.* **20,** 324 (1964).

44. B. Carlson, Numerical Solution of Transient and Steady State Neutron Transport Problems, Rept. LA-2260, *Los Alamos Sci. Lab.*, Los Alamos, New Mexico (1959).

45. C. E. Lee, The Discrete Sn Approximation to Transport Theory, Rept. LA-2595, *Los Alamos Sci. Lab.*, Los Alamos, New Mexico (1962).

46. B. G. Carlson and G. I. Bell, Solution of the Transport Equation by the Sn Method, *Proc. Second Intern. Conf. Peaceful Uses of Atomic Energy* **16,** 535 (1959).

47. E. P. Blizard and L. S. Abbott, Shielding, *Reactor Handbook* **3,** Part B, Wiley (Interscience), New York (1962).

48. B. T. Price, C. C. Horton, and K. T. Spinney, "Radiation Shielding." Pergamon Press, Oxford, 1957.

49. H. Goldstein, "Fundamental Aspects of Reactor Shielding." Addison-Wesley, Reading, Massachusetts, 1959.

50. T. Rockwell, "Reactor Shielding Design Manual." Van Nostrand, Princeton, New Jersey, 1956.

51. A. D. Krumbein, Summary of NDA Unclassified Results of Moments Calculations for the Penetration of Neutrons through Various Materials, Rept. NDA-92, *Nuclear Develop. Assoc., White Plains, New York* (1958).

52. R. D. Albert and T. A. Welton, A Simplified Theory of Neutron Attenuation and Its Application to Reactor Shield Design, Rept. WAPD-15, *Westinghouse Electric Corp., Atomic Power Div., Pittsburgh* (1950).

53. G. T. Chapman and C. L. Storrs, Effective Neutron Removal Cross Sections for Shielding, Rept. ORNL-1843, *Oak Ridge Natl. Lab, Oak Ridge, Tennessee* (1955).

54. A. W. Casper, Comparison of Bulk Shielding Reactor Centerline Measurements in Water with Predictions, Rept. APEX-504, General Electric Co., *Aircraft Nucl. Propulsion Dept., Cincinnati, Ohio* (1958).

214        *VI. Uncharged Radiation Attenuation*

55. J. W. Haffner, Neutron Energy Spectrum Calculations in Reactor Shields, Paper V-84, *Nucl. Energy Congr., Cleveland, Ohio* (1959).
56. A. F. Avery, J. Butler, A. K. McCracken, and A. Packwood, Neutron Penetration in Bulk Media, *Trans. Am. Nucl. Soc.* **5,** 400 (1962).
57. M. H. Kalos, On the Estimation of the Flux at a Point by Monte Carlo, *Nucl. Sci. Eng.* **16,** 111 (1963).
58. M. B. Wells, A Monte Carlo Study of the Transport of Neutrons Resulting from Proton-Induced Nuclear Evaporation, *Trans. Am. Nucl. Soc.* **7,** 17 (1964).
59. H. E. Hungerford, A New Approach to Stochastic Neutron Transport, *Trans. Am. Nucl. Soc.* **8,** 187 (1965).
60. J. J. Loechler and J. E. MacDonald, Flexible Monte Carlo Programs FMC-N and FMC-G, Rept. APEX-706, *General Electric Co., Flight Propulsion Lab. Dept., Cincinnati, Ohio* (1961).
61. Monte Carlo Method, Rept. 12, *Appl. Math. Series, Natl. Bur. Std., Washington, D.C.* (1949).
62. H. Rossi (ed.), Protection against Neutron Radiation up to 30 Million Electron Volts, *Natl. Bur. Std., U.S., Handbook* **63,** (1957).
63. W. D. Lanning, Application of the Spherical Harmonics Technique to Problems in Gamma Transport, *Nucl. Sci. Eng.* **15,** 259 (1963).
64. L. V. Spencer and U. Fano, Penetration and Diffusion of X-Rays—Calculation of Spatial Distributions, *Phys. Rev.* **81,** 464 (1951).
65. H. Goldstein and J. E. Wilkins, Calculations of the Penetration of Gamma Rays, Rept. NYO-3075, *U.S. At. Energy Comm.* (1954).
66. D. K. Trubey, Tabulated Values of Scattered Gamma Ray Fluxes in Water Interpolated from Moments Method Calculations, Rept. ORNL-3466, *Oak Ridge Natl. Lab.,* Oak Ridge, Tennessee (1963).
67. G. S. Weller and B. J. Workman, Single Scattering of Neutrons in Air, Rept. CVAC-211T, *General Dynamics Corp., Convair Div. Ft. Worth, Texas* (1954).
68. L. S. Burns, Relative Contributions of Scattered and Secondary Radiation Inside a Realistic Crew Shield, Rept. XDC-60-6-70, *General Electric Co., Cincinnati, Ohio* (1959).
69. A. Prince, The Scattering of Neutrons by Air Ducts in Shields, Rept. XDC-59-7-119, *General Electric Co., Aircraft Nucl. Propulsion Dept., Cincinnati, Ohio* (1959).
70. C. E. Clifford, Gamma Shielding Provided by Ducts, Rept. 370, *Can. Defence Res. Board, Defence Res. Chem. Lab., Ottawa, Canada* (1962).
71. K. T. Spinney, Radiation Streaming Through Ducts—A Survey of the Present Situation, *Trans. Am. Nucl. Soc.* **5,** 390 (1962).
72. M. D. Clark, E. W. Etherington, D. S. Greenway, and W. J. Paterson, The Streaming of Scattered Gamma Radiations through a Duct in a Shield, *Trans. Am. Nucl. Soc.* **5,** 395 (1962).

# *VII*

## SPACE RADIATION SHIELDING
## COMPUTER CODES

### A.  Introduction

It is possible to compute fluxes, energy spectra, and doses due to space radiations by hand for only relatively simple situations. Typically such a simple situation deals with a spherical or slab geometry and an isotropic or monodirectional flux of incident particles whose energy spectrum is of the form $E^{-\alpha}$. In addition secondary radiations are usually neglected. Thus the considerations which tend to impel one to use an electronic computer to solve problems in space radiation shielding are as follows:

Complicated spacecraft geometry (i.e., not slab or spherical)
Nonanalytical incident radiation energy and/or angular distributions (i.e., not readily fit mathematically)
Thick shielding (i.e., secondary radiations important)
Time and/or spatially dependent radiation environment (e.g., as encountered in mission analysis studies)
Several similar problems will be handled (thus resulting in an overall time saving)

The various factors are self-explanatory, with the last being the chief motive behind most computer programs. If the human effort can be reduced by programming a computer to carry out the calculations to the desired degree of refinement, a computer code usually results. (Note that code is identical with program in this chapter.)

215

## B.  Computer Code Centers

The descriptions, albeit brief, of every computer code which has been or could potentially be, applied to radiation shielding would comprise a book by itself. Fortunately code centers have been established which not only maintain current files on various computer codes but through which (in many cases) one can obtain the codes themselves and related material. The Argonne Code Center collects and periodically distributes abstracts of computer programs pertaining to nuclear technology, principally applying to reactors [1]. Table 7-2 at the end of this chapter presents material from a recent listing of programs available (as of 1965) from or through the Argonne Code Center at ANL (Argonne National Laboratory). These listings are kept up to date as new programs become available and old ones become obsolete or are otherwise superseded.

Another source of information on nuclear shielding literature generally and shielding computer codes specifically is the RSIC (Radiation Shielding Information Center) at the Oak Ridge National Laboratory (ORNL). The RSIC is concerned with reactor, accelerator, and weapon radiation shielding as well as with space radiation shielding. A list of code packages available from the RSIC as of March, 1965, is listed in Table 7-3[2]. Additional codes are being made available continually. The material in Table 7-3 at the end of this chapter may be considered as illustrative of the sort of programs which the RSIC handles and distributes.

In addition, computer code abstracts of interest to the nuclear field are listed from time to time in *Nuclear Science and Engineering*, a technical journal published monthly by the American Nuclear Society. The information for each code is presented in outline form, and includes the following:

Name of the program

Computer required to use the program (e.g., IBM 7094)

Computer language the program is written in (SAP, FORTRAN, etc.)

Type of problem solved (e.g., neutron transport in reactor shields, secondary $\gamma$ ray production in slabs, etc.)

Method of solution (e.g., multigroup $P_3$, moments method, modified Monte Carlo, etc.)

Restrictions on use of the program (e.g., maximum number of regions allowed, if void regions allowed, etc.)

Typical computer running time
Current status (checked out, in use, etc.)
Literature references (where the program is described in more detail)
What material is available and how to obtain it (e.g., reports, card decks, etc.)

The lists and abstracts of computer codes discussed above are excellent sources of information on computer programs which have been checked out and are in operation. In addition, the personnel at the code centers often are aware of work in progress on other computer programs. There are often technical meetings and symposiums at which nuclear radiation computer codes are discussed. In short, there are several sources of information available, and the code centers are logical places to begin looking for information in this area.

## C. Brief Descriptions of a Few Selected Codes

Historically the use of computer programs in a given technical field begins when that field has reached the level of development where the basic relationships are understood. In other words, when one knows how to calculate the desired quantities, but finds the actual calculations tedious, difficult, and time-consuming, then it makes sense to resort to computers. Space radiation shielding appears to be essentially at this point, with the result that computer programs specifically designed for handling the attenuation and interaction of space radiations in matter are becoming available. While some organizations tend to consider computer programs as proprietary, several space radiation shielding computer programs have been described in the open literature. The remainder of this chapter is devoted to brief descriptions of a few such programs.

Computer codes generally fall into one or more of three categories. The first is that of electrical (or other) analogs. If an electrical, mechanical, or other analog can be found to the problem of interest, the behavior of that analog under certain conditions yields information concerning the solution of the problem. The difficulty with this approach is that finding a suitable analog is often not easy. In general the behavior of the analog should be describable by the same mathematics as the problem of interest. For space radiation shielding studies, this approach is seldom attempted because satisfactory analogs have not been found.

The second category of code is that of analytical evaluation. This approach is used when the equations describing the integral behavior of a system as a function of integral (macroscopic) parameters are known. In other words the computer evaluates the integrals, solves the equations, and the rest, in essentially the same way a person might by hand. This requires relatively little computer time, but is limited to those problems which can be formulated analytically.

The third category of computer code is that of stochastical evaluation (Monte Carlo). This approach is used when the integral behavior of a system can be described as a function of differential (microscopic) parameters, but for some reason it is not possible or desirable to describe it in terms of integral (macroscopic) parameters. Here the computer, in effect, performs the experiment itself in order to obtain the desired answer. This approach may be quite time-consuming, but it is often the only available one. It is especially useful where complex geometries are involved.

It will be noted that the second and third approaches require digital computers, as contrasted to the first approach, which involves using an analog type. In a sense the first and third approaches differ primarily as to whether an analog or a digital technique is used.

The programs described below are chosen as representative samples of the growing library of digital computer codes used for space shielding studies.

## 1.   INTERNUCLEAR CASCADE CODE

One of the major problems in all shielding calculations is to obtain the required reaction cross sections and secondary yields and energies. In many cases actual, measured data is either unavailable or not sufficiently known. Therefore it is often necessary to calculate the desired cross sections using theoretical approaches which agree fairly well with the measured data which is available.

A useful and widely used computer program by Bertini [3] calculates the multiplicities and energies of cascade secondaries resulting from $\pi$ meson and nucleon interactions with nuclei. The Serber free-particle approach [4] is used to extend the work of Metropolis *et al.* [5]. A three-step nuclear density model is used, and by varying the parameters of this model it has been possible to fit the energies and multiplicities which have been measured. In order to accomplish this it was necessary to write a Monte Carlo program to follow the chain of reactions which take place when the incident particle strikes such a nuclear model. Beginning with a given incident particle and target nucleus, the point of collision inside the nuclear model and the type of reaction are selected simultaneously by the usual Monte Carlo techniques [6]. If the reaction is a scattering reaction, the scattering angles are obtained by sampling the differential free-nucleon cross sections. If the reaction is a pion absorption reaction, the collision products are emitted isotropically in the CM system. All kinematics are treated relativistically.

With the energies and directions of the two collision products determined, one is stored temporarily while the other is followed. If additional inter-actions take place the process is repeated. All such affected particles are followed this way until they are either absorbed or escape from the nucleus. Effects of the exclusion principle are taken approximately into account.

This program has been used to calculate the cross sections, multiplicities and energetics of reaction products for various nuclei with good results. It has been incorporated into various other computer codes to generate cross sections and related quantities.

## 2. NUCLEON TRANSPORT CODE

A series of computer codes, all written for the IBM-7090 has been pre-pared by Kinney *et al.* [7] of ORNL (Oak Ridge National Laboratory) to handle the transport of nucleons up to 400 Mev. Based upon the Monte Carlo approach, these codes will accommodate complex geometries. Nucle-ons are introduced into the system, and so long as the incident nucleons have energies between 400 and 50 Mev, they are handled by the High Energy Transport Code. When a nucleon escapes from a nucleus, has a collision, or slows down to below 50 Mev, the position and velocity of the particle are recorded on tape.

The High Energy Transport Code divides the energy region to be treated into a hundred and one equally spaced groups. Following the selection of the initial position and velocity coordinates of the incident nucleon, the flight distance data is selected from the distribution

$$\Sigma e^{-\Sigma d}$$

where $\Sigma$ is the total macroscopic geometric cross section. If the particle is a proton its energy at the end of this portion of its flight is computed from the range-energy relationships; it is a neutron it is assumed to have lost no energy. The type and other parameters of the interactions at the end of this flight distance *d* are next computed from either input data or Bertini's cascade subroutine. The flow chart for the High Energy Transport Code is shown in Fig. 7-1.

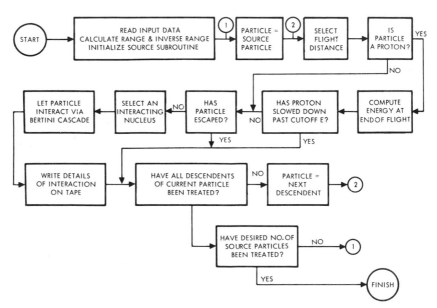

FIG. 7-1.   Flow diagram for ORNL high-energy transport code.

In this way all particles either are absorbed, migrate away from the geometrical region of interest, or slow down to 50 Mev. Below 50 Mev, protons are allowed to proceed straight ahead with no additional nuclear interactions (only atomic ionization) until they reach the end of their ranges. Neutrons below 50 Mev are handled by the 05R Monte Carlo Code. In this code the statistical weight of the neutron is constantly reduced at each collision until the neutron reaches thermal energy [8].

For one source energy and one material it requires on the order of an hour to follow two thousand incident nucleons and all their secondaries for shield thicknesses of $\sim 120$ gm/cm$^2$.

A fairly comprehensive report on the Lockheed space shielding computer programs has been prepared by Hill *et al.* [9]. While restricted to the programs of that aerospace firm, it is in many respects typical of the current

(1964–1965) technology in the area of space radiation shielding [10–12]. The following five program descriptions (LRSPC, LPPC, LIGHT, LEBC, and LMFC) are abstracted from that report.

### 3. RANGE AND STOPPING POWER CODE

The Lockheed Range and Stopping Power Calculator (LRSPC) is a computer code designed to estimate the energy loss, due to ionization and excitation, of charged particles passing through matter. This loss (i.e., stopping power) is calculated as a function of kinetic energy for charged particles penetrating materials composed of ten or less elements. Appropriate correction factors are introduced in the stopping power calculation to account for the "density effect," the "shell effect," and the "physical state effect." Protons with kinetic energies ranging from 2 Mev–100 Bev are considered in the calculations.

The range of protons in matter is given by

$$R(E) = R(2 \text{ Mev}) + \int_{2 \text{ Mev}}^{E} \frac{dE}{SP(E)} \tag{7.1}$$

where $R(E)$ is the range of a proton with kinetic energy $(E)$, $R(2 \text{ Mev})$ is the experimentally determined range of protons with kinetic energy of 2 Mev, and $SP(E)$ is calculated stopping power of protons with kinetic energy $(E)$.

The stopping power, $SP(E)$, is calculated from the Bethe–Bloch formula [13]:

$$SP(E) = -\left(\frac{dE}{dx}\right)\left(\frac{1}{\rho_t}\right) = \frac{2\pi N e^4}{mc^2 \beta^2} \sum \frac{Z_k \rho_k}{A_k \rho_t} (\text{BRAK}) \tag{7.2}$$

where $-(dE/dx)$ is the proton energy loss rate due to ionization in the material, $\rho_t$ is the density of the stopping material in units of gm/cm³, $N$ is Avogadro's number in units of atoms/mole, $e$ is the electronic charge in units of (Mev–cm)$^{\frac{1}{2}}$, $mc^2$ is the electron rest mass in units of Mev; $\beta$ is the ratio of the velocity of the incident proton to the velocity of light, $Z_k$ is the atomic number of the $k$th element of the stopping material, $\rho_k$ is the partial density of the $k$th element of the stopping material in units of gm/cm³, $A_k$ is the atomic weight of the $k$th element of the stopping material, and BRAK is a term of convenience defined as

$$\text{BRAK} = \ln\left[\frac{2mc^2\beta^2}{I^2(1-\beta^2)} W_{\max}\right] - 2\beta^2 - U - \delta \tag{7.3}$$

where *I* is the mean ionization potential of the stopping material in units of Mev, *U* is the "shell effect" correction term, $\delta$ is the "density effect" correction term, and $W_{\text{max}}$ is maximum energy transfer from the incident proton to an atomic electron.

The "shell effect" correction term ($U$) is introduced to prevent an over-estimation of the stopping power of a material when the velocity of the incident charged particle is not much greater than the velocity of the inner electrons of the elements present.

The "density effect" is the reduction in the ionization loss of a charged particle due to polarization of the stopping medium. The density effect correction term to be applied to the Bethe–Bloch formula is directly dependent on the value of the mean ionization potential of the stopping medium and is calculated by a method similar to that of Sternheimer [14–16]. It differs chiefly as to the large number of electron shells considered.

In short, the program facilitates very accurate determinations of the proton stopping power $dE/dx$ and range $R(E)$ in spacecraft materials. A set of tables giving the stopping powers and ranges in sixteen materials at eighty seven energies from 2 Mev–10 Bev is presented in an appendix to the report [9]. While the neglect of nuclear interactions is a limitation, the program is apparently quite accurate for computing ranges and stopping powers for protons up to a few hundred million electron volts.

### 4. PROTON PENETRATION CODE

The Lockheed Proton Penetration Code (LPPC) is an IBM 7094 program which calculates primary and secondary doses behind multistrata slab shields due to an incident proton flux. A number of options are available for treating diverse proton angular and energy distributions and providing several types of output data. Early versions of this code have been given in several previous reports [17, 18].

The incident proton flux may be monodirectional or isotropic. The monodirectional flux option treats protons impinging on a slab shield at an arbitrary angle. The isotropic flux option considers isotropic protons incident on a slab shield and applies a transformation to convert to a spherical shell shield. The slab doses are available as intermediate output, if desired.

The energy spectrum of the initial protons is specified as the number flux, differential in energy, or as monoenergetic. Spectrum option one computes the spectrum from the power law given below:

$$\phi(E) = AE^{-B} \tag{7.4}$$

*A* and *B* are input constants and *E* is the energy in Mev. Spectrum option two computes the spectrum from an exponential of the form:

$$\phi(E) = Ae^{(-E/B)} \tag{7.5}$$

Low- and high-energy cutoffs may be applied to spectrum options one and two. Spectrum option three causes the code to read a table of the number flux, differential in energy, versus energy. A parabolic interpolation routine automatically computes the flux at the energy mesh points used in the calculation. Option four treats a monoenergetic proton flux.

The shield is composed of one to ten homogeneous strata. A stratum may contain a single element, compound, or mixture. Each stratum may be subdivided into a number of layers. The layer size defines the thickness mesh used in solving the transport equations.

Dose components are computed for zero shield thickness and after each layer. These doses include primary proton dose, cascade proton dose, cascade neutron dose, and evaporation neutron dose. In addition, gamma ray source terms as a function of energy and depth may be calculated.

The computational model applies to a beam of protons incident on a slab shield. Isotropic flux is approximated by taking eleven beams at equal intervals in the cosine of the incident angle and performing a numerical integration over solid angle. The calculation proceeds by treating in sequence the penetration of radiation through successive shielding layers, each of which is of thickness substantially smaller than the mean free path for nuclear collisions. Given the absolute energy spectrum of nucleons incident on the first layer, the spectra of emerging nucleons are calculated on the basis of the ionization energy losses and nuclear collisions within the layer. These spectra are then taken to represent the spectra of protons and neutrons incident on the second layer, and the calculations are repeated until the desired range of shield thicknesses has been covered.

An approximate computational method for generating secondary nucleons within the shield has been devised on the basis of the simplifying assumption that the high-energy neutrons and protons resulting from the initial stage of the nuclear reaction are emitted in the direction of the incident nucleon giving rise to the reaction. An energy distribution of these straight-ahead nucleons is derived from the Metropolis [5] data. The more nearly isotropic evaporation nucleons are treated in a separate calculation.

The assumptions used in the program include the following:

• The flux of particles available for producing inelastic collisions is unaffected by nuclear collisions within the layer.

• The flux of cascade particles generated throughout a layer is not attenuated by nuclear collisions. Layer thickness is generally a scant percentage of the inelastic mean free path inside the layer and does not produce additional cascade particles within the layer.

• The cascade nucleon sources are distributed realistically through the layer.

• The effect of energy losses due to ionization within the layer is taken into account, both for proton-initiated reactions and for cascade protons produced in the layer.

• The effect of nuclear attenuation and ionization losses is considered in attenuating particles which are incident on the layer.

• Finally, it is assumed that the cascade nucleon production function is separable.

The code proceeds step by step through the shield, calculating the energy spectra of primary protons and cascade protons and neutrons after each layer. The energy mesh may contain up to two hundred and fifty points divided into four ranges with constant energy spacing within each range. The shield may contain up to a hundred layers divided into ten or fewer homogeneous strata.

The treatment of cascade nucleons has already been described. The energy spectrum of the evaporation neutrons is continuous, with an upper bound of 10–20 Mev. The data [19–23] available indicate that the spectrum peaks below 1 Mev and resembles the fission spectrum–within experimental error.

The neutron attenuation scheme incorporated into the proton penetration code is a point kernel approach based upon experimental removal cross sections for nonhydrogenous materials proposed by Albert and Welton [24]. Certain constants in the equations are adjusted to normalize to moments method data for light elements and water and to Monte Carlo data for iron and other heavy elements.

The Lockheed Source Spectrum Code (LSSC) was written to facilitate preparation of proton input spectra in a format suitable for the Lockheed Proton Penetration Code (LPPC).

The code, LSSC, may be used to convert five types of proton spectral data to differential number flux versus energy. These types are

Option 1–Integral number flux versus rigidity
Option 2–Integral number flux versus energy
Option 3–Differential number flux versus rigidity
Option 4 Power law representation of integral number flux versus rigidity
Option 5–Power law representation of integral number flux versus energy

## 5. SECONDARY GAMMA RAY CODE

The LIGHT code estimates gamma ray spectra resulting from inelastic nucleon-nucleus collisions. Gamma ray transitions from excited levels of the nucleus are traced, and an estimate of gamma ray production following direct interactions and nucleon evaporation may be made. Gamma rays due to proton bremsstrahlung, beta ray bremsstrahlung, annihilation radiation, and collective dipole effects are not considered.

The calculation is based upon a simple statistical model of the nucleus supplemented by knowledge of the low-lying nuclear levels. The method is based upon the work of Troubetzkoy [25]. Given the level density, level population, and transition probabilities, it is possible to compute the resulting gamma ray spectrum.

A discrete spectrum is obtained by computing transitions between discrete levels. Since fifty excited states are permitted by the dimensions in LIGHT, a maximum of $(50/2)(50 + 1)$ or 1275 discrete transitions may be calculated. The LIGHT program sums these transitions into 10 energy groups ranging from 1–10 Mev. The number flux is corrected to insure energy conservation in the summing process.

A continuous gamma ray spectrum is obtained by computing transitions within the continuum and from the continuum to discrete states.

Gamma ray production following nucleon evaporation is roughly estimated in the following way. The LIGHT code is run at energies near the nucleon emission threshold, where discrete gamma ray transitions are the dominant decay mode. The intensity distribution of these discrete gamma rays is assumed to be valid for neighboring excited nuclei which are the products of nucleon evaporation. At higher bombarding energies, the discrete transition spectrum decreases due to the small $\Gamma_\gamma/\Gamma$ ratio ($\Gamma =$ nuclear energy level width), but the above assumption partially compensates for the loss. No attempt is made to compute transitions in the continuum after nucleon evaporation because of their minor importance.

The proton penetration code, LPPC, uses spectral yield data developed by LIGHT to calculate and sum gamma ray production as a function of incident particle energy and the type of target nucleus. Interactions produced by primary protons, cascade protons, and cascade neutrons are taken into account. The resulting gamma ray sources become output on punched cards in the form of energy and depth distributions.

Gamma ray dose is computed by program MSGAM, using source data from the proton penetration code. A calculation is performed for each of ten gamma ray energies for which isotropic sources are distributed throughout the shield. Moments method buildup factors [26] are used for the gamma ray transmission calculations.

### 6.  BREMSSTRAHLUNG CODE

The Lockheed Electron Bremsstrahlung Code (LEBC) considers photons generated by electrons incident upon a shield material. The photons are attenuated through the remainder of the shield and the resulting dose is calculated.

The incident electron flux is assumed to be normal to the surface of the shield. The cross section for bremsstrahlung production differential in photon energy is calculated using the Born approximation. This approximation underestimates the true cross section at very low energies and overestimates it at extreme relativistic energies. The energy region in which the Born approximation is only slightly in error is the range from 4–10 Mev. Roughly, the Born approximation is within 10% above 2 Mev and within a factor of 2 below 2 Mev.

With the photon differential energy flux determined, the bremsstrahlung dose rate emerging from the shield may be calculated. The formula used is

$$D(x) = 0.511 \int_{k_{min}}^{k_{max}} I(k)F(E)e^{-\mu(k)x} \, B(k, x) \, dk \qquad (7.6)$$

where $F(E)$ is the photon energy flux-to-dose conversion factor, $r$–cm²– sec–hr$^{-1}$–Mev$^{-1}$, $k$ the mass attenuation coefficient [27], in cm²/gm,

$x$ the normal thickness of shield, in $gm/cm^2$, $B(k, x)$ the point isotropic source dose buildup factor [26], and $D(x)$ the photon dose rate in r/hr.

The numerical constant, 0.511, is used to convert the Mev energy units in the flux-to-dose conversion factor to $m_0c^2$ energy units.

In the bremsstrahlung code, the dose rate integration is actually the sum of two integrations. In the first, the integration is from the minimum photon energy to the K-edge energy; and in the second, the integration is from the K-edge energy to the maximum photon energy. This is done in order not to integrate over the discontinuity generated in the attenuation coefficients at the K-edge. The program is used to compute dose rates due to bremsstrahlung produced by Van Allen belt electrons.

### 7. MISSION FLUX CODE

The Lockheed Mission Flux Code (LMFC) calculates the electron and proton fluxes due to trapped (Van Allen) radiation encountered for a specified mission. Tables of integral number fluxes as functions of geomagnetic and geographic coordinates are stored in the code library (input data). Vehicle geographic coordinates tabulated at equal time intervals which describe the desired mission are also entered as input. The program transforms these vehicle locations to geomagnetic coordinates, facilitating the calculation of electron and proton flux rates as a function of time. Simpson's rule integration over time is used to obtain the mission fluxes.

Along the same lines, a modification of McIlwain's original FLUX code has been reported by Russak and Richardson [28]. In addition to allowing a wider choice of incident spectra, the modification permits the direct computation of the rad dose. Other similar programs have also been coded by various groups.

### 8. ELECTRON TRANSPORT CODE

While shielding computer codes written for electrons are not nearly as numerous as those written for protons (which in turn are less numerous than those written for neutrons), a few electron attenuation programs do exist [29, 30]. A Monte Carlo code by Perkins [31] for the IBM 7090 is a good example of such a code, and it serves as a model for other similar codes.

The basic problem in a Monte Carlo code for electron attenuation is that an electron makes thousands of collisions in its lifetime, any one of which may appreciably alter its direction and/or energy. In order to avoid the excessive computation time which would result if each and every collision were treated by conventional Monte Carlo techniques, the shield material being penetrated is divided into a series (ten to fifty) of layers, each of finite thickness. By computing the energy and direction of the electron at each interface in turn, the computing time is kept within bounds. The thickness of each layer is on the order of $\lesssim 5\%$ of the electron range, resulting in an approximately constant specific ionization throughout the layer. In addition the small layer thickness results in only small angular deflections.

The mechanics of the program are relatively straightforward. The ionization within each layer is computed using the table of Nelms [32], and the angular deflection is determined from the Moliere relationships discussed by Bethe [33]. Landau's straggling function is used, so normalized as to agree with the Bethe–Bloch formula [13].

The results obtained by the use of the code agree well with measurements of both electron attenuation and electron backscattering. A modification of this code by Mar [29] includes bremsstrahlung calculations based upon the work of Bethe and Heitler [34]. This modification is capable of handling up to twelve materials and electron energies of up to 10 Mev (Perkins' original work covered the 0.4–4.0 Mev incident energy region).

## 9. COMBINED ELECTRON AND PROTON TRANSPORT CODE

A space radiation shielding program capable of handling both protons and electrons and their secondaries has been coded by Yucker and Lilley [35] of the Douglas Aircraft Company. This program, called CHARGE, performs range-energy calculations using the straight-ahead approximation. The source spectrum is divided into energy intervals, within each of which a power law expression is used. The transmission factors of B. Mar [29] are used to account for electron straggling. Either the Born approximation or the Kulenkampf formula [36] is used to calculate bremsstrahlung production. Monte Carlo calculations and experimental data are used to estimate cascade and evaporation secondary nucleons [37]. Both rad and rem doses behind multilayer shields can be calculated.

## 10. SPHERICAL SPACECRAFT CODE

A straightforward analytical computer program which has been widely adopted and used is the spherical spacecraft code of Dye and Butler [38] of the Boeing Aircraft Company. While primarily designed for a shield which can be described by a series of spherical sections, as long as the limitation of radial propagation of radiation is acceptable, it may be applied to a large number of situations. It can handle slab geometries as a special case. It is programmed for the IBM 7090 in FORTRAN.

The geometry handled consists of spherical wedges of azimuthal angle $\psi_i$ and polar angle $\theta_i$, where $i$ is the wedge index number. Any combination of these wedges which do not overlap and which sum to $4\pi$ sterradians may be used. Each wedge consists of a series of layers $X_{ij}$, where each layer has a

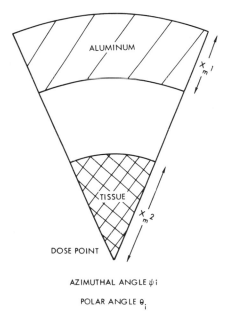

ALUMINUM

$X_{m}1$

TISSUE

$X_{m}2$

DOSE POINT

AZIMUTHAL ANGLE $\psi_i$

POLAR ANGLE $\theta_i$

FIG. 7-2.   Sector of spacecraft for spherical spacecraft code.

composition which is constant throughout that layer. Usually, two layers are used—the outer representing an aluminum spacecraft and the inner representing the man (tissue) (Fig. 7-2). A complicated geometry may be handled by decomposing it into solid angle regions about the desired dose point. In Fig. 7-3 a typical spacecraft consisting of command module (where the astronauts ride) and the service module (containing the power and environmental systems) is schematically shown. Around a representative dose point within the command module solid angles are generated

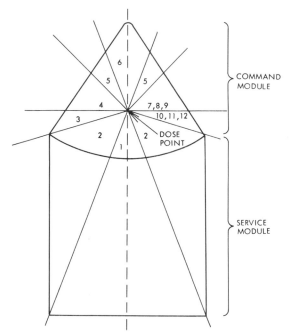

FIG. 7-3.   Angular divisions of Apollo spacecraft for 12 region shielding analysis.

within which the amount of shielding may be considered constant without undue error. The spacecraft is then removed and replaced by a series of spherical shells whose attenuations are equal on a gm/cm² basis to that of the spacecraft. The result is a geometry such as that shown in Fig. 7-4. In both Figs. 7-3 and 7-4 only the polar distributions are shown, since the spacecraft is approximately cylindrically symmetric. If desired, the small amount of cylindrical asymmetry present in the spacecraft may be taken into account by making $\theta_i$ less than 360 deg for the appropriate spherical shells.

The source function handled is time-independent and isotropic but has a differential energy distribution described by $AE^{-\alpha}$, where $A$ and $\alpha$ are constants and $E$ is the particle energy. In practice, by running a series of different problems, an intensity or energy distribution which is a function of direction can be handled.

In operation the program computes the energy lost in traversing each spherical shell using the range-energy relation as approximated by

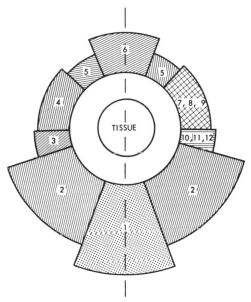

FIG. 7-4.   Spherical spacecraft code mockup of Apollo spacecraft.

$$R = \delta E^n \tag{7.7}$$

where $\delta$ and $n$ are constants, and $E$ is the particle energy.

The dose received by the tissue is computed from the energy lost in the tissue and the flux-to-dose conversion factor. In addition secondaries (cascade and evaporation neutrons and protons) may be taken into account by computing the approximate source functions and attenuating the secondaries radially. Cascade neutrons are assumed to have 50 Mev, evaporation neutrons, 2 Mev. Cascade and evaporation proton energies are computed from the incident proton energy.

The output of the program consists of the rad dose in each spherical segment due to each type of particle (primary and secondary; neutrons and protons). The total dose is also printed out. The running time depends upon the geometrical complexity and the number of secondary processes taken into account. For twelve spherical shells each of two layers, the running time is about three minutes if all secondaries are taken into account.

A very similar code has been used by Schaefer [39] to compute doses due to protons and alpha particles in a typical spacecraft. Eighteen solid angle elements were used, varying from 1.75–212 $gm/cm^2$. While the average shield thickness is $\sim 18$ $gm/cm^2$, the effective thickness is more like 4–5 $gm/cm^2$ because most of the radiation penetrates the thin regions as shown by Schaefer's studies. (Table 7-1).

TABLE 7-1

SOLID ANGLE BREAKDOWN OF APOLLO COMMAND MODULE [36]
USED BY SCHAEFER

| Section number | Shield thickness $(gm/cm^2)$ | Solid angle (steradians) | Solid angle ($\%$ of total) |
|---|---|---|---|
| C1  | 1.75  | 0.955 | 7.6  |
| C2  | 3.5   | 0.298 | 2.4  |
| C3  | 5.25  | 0.470 | 3.7  |
| C4  | 6.5   | 0.564 | 4.5  |
| C5  | 7.0   | 1.292 | 10.3 |
| C6  | 7.5   | 0.571 | 4.5  |
| C7  | 8.5   | 1.038 | 8.3  |
| C8  | 8.75  | 0.672 | 5.3  |
| C9  | 10.75 | 0.804 | 6.4  |
| C10 | 11.25 | 0.565 | 4.5  |
| C11 | 14.25 | 1.109 | 8.8  |
| C12 | 15    | 0.949 | 7.6  |
| C13 | 21    | 0.799 | 6.4  |
| C14 | 28    | 1.593 | 12.7 |
| C15 | 38    | 0.397 | 3.1  |
| C16 | 62    | 0.130 | 1.0  |
| C17 | 102   | 0.151 | 1.2  |
| C18 | 2.2   | 0.209 | 1.7  |

A somehwat similar program for calculating the primary and secondary dose rates in spheres and slabs of tissue has been reported by Wallace *et al.* [40]. Special attention is paid to the depth dose distribution in the tissue. Mention should be made of the explicit list of approximations and assumptions included in the program. Several calculated dose depth distributions for monoenergetic protons in 2.5 and 10 cm radius spheres are presented.

## 11.  APOLLO SPACECRAFT CODE

This code was prepared by Blaine and Alter [41] and by Rooney *et al.* [42] of North American Aviation, Inc., for use on the Apollo Project. While capable of handling fairly complex geometries generally, it was specifically designed to handle the geometry of the Apollo spacecraft. It was written in FORTRAN for the IBM 7094, and consists of two stages. In the first stage the geometry and composition of the various regions constitute the input from which the first part (Intermediate Tape Program) computes the macroscopic attenuation parameters using microscopic tape data. This tape data consists of cross sections and the like for each chemical element, and part of the input to the Intermediate Tape Program consists of the elemental volume fractions and densities in each geometrical region. The second part of the program (SERAPH) tracks the radiation through the spacecraft and

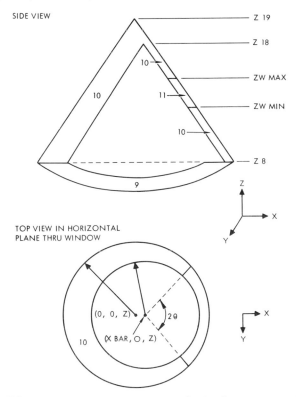

FIG. 7-5.  Command module regions for Apollo computer code.

computes the dose received by a man and/or a unit spherical dosimeter (meatball).

The geometry handled consists of a cone sitting on a circular cylinder, with the interface between the two being a spherical surface. The spherical-bottomed cone is the command module occupied by the astronauts, while the cylindrical body below it is the service module containing many of the power and environmental systems of the spacecraft. The command module shell consists of three regions—nine, ten, and eleven (Fig. 7-5), of which the side wall is described by two cones (one within the other) the inner cone being possibly off center. The section of the wall (region eleven) is the space-craft window. The interior of the command module may be sliced into eleven horizontal regions, each of which may be divided into a maximum of four radial zones. The radial zones may be divided into eight sectors, and all zones must be divided into sectors the same way (Fig. 7-6). The service module shell consists of three regions—six, seven, and eight (Fig. 7-7), and the interior of the service module is divided into four cylinders and two spheres. These cylinders and spheres may be placed anywhere within the

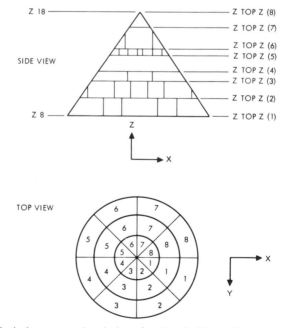

FIG. 7-6.   Typical computer description of regions inside Apollo command module.

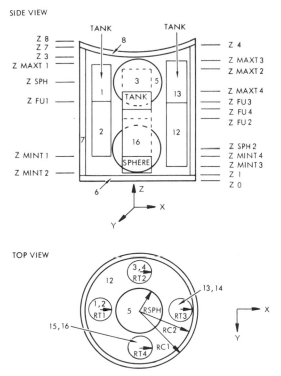

FIG. 7-7. Typical computer description of regions in the Apollo service module.

service module so long as they do not intersect each other. In both the command and service modulus any region may have any density and elemental composition available from the microtape (eighteen elements ranging from hydrogen to lead). Void regions are not allowed, but finite, very low densities (e.g., $10^{-5}$) accomplish the same purpose.

Up to three men-models are allowed in the command module, each consisting of a right circular cylinder made up of up to eight axial divisions, four radial divisions, and four angular sectors. The men-models are all of composition one, and must be horizontal (i.e., perpendicular to the axis of the command module), except for man one (the target man), who may be either horizontal or vertical. The men-models cannot intersect each other but take precedence over, and may intersect any of, the interior regions in the command module.

The energy distribution of source extends from 1.0–2000 Mev and may be divided into 10, 20, or 30 energy groups. These energy groups are specified and increase geometrically rather than linearly from 1–2000 Mev. Three possible source angular distributions may be selected—isotropic, mono-directional, or anisotropic. For the monodirectional and anisotropic sources, direction cosines must be specified, and for the anisotropic source, the polar angular distribution also can be described at twenty-one points. The energy spectrum handled is the same for all directions and is time-invariant.

In operation the main program (SERAPH) starts with the target man and the dosimeter and draws straight lines radially to the outside of the space-craft (command plus service module). From the points on the spacecraft surface the attenuation of the protons through the spacecraft to the target man and/or dosimeter is obtained, using the Sternheimer range-energy relation. Either primary protons only or primary protons and secondaries (protons and neutrons) may be considered. If secondaries are included, a Monte Carlo technique is used to generate secondary sources along the paths of the primary protons. Secondary protons are attenuated using the Sternheimer relation, while secondary neutrons are attenuated in number, but not in energy (e.g., uncollided neutrons only are followed).

The SERAPH output consists of the rad dose received by the dosimeter and/or each region of the target man for every $N$ histories ($N$ is an input parameter). For each case the dose contribution by primary protons and secondary protons and neutrons is given, as is the total dose—both by region and for the man as a whole. For the dosimeter no geometrical sum-ming is necessary.

The running time for the two parts of the program depends upon the complexity of the geometry and physical processes treated. If primary protons only are considered and the command module is divided into the maximum number of regions, each 100 case histories requires $\sim 15$ min. Including secondaries increases this to $\sim 1$ hr.

Several studies using this code have been carried out. Raymes [43] has calculated the eye, skin, and bloodforming-organ dose expected by astro-nauts on a lunar mission inside the Apollo command module. Liley and Schaedle [44] have compared the results obtained by use of this program with those derived using a spherical spacecraft code. Undoubtedly additional studies will be carried out with this or similar programs.

## 12. SHIELD WEIGHT OPTIMIZATION CODES

A number of shield weight optimization codes have been prepared. Such codes have the limitations of generally being applicable only for simplified geometries but are useful for indicating desirable shield compositions. All such programs involve comparing the shielding effectiveness of a differential "patch" of material as a function of either location on the spacecraft or as a function of composition. If the dose at the point in question can be reduced by the relocation of the patch on the spacecraft or by its replacement by another of equal weight, the shield is not optimum (from a weight standpoint). The computer programs of Krumbein *et al.* [45] and Celnik *et al.* [46] involve selecting materials with a minimum total weight for spherical shields, although the technique can be extended to nonspherical shields if assumptions are made concerning secondary radiations. Somewhat more elaborate geometries can apparently be accommodated by the optimization program of Bouquet [47]. Other optimization studies have been carried out for other specialized conditions. The results of some of these studies are discussed in Chapter IX.

## D. Concluding Remarks

This chapter was written for the reader who wishes to go beyond this book and to carry out detailed space radiation shielding calculations of his own. It must be pointed out that the material in this chapter is intended to be illustrative rather than comprehensive, and that the inclusion or exclusion of any code description in no way implies a judgment of such a code. In any situation certain codes will be more useful than others, but the number of variables is so great that each reader must make his own judgments. It is hoped that the material here will acquaint the reader with some of the literature sources and code centers which will facilitate his task.

TABLE 7-2

Sample Index of Programs Available at Argonne Code Center

| Name, type, computer, and originator of program | Program language | Tape(s) required | | Abstract number |
|---|---|---|---|---|
| EQUIPOISE, A 2-GP 2-D CYL DIFFUSION CODE FOR 704 BY ORNL | F | | | 1 |
| NIGHTMARE, A GAMMA HEATING CYL CODE FOR 704 BY ORNL | F | | | 2 |
| CRUNCH, AN ISOTOPE PRODUCTION-DECAY CODE FOR 704 BY ORNL | F+SAP | | | 3 |
| FIRN, A 2-D S4 CYCLE TRANSPORT CODE FOR 709 BY LRL-L | F | RS | | 7 |
| FIRE, 1-D AGE DIFFUSION SLAB CYL SPH FOR 704 BY LASL | LA871 | R B | | 9 |
| EQUIPOISE-2, A 7090 VERSION OF EQUIPOISE-1 BY ORNL | F | | | 10 |
| FF-MOCCA, FAST-FISSION RATIO FACTOR, FOR 704 BY BNL | F+SAP | | | 11 |
| HAFEVER, INELASTIC SCATTERING CODE FOR 704 BY APDA | F | RS | | 14 |
| HAFEVER, INELASTIC SCATTERING CODE FOR 1604 BY APDA (CDC) | F | RS | | 14 |
| APWRC-SYNFAR, 2-D SYNTHESIS SLAB CYL SPH FOR 709, MARTIN | F+FAP | RSBP | T | 15 |
| APWRC-CSDT, 7090 CROSS SECTION DATA REDUCTION, MARTIN | F+FAP | | | 16 |
| APWRC-BLACKNESS, BLACKNESS COEFFICIENT 709 CODE, MARTIN | F+FAP | | | 17 |
| 2DXY, 2-D X-Y SN APPROXIMATION CODE FOR 704 BY AGN | FLOCO | R BP | | 18 |
| 2DXY, 2-D X-Y SN APPROXIMATION CODE FOR 7090 BY AGN | FLOCO | R BP | | 18 |
| AIM-5, 1-D DIFFUSION CODE BY AI FOR 7090, SLAB CYL SPH | F | | | 27 |
| FOG, 7090 1-D FEW-GP DIFFUSION CODE BY AI, SLAB CYL SPH | F | RS | T | 28 |
| FOG, 1604 1-D FEW-GP DIFFUSION CODE BY AI, SLAB CYL SPH | F | RS | T | 28 |
| AIM6, 1-D MULTI-GP PL CYL SPH DIFFUSION 7090 BY AI | F+FAP | RS | T | 29 |
| AIM6, 1-D MULTI-GP PL CYL SPH DIFFUSION 1604 BY AI (CDC) | F+CDP | RS | | 29 |
| PERT, 1-D PERTURBATION CALC. FOR AIM, FOG CODES 7090 AI | F | RS | | 30 |
| PERT, 1-D PERTURBATION CALC. FOR AIM, FOG CODES 1604 AI | F | RS | | 30 |
| APWRC-CELCOR, 709 CELL CORRECTION CALCULATION BY MARTIN | F+FAP | RSBP | T | 31 |
| WHIRLAWAY, 2-GP 3-D XYZ, DIFFUSION CODE BY ORNL FOR 7090 | F | RS | T | 32 |
| WHIRLAWAY, 2-GP 3-D XYZ, DIFFUSION CODE BY ORNL FOR 1604 | F | RS | T | 32 |

| | | | | |
|---|---|---|---|---|
| GAM-1, SLOWING DOWN SPECTRUM CODE BY GA FOR 7090 | F | RS | LT | 33 |
| GAM-1, SLOWING DOWN SPECTRUM CODE BY GA(CDC) FOR 1604 | F | RS | LT | 33 |
| EQUIPOISE-3, 2-D 2-GP SLAB OR CYL 7090 DIFFUSION, ORNL | F | RS | T | 39 |
| EQUIPOISE-3, 2-D 2-GP SLAB OR CYL 1604 DIFFUSION, ORNL | F | RS | T | 39 |
| TWENTY GRAND, 2-D FEW-GP SLAB CYL DIFFUSION 7090 BY ORNL | F | RS | T | 40 |
| TWENTY GRAND, 2-D FEW-GP SLAB CYL DIFFUSION 1604 BY ORNL | F | RS | T | 40 |
| ZUT, RESOLVED RESONANCE INTEGRAL CODE FOR 7090 BY GA | F+FAP | RSB | T | 41 |
| TUZ, UNRESOLVED RESONANCE INTEGRAL CODE FOR 7090 BY GA | F+FAP | RSB | T | 42 |
| RE224, REACTOR ECONOMICS CODE ON 704 BY ANL | F | RS | | 44 |
| GRACE-I, SLAB GAMMA RAY ATTENUATION CODE FOR 7090 BY AI | F | RS | | 45 |
| GRACE-I, SLAB GAMMA RAY ATTENUATION CODE FOR 1604 BY AI | F | RS | | 45 |
| GRACE-II, CYL OR SPH GAMMA RAY ATTENUATION 7090 CODE, AI | F | RS | | 46 |
| GRACE-II, CYL OR SPH GAMMA RAY ATTENUATION 1604 CODE, AI | F | RS | | 46 |
| CLOUD, GAMMA RAY DOSE RATE FROM A CLOUD, 7090 CODE BY AI | F | RS | | 47 |
| CLOUD, GAMMA RAY DOSE RATE FROM A CLOUD, 1604 CODE BY AI | F | RS | | 47 |
| FUGUE, STEADY STATE ANALYSIS IN CLOSED CHANNELS 7090 AI | F | RS | | 48 |
| AIREK II, REACTOR KINETICS CODE FOR 7090 BY AI | F | RS | | 49 |
| AIREK II, REACTOR KINETICS CODE FOR 1604 BY AI(CDC) | F | RS | | 49 |
| TEMPEST II, A THERMAL SPECTRUM CODE FOR 7090 BY AI | F | RS | T | 50 |
| TEMPEST-II, A THERMAL SPECTRUM CODE FOR 1604 BY AI(CDC) | F | RS | T | 50 |
| FORM, FOURIER TRANSFORM FAST SPECTRUM CODE 7090 AI | F | RS | LT | 51 |
| FORM, FOURIER TRANSFORM FAST SPECTRUM CODE 1604 AI(CDC) | F | RS | LT | 51 |
| SAIL, SN 1-D PLANE CELL CALCULATION FOR 7090 BY AI | F | RS | | 52 |
| S4 CYLINDRICAL CELL CODE, 1-D SOLUTION FOR 7090 BY AI | F | RS | | 53 |
| S4 CYLINDRICAL CELL CODE, 1-D SOLUTION FOR 1604, AI(CDC) | F | RS | | 53 |
| FORTRAN SNG, SN APPROXIMATION SLAB CYL SPH 7090 AI | F | RS | | 54 |
| FORTRAN SNG, SN APPROXIMATION SLAB CYL SPH 1604 AI(CDC) | F | RS | | 54 |
| AIMFIRE, URANIUM FUEL CYCLE ECONOMICS CODE, 7090, AI | F | RS | T | 55 |
| SUMMIT, 7090 CRYSTALLINE SCATTERING KERNEL, GA | F | RS | T | 56 |

TABLE 7-2 *(continued)*

| Name, type, computer, and originator or program | Program language | Tape(s) required | Abstract number |
|---|---|---|---|
| AETRA, AETR CRITICAL ASSEMBLY ANALYSIS CODE FOR 7090, AI | F | RS | T | 57 |
| SIZZLE, 1-D MULTI-GP DIFFUSION BURNUP CODE 7090 AI | F | RS | T | 58 |
| MIST, 1-D SLAB SN, DOUBLE SN CODE FOR 7090, INTERNUCLEAR | F | RS | T | 59 |
| GREEN, POINT SOURCE FLUX COEFFICIENT CALCULATION 704 UF | F | | | 60 |
| DETECTOR, DISTURBED FLUX IN OR NEAR A DETECTOR, 704, UF | F | | | 61 |
| LASL LEAST SQUARES, GENERAL CURVE FITTING 704 LASL | F | | | 62 |
| 9-RENUPAK, A 7090 NEUTRON MOMENTS CALCULATION BY UNC | FAP | R B | | 63 |
| 9-NIOBE, MULTI-ENERGY TRANSPORT SOLUTION, SPH, 7090, UNC | FAP | R B | | 64 |
| TET, MULTI-GP PN FOR SLAB, P1, 2, 3, ON 7090 BY DTMB | F | RS | T | 66 |
| TET, MULTI-GP PN FOR SLAB, Pl, 2, 3, ON S-2000 BY DTMB | F | RS | | 66 |
| 2DGH, GAMMA RAY DOSE WITHIN A CYL, 2-D FOR 7090 BY ORNL | F | | | 67 |
| TRG-RS(GAMMA), MC CALC OF GAMMA FLUX IN CYL DETECTOR 704 | F | | | 68 |
| TRG-RS(N), MC CALC OF NEUTRON FLUX IN CYL DETECTOR 704 | F | | | 69 |
| SHADOW, MC CALC OF GAMMA CURRENT, SPH, FOR 704 BY TRG | F | | | 70 |
| TRIGR-S, MC CALC OF GAMMA EMISSION OF SPH 704 TRG | SAP | | | 71 |
| TRIGR-P, MC CALC OF GAMMA TRANSMISSION PLANE, 704, TRG | SAP | | | 72 |
| ABCD, MC CALC OF NEUTRON DOSE IN CYL COMPARTMENT 704 TRG | SAP | | | 73 |
| GE-HAPO-SXII, DOUBLE SN FOR SLAB, CYL, SPH 7090 BY HAPO | FLOCO | RSBP | T | 75 |
| KERNMAT, SMALL SOURCE THEORY REACTOR CODE 7090 WAPD | F | RS P | T | 76 |
| PDS, 1-D MULTI-GP POWER DISTRIBUTION SEARCH 7090 DAC | F | RS | | 81 |
| CURE-7090, 2-D FEW-GP X-Y R-Z R-THETA CODE BY MARTIN | FAP | RS | T | 82 |
| GMCM, MC REACTOR AND SHIELDING CODE ON 7090, BY MARTIN | F | RS P | T | 83 |
| ZORCH, MSRE POWER TRANSIENT ANALYSIS ON 7090 BY ORNL | F | RSB | | 86 |
| EQUIPOISE-3A, 2-D 2-GP DIFFUSION CYL OR SLAB, 7090, ORNL | F | RS | T | 87 |
| EQUIPOISE-BURNOUT, 2-D 2-GP DEPLETION SLAB CYL 7090 ORNL | F | RS | | 88 |

| | | | | |
|---|---|---|---|---|
| ARES-2, RESONANCE INTEGRAL GROUP CONSTANT CODE, 7090, AI | F | RS | T | 89 |
| ARES-2, RESONANCE INTEGRAL GROUP CONSTANT CODE, 1604, AI | F | RS | T | 89 |
| INDEXING POWDER PATTERNS, CRYSTAL STRUCTURE 7090 AI | F | RS | T | 90 |
| FARSE-1A, NEUTRON LEAKAGE FROM SHIELD ANNULUS, 7090, AI | F | RS | | 91 |
| PLATYPUS, REACTIVITY AND RUNNING COST CODE FOR 7070, RR | AC72 | R | | 92 |
| APWRC, CRITICALITY FLUX AND BURNUP SYSTEM, 7094, MARTIN | F+FAP | RSBP | LT | 93 |
| APWRC-SYNFARO2, SYNTHESIS X-Y R-Z CODE 7090 MARTIN | F+FAP | RSBP | T | 94 |
| APWRC-GAMICO, SLOWING DOWN SPECTRUM CODE 7090 MARTIN | F+FAP | RSBP | T | 95 |
| APWRC-SYBURN, 1-D DEPLETION ON PI OR SN FOR 7090, MARTIN | F+FAP | RSBP | T | 96 |
| DDB, 2-D R-Z DIFFUSION DEPLETION CODE 7090 GA | F+FAP | RSBP | T | 99 |
| QUADRIFIT, QUADRATIC EXPRESSION FIT FOR 704 BY EDC | F | RSB | | 100 |
| NDC, UNIT CELL DESIGN CALC. FOR LATTICES FOR 704 BY WAPD | F | RSB | T | 101 |
| AX-1, COUPLED NEUTRONICS-HYDRODYNAMICS SPH CODE 704 ANL | F | RS | | 102 |
| CRAM, 1,2-D MULTI-GP DIFFUSION CODE 7090 UKAEA-R | F+FAP | RSBP | LT | 103 |
| 2D-PERT, MULTI-GP PERTURBATION FOR CUREM ON 704 BY ANL | F+SAP | RS P | | 104 |
| PLMCN-1, MC NEUTRON DOSE RATE, PLANE SOURCE 7090 MARTIN | F | | | 105 |
| M-1, MC RADIOISOTOPE CYL SHIELDING CODE FOR 7090, MARTIN | F | | | 106 |
| MURGATROYD, MSRE KINETICS CODE FOR 7090 BY ORNL | F | RS | | 107 |
| MURGATROYD, MSRE KINETICS CODE FOR 1604 BY ORNL | F | RS | | 107 |
| BAM, THERMAL CONSTANTS BY S4 AND TEMPEST FOR 7090 BY AI | F | RS | | 108 |
| 4 RESTRAINT PIPE STRESS, FORCES AND MOMENTS FOR 7090, AI | F | RS | T | 109 |
| SCARF2, SNAP SCATTER FROM RADIATOR FINS, FOR 7090 BY AI | F | RS | T | 110 |
| SCAR1, SNAP SCATTER FROM RING, FOR 7090 BY AI | F | RS | T | 111 |
| CROCK, SPACE POWER PLANT DESIGN OPTIMIZATION 7090 AI | F | RS | T | 112 |
| ZOT, CROSS SECTION GROUP COLLAPSING CODE 704 LASL | FLOCO | RSBP | | 113 |
| ZOT, CROSS SECTION GROUP COLLAPSING CODE 7090 LASL | FLOCO | RSBP | | 113 |
| SHOCK, SPACE POWER PLANT DESIGN OPTIMIZATION 7090 AI | F | RS | T | 114 |
| GAZE-II, 1-D MULTI-GP FULL SCATTER SLAB CYL SPH 7090 GA | F+FAP | | | 115 |
| FEVER, 1-D FEW-GP DEPLETION CODE SLAB CYL SPH, 7090, GA | F | RS | T | 117 |

TABLE 7-2 (*continued*)

| Name, type, computer, and originator of program | Program language | Tape(s) required | Abstract number |
|---|---|---|---|
| ULCER, 1-D MULTI-GP FULL SCATTER SLAB CYL SPH, 7090, AI | F+FAP | RS P   LT | 118 |
| QUICKIE, MULTI-GP REACTIVITY 1-REGION SYSTEMS, 7090, AI | F | RS   LT | 119 |
| FAIM, 1-D MULTI-GP DOWN SCATTER, SLAB CYL SPH, 7090, AI | F+FAP | RS P   LT | 120 |
| AIREK-III, SPACE INDEPENDENT REACTOR KINETICS 7090 AI | F | RS   T | 121 |
| SNAPKIN-5, 5A, SNAP PERTURBATION EFFECT STUDY 7090 AI | F | RS   T | 122 |
| LIPRECAN-1, MC NEUTRON PENETRATION IN HYDROGEN, 7090, HN | F | | 123 |
| SPMCN-1, NEUTRON MC CODE FOR SPH GEOM FOR 7090 BY MARTIN | F | | 126 |
| SANE-SAGE, NEUTRON OR GAMMA SPH SHIELDING CODE 7090 UNC | F+FAP | RS   T | 127 |
| ADONIS, 3-D NEUTRON OR GAMMA SHIELDING CODE 7090 UNC | F+FAP | RS   T | 128 |
| CONEC, COUPLED NEUTRON-HYDRODYNAMICS SPH CODE 7090 LRL-L | F | RS | 129 |
| ADJUST, PULSE-HEIGHT SPECTRA GAIN CORRECTION, 7090, ORNL | F | R | 131 |
| W-DSN, 1-D CYL CELL SN REACTIVITY CALCULATION 7030 AEE-W | SI | R | 132 |
| W-DSN, 1-D CYL CELL SN REACTIVITY CALCULATION 7090 AEE-W | F | RS   T | 132 |
| WED, W-DSN EDIT OF REACTION RATE SUMMARIES 7030 AEE-W | SI | R | 133 |
| WED, W-DSN EDIT OF REACTION RATE SUMMARIES 7090 AEE-W | F | RS   T | 133 |
| NUCY, SOLUTION OF NUCLIDE CHAIN EQUATIONS, 7090, ORNL | F | RS | 134 |
| NUCY, SOLUTION OF NUCLIDE CHAIN EQUATIONS, 1604, ORNL | F | RS | 134 |
| TRAFICORPORATION, TRANSFER FUNCTION SYNTHESIS, 704, ANL | F | R B | 135 |
| HERESY-1, HETEROGENEOUS REACTOR CALCULATION, 704, FMA | F | R | 136 |
| HERESY-1, HETEROGENEOUS REACTOR CALCULATION, 7090, FMA | F | RSBP | 136 |
| CCCl, SHIELD PENETRATION CALCULATED CYL SOURCE 704 7090 | S,FAP | R B | 137 |
| CCC2, SHIELD PENETRATION INPUT CYL SOURCE 704 7090 | S,FAP | R B | 138 |
| CCC3, SHIELD PENETRATION INPUT RECT SOURCE 704 7090 | S,FAP | R B | 139 |
| CCC4, MC CALC OF GAMMA RAY SCATTERING IN AIR 704 7090 | S,FAP | R B | 140 |
| RATRAP, SNAP GEOM DOSE RATE CALCULATION 7090 BY AI | F | RS | 141 |

TABLE 7-2 (*continued*)

| Name, type, computer, and originator of program | Program language | Tape(s) required | Abstract number |
|---|---|---|---|
| CRE, CONTROL ROD EFFECT CYL GEOM 7090 CODE BY EURATOM | F | RS P | | ENEA 003 |
| MAC-RAD, EXTENSION OF MAC SHIELDING CODE 7090 EURATOM | F | RS P | LT | ENEA 006 |
| METHUSELAH-1, LIQUID-MOD REACTOR CELL 7090,30 CODE UKAEA | F | RS P | LT | ENEA 007 |
| MUFT-EUR, FEW-GP CONSTANTS + RES ESCAPE 7090 EURATOM | F | RS P | L | ENEA 008 |
| PINETO, REACTOR KINETICS W/FEEDBACK ON 7090 BY EURATOM | F | RS P | | ENEA 009 |
| THESIS-2, THERMAL SPECTRUM + X-SEC CALC 7090 EURATOM | F | RS P | | ENEA 011 |
| ZIP-ZIP1, SLAB GEOM TRANSPORT INTEGRAL CODE 7090 EURATOM | F | RS P | | ENEA 015 |
| ZIP-ZIP2, CYL GEOM TRANSPORT INTEGRAL CODE 7090 EURATOM | F | RS P | | ENEA 016 |
| PERSEUS, COLLISION PROB MULTIGP CYL CELL CALC 7090 AEE-W | F | RS P | | ENEA 018 |
| PIP-1, COLLISION PROB MULTIGP TRANSPORT 7090 CODE AEE-W | F | RS P | | ENEA 019 |
| PIXSE, THERMAL ENERGY SCAT MATRIX CALC 7090 AEE-W | F | RS P | | ENEA 020 |
| TED, EDIT PROGRAM FOR WDSN OUTPUT TAPE 7090 AEE-W | F | RS P | | ENEA 021 |
| THESEUS, MULTIGP COLLISION PROB IN CYL GEOM 7090 AEE-W | F | RS P | | ENEA 022 |

*a* Explanation of symbols: F = FORTRAN, R = Reference document, S = Source deck or symbolic listing, B = Binary or object deck, P = Test problem, L = Library, T = Tape(s) required for transmittal, and ENEA = European nuclear energy authority.

TABLE 7-3

<small>SAMPLE LISTING OF PROGRAMS AVAILABLE AT THE RADIATION
SHIELDING INFORMATION CENTER (RSIC) OF OAK RIDGE</small>

---

CCC-1: 14–0 and 14-3
KERNEL INTEGRATION CODE AND DATA CHECK—CALCULATED SOURCES DESCRIBED IN CYLINDRICAL COORDINATE SYSTEM, contributed by General Electric, Cincinnati, Nuclear Materials and Propulsion Operation
SAP-FAP, IBM 704 and 7090
(Reference: XDC 59-2-16 and XDC 59-3-52)

CCC-2: 14-1 and 14-3
KERNEL INTEGRATION CODE AND DATA CHECK—INPUT SOURCES DESCRIBED IN CYLINDRICAL COORDINATE SYSTEM, contributed by General Electric, Cincinnati, Nuclear Materials and Propulsion Operation
SAP-FAP, IBM 704 and 7090
(Reference: XDC 59-2-16 and XDC 59-3-52)

CCC-3: 14-2 and 14-3
KERNEL INTEGRATION CODE AND DATA CHECK—SOURCES DESCRIBED IN RECTANGULAR COORDINATE SYSTEM, contributed by General Electric, Cincinnati, Nuclear Materials and Propulsion Operation
(Reference: XDC 59-6-173 and XDC 59-3-52)

CCC-4: 15-2
MONTE CARLO CALCULATION—GAMMA-RAY SCATTERING IN AIR, contributed by General Electric, Cincinnati, Nuclear Materials and Propulsion Operation
SAP-FAP, IBM 704 and 7090
(Reference: XDC 61-5-1 and DC 60-10-150)

CCC-5: C-17 and R-29
KERNEL INTEGRATION CODE AND DATA GENERATOR—FRUSTRA OF RECTANGULAR PYRAMIDS AND CYLINDERS, contributed by General Dynamics, Fort Worth, USAF Nuclear Aerospace Research Facility
SAP-FAP, IBM 704 and 7090
(Reference: NARF 61-39T, FZK-9-170)

CCC-6: L-63 and R-29
KERNEL INTEGRATION CODE AND DATA GENERATOR—CYLINDERS, SPHERES, AND COMPLEX GEOMETRY, contributed by General Dynamics, Fort Worth, USAF Nuclear Aerospace Research Facility
SAP-FAP, IBM 704 and 7090
(Reference: NARF 61-39T, FZK-9-170)

CCC-7: NTC
A MONTE CARLO HIGH ENERGY NUCLEON TRANSPORT CODE INCORPORATING CASCADE AND EVAPORATIVE PROCESSES, contributed by Neutron Physics Division, Oak Ridge National Laboratory, Oak Ridge, Tennessee

---

TABLE 7-3 (*continued*)

---

FORTRAN/FAP, IBM 7090
(Reference: ORNL-3610)

CCC-8:    K-74
MONTE CARLO CALCULATION OF NEUTRON FLUX IN INFINITE MEDIUM FOR POINT ISOTROPIC SOURCES, contributed by General Dynamics, Fort Worth, USAF Nuclear Aerospace Research Facility
FAP, IBM 7090
(Reference: NARF 60-8T, FZK-9-147)

CCC-9:    L-05
MONTE CARLO MULTIBEND-DUCT SHIELDING CODE, contributed by General Dynamics, Fort Worth, USAF Nuclear Aerospace Research Facility
FAP, IBM 7090
(Reference: NARF 61-33T, MR-N-286 and NARF 62-13T, MR-N-297)

CCC-10:    C-18, R-35, and R-65
MONTE CARLO MULTILAYER SLAB GEOMETRY SHIELDING CODES, contributed by General Dynamics, Fort Worth, USAF Nuclear Aerospace and Research Facility and U.S. Army Tank-Automotive Center, Warren, Michigan
SAP-FAP, IBM 704 and 7090
(Reference: FZK-134-3)

CCC-11:    SANE
MONTE CARLO SPHERICAL MULTILAYER GEOMETRY NEUTRON TRANSPORT SHIELDING CODE, contributed by United Nuclear Corporation, White Plains, Development Division—NDA
FORTRAN-FAP, IBM 7090
(Reference: UNUCOR-633 and UNUCOR-634)

CCC-12:    SAGE
MONTE CARLO SPHERICAL MULTILAYER GEOMETRY GAMMA TRANSPORT SHIELDING CODE, contributed by United Nuclear Corporation, White Plains, Development Division—NDA
FORTRAN-FAP, IBM 7090
(Reference: UNUCOR-633 and UNUCOR-634)

CCC-13:    ADONIS
MONTE CARLO THREE-DIMENSIONAL RECTANGULAR GEOMETRY SHIELDING CODE, contributed by United Nuclear Corporation, White Plains, Development Division—NDA
FORTRAN-FAP/CODAP, IBM 7090 and CDC-1604
(Reference: UNUCOR-635)

CCC-14:    FMC-G
MONTE CARLO SIMULATION OF GAMMA-RAY LIFE HISTORIES IN A SOURCE-SHIELD CONFIGURATION, contributed by General Electric, Cincinnati, Nuclear Materials and Propulsion Operation
SAP-FAP, IBM 704 and 7090
(Reference: APEX-706)

---

TABLE 7-3 *(continued)*

---

CCC-15: FMC-N
MONTE CARLO SIMULATION OF NEUTRON LIFE HISTORIES IN A SOURCE-SHIELD CONFIGURATION, contributed by General Electric, Cincinnati, Nuclear Materials and Propulsion Operation
SAP-FAP, IBM 704 and 7090
(Reference: APEX-706)

CCC-16: 18-0 and Auxiliary Routines
MONTE CARLO SIMULATION OF NEUTRON AND GAMMA-RAY LIFE HISTORIES IN REACTOR-SHIELD ASSEMBLIES, contributed by General Electric, Cincinnati, Nuclear Materials and Propulsion Operation
FORTRAN-FAP, IBM 7090
(Reference: XDC 61-1-91)

CCC-17: 05R
A GENERAL PURPOSE MONTE CARLO NEUTRON TRANSPORT CODE, contributed by Neutron Physics Division, Oak Ridge National Laboratory, Oak Ridge, Tennessee
FORTRAN-FAP/CODAP, IBM 7090 and CDC-1604
(Reference: ORNL-3622)

CCC-18: 05-0
ANISOTROPIC POINT SOURCE CODE—SINGLE SCATTERED GAMMA-RAYS INFINITE HOMOGENEOUS MEDIUM, contributed by General Electric, Nuclear Materials and Propulsion Operation, Cincinnati, Ohio
SAP-FAP, IBM 704 and 7090
(Reference: XDC-50-8-218)

CCC-19: 09-0
ANISOTROPIC POINT SOURCE CODE—SINGLE SCATTERED NEUTRONS IN INFINITE HOMOGENEOUS MEDIUM, contributed by General Electric, Nuclear Materials and Propulsion Operation, Cincinnati, Ohio
SAP-FAP, IBM 704 and 7090
(Reference: APEX-533)

CCC-20: TRIGR
MONTE CARLO GAMMA-RAY PENETRATION CODES—PLANE AND SPHERICAL GEOMETRY, contributed by TRG, Incorporated, Melville, New York, and Aeronautical Research Laboratories, Wright Air Development Center, Wright-Patterson Air Force Base, Ohio
SAP, IBM 704
(Reference: WADC 59-771)

CCC-21: MORTIMER
KERNEL INTEGRATION CODE—TWO-COMPONENT ANALYSIS FOR SNAP SHIELD GEOMETRIES, contributed by Atomics International, Canoga Park, California
FORTRAN-FAP, IBM 7090
(Reference: NAA-SR-9327)

---

TABLE 7-3 *(continued)*

---

CCC-22:      MAC

NEUTRON GAMMA-RAY ATTENUATION CODE—SPINNEY (REMOV-
AL-DIFFUSION) CALCULATION IN PLANE GEOMETRY, contributed by
General Electric, Hanford Atomic Products Operation, Richland, Washington
FORTRAN, IBM 7090
(Reference: HW-73381)

CCC-23:      MAVRAC

MODEL ASTRONAUT AND VEHICLE RADIATION ANALYSIS CODE,
contributed by Northrop Space Laboratories, Hawthorne, California, and
Aerospace Medical Research Laboratory, Wright-Patterson Air Force Base,
Ohio
FORTRAN, IBM 7090
(Reference: NSL 63-159)

CCC-24:      CARSTEP

TRAJECTORY AND ENVIRONMENT CODE—ELECTRON AND PRO-
TON FLUXES IMPINGING ON SPACECRAFT IN ORBIT, contributed by
Northrop Space Laboratories, Hawthorne, California, and Aerospace Medical
Research Laboratory, Wright-Patterson Air Force Base, Ohio
FORTRAN, IBM 7090
(Reference: NSL 63-63R-1)

CCC-25:      TRG-SGD

A MONTE CARLO PROGRAM TO CALCULATE SECONDARY GAMMA
RAY DOSE FROM A NUCLEAR WEAPON DETONATION, contributed by
Research and Technology Division, Air Force Weapons Laboratory, Kirtland
Air Force Base, New Mexico
FORTRAN, CDC-1604
(Reference: WL-TDR-64-46)

CCC-26:      GRACE-II

GAMMA-RAY KERNEL INTEGRATION DOSE RATE AND HEATING
CODE (CYLINDERS AND SPHERES), contributed by Atomics International,
Canoga Park, California
FORTRAN, IBM-7090-4, CDC-1604
(Reference: WL-TDR-64-40)

CCC-27:      ACT II

ACTIVATION GAMMA-RAY SOURCE STRENGTH CODE, SIMPLE
GEOMETRY, FINITE DILUTION, contributed by Westinghouse Electric
Company, Astronuclear Laboratory, Pittsburgh, Pennsylvania
FORTRAN, IBM-7090-4
(Reference: NAA-SR-4649)

CCC-28:      QAD

KERNEL INTEGRATION CODE, PENETRATION AND HEATING IN
COMPLEX GEOMETRY, contributed by Los Alamos Scientific Laboratory,
N Division, Los Alamos, New Mexico

---

TABLE 7-3 (*continued*)

FORTRAN, IBM 7090-4
(Reference: to be published)

CCC-29: MARTY-G
MONTE CARLO GAMMA-RAY RADIATION TRANSPORT AND HEAT DEPOSITION RATES IN LIQUID HYDROGEN—SLABS AND CYLINDERS, contributed by NASA, George C. Marshall Space Flight Center, Huntsville, Alabama
FORTRAN, IBM 7090
(Reference: NASA TN D-1115)

CCC-30: MARTY-N
MONTE CARLO NEUTRON RADIATION TRANSPORT AND HEAT DEPOSITION RATES IN LIQUID HYDROGEN—SLABS AND CYLINDERS, contributed by NASA, George C. Marshall Space Flight Center, Huntsville, Alabama
FORTRAN, IBM 7090
(Reference: NASA TN D-1115)

CCC-31: BREMRAD
EXTERNAL AND INTERNAL BREMSSTRAHLUNG CALCULATION CODE, contributed by Chemical Laboratory, Batelle-Northwest Laboratories, Richland, Washington
FORTRAN, IBM 7090
(Reference: HW-83784)

CCC-32: LIGHT
INELASTIC GAMMA PRODUCTION CODE, contributed by Lockheed Nuclear Products, Lockheed-Georgia Company and NASA, George C. Marshall Space Flight Center, Huntsville, Alabama
FORTRAN, IBM 7090
(Reference: ER-6643)

CCC-33: SALOMON
MONTE CARLO GAMMA TRANSPORT CODE LAMINATED SLABS, contributed by Research Institute of National Defense, Stockholm, Sweden
FORTRAN, IBM 7090-4
(Reference: A-4403-441)

CCC-34: TOPIC
A FORTRAN PROGRAM FOR CALCULATING TRANSPORT OF PARTICLES IN CYLINDERS, contributed by Phillips Petroleum Co., Atomic Energy Division, Idaho Falls, Idaho
IBM 7090-4
(Reference: IDO-16968)

CCC-35: DIPSEA
MONTE CARLO DOSE CALCULATION, ISOTROPIC POINT SOURCE, EXPONENTIAL ATMOSPHERE, contributed by Technical Operations Re-

TABLE 7-3 (*continued*)

---

search, Burlington, Massachusetts, and MIT Lincoln Laboratory, Lexington, Massachusetts
FORTRAN-FAP, IBM 7090-4
(Reference: TO-B 64-12)

CCC-36:   EMPIRE-II
MULTI-GROUP DISCRETE ORDINATE TRANSPORT CODE, SLAB GEOMETRY, contributed by Estinghouse Corporation, Bettis Atomic Power Laboratory, Pittsburgh
FORTRAN, PHILCO-2000
(Reference: WAPD-TM-436)

---

## REFERENCES

1.  M. Butler, "Code Abstracts." Argonne Code Center, Argonne Natl. Lab. (1961 to present).
2.  K. Penny (ed.), RSIC Newsletter, *Oak Ridge Natl. Lab.*, Oak Ridge, Tennesse (1964 to present).
3.  H. W. Bertini, Monte Carlo Calculations on Intranuclear Cascades, Rept. ORNL-3383, *Oak Ridge Natl. Lab.*, Oak Ridge, Tennessee (1963).
4.  R. Serber, Nuclear Reactions at High Energies, *Phys. Rev.* **72,** 1114 (1947).
5.  N. Metropolis, R. Bivins, M. Storm, A. Turkevich, J. M. Miller, and G. Friedlander, Monte Carlo Calculations on Intranuclear Cascades, I and II, *Phys. Rev.* **110,** 185 (1958).
6.  A. S. Householder *et al.*, Monte Carlo Method, Rept. 12, *Appl. Math. Ser., Natl. Bur. Std.* (1951).
7.  W. E. Kinney, R. R. Coveyou, and C. D. Zerby, A Series of Monte Carlo Codes to Transport Nucleons through Matter, pp. 608 ff., *Proc. Symp. Protection against Radiation Hazards in Space,* TID-7652 (1962).
8.  R. R. Coveyou, J. G. Sullivan and H. P. Carter, "The 05R Code—A General Purpose Monte Carlo Reactor Code for the IBM-704 Computer, pp. 267 ff., *Codes for Reactor Computations, IAEA, Vienna* (1961).
9.  C. W. Hill, C. C. Douglass, W. B. Ritchie, and K. M. Simpson, Computer Programs for Shielding Problems in Manned Space Vehicles, Repts. ER-6643, and ER-7777 *Lockheed Aircraft*, Marietta Georgia (1964).
10.  K. S. McGarrigle and B. W. Mar, Computer Codes for the Evaluation of Space Radiation Hazards, Rept. D2-90418, Boeing Airplane, Seattle, Washington (1963).
11.  J. A. Barton and B. W. Mar, Computer Codes for Space Radiation Environment and Shielding, Rept. WL-TDR-64-71, *U.A. Air Force Weapons Lab., Kirtland, Air Force Base, New Mexico* (1964).

12. R. E. Fortney, Computer Analysis of Radiation Shielding, Rept. AMRL-TDR-64-11, *Biophys. Lab., Wright-Patterson Air Force Base, Dayton, Ohio* (1964).

13. H. A. Bethe, On the Theory of Penetration of Fast Corpuscular Radiation through Material, *Ann. Physik* **5**, 325 (1930).

14. R. M. Sternheimer, The Density Effect for the Ionization Loss in Various Materials, *Phys. Rev.* **88**, 851 (1952).

15. R. M. Sternheimer, The Density Effect for the Ionization Loss in Various Materials, *Phys. Rev.* **103**, 511 (1956).

16. R. M. Sternheimer, Range-Energy Relations for Protons in Be, C, Al, Cu, Pb, and Air, *Phys. Rev.* **115**, 137 (1959).

17. R. I. Allen *et al.*, Shielding Problems in Manned Space Vehicles, Rept. NR-140, *Lockheed Airplane, Marietta, Georgia* (1961).

18. W. M. Schofield *et al.*, Shielding Problems in Manned Space Vehicles, Rept. ER-5997, *Lockheed Airplain, Marietta, Georgia* (1962).

19. I. Dostrovsky, Z. Fraenkel and G. Friedlander, Monte Carlo Calculations of Nuclear Evaporation Processes III—Application to Low Energy Reactions, *Phys. Rev.* **116**, 683 (1959).

20. I. Dostrovsky, Z. Fraenkel and L. Winsberg, Monte Carlo Calculations of Nuclear Evaporation Processes IV—Spectra of Neutrons and Charged Particles from Nuclear Reactions, *Phys. Rev.* **118**. 781 (1960).

21. E. Gross, The Absolute Yield of Low Energy Neutrons from 90 MeV Proton Bombardment of Gold, Silver, Nickel, Aluminum, and Carbon, Rept. UCRL-3330, *Univ. Calif. Berkeley, California* (1956).

22. K. J. Le Couteur and D. W. Long, Neutron Evaporation and Level Densities in Excited Nuclei, *Nucl. Phys.* **13**, 32 (1959).

23. K. J. Le Couteur, The Evaporation Theory of Nuclear Disintegrations, *Proc. Roy. Soc. (London)*, **A63**, 259 (1950).

24. R. D. Albert and T. A. Welton, A Simplified Theory of Neutron Attenuation and Its Application to Reactor Shield Design, Rept. WAPD-15, *Westinghouse Electric Corp., Pittsburgh, Pennsylvania* (1950).

25. E. S. Troubetzkoy, Continuous Theory of Gamma Ray Spectra Following Inelastic Scattering, Rept. NDA-2111-3, *Nucl. Develop. Corp., White Plains, New York* (1959).

26. H. Goldstein and J. E. Wilkins, Calculations of the Penetration of Gamma Rays, Rept. NYO-3075, *U.S. At. Energy Comm.* (1954).

27. G. W. Grodstein, X-Ray Attenuation Coefficients from 10 keV to 100 MeV, Circular 583, *Natl. Bur. Std., Washington, D.C.* (1957).

28. S. Russak and K. Richardson, Proton Flux, Dosages, and Damage Estimates in the Van Allen Belt, pp. 251 ff., *Second Symp. Protection against Radiations in Space*, NASA-SP-71 (1964).

29. B. W. Mar, Electron Shielding Codes for Evaluation of Space Radiation Hazards, Rept. D2-90414, *Boeing Airplane Co., Seattle, Washington* (1963).

30. R. E. Fortney, Computer Analysis of Radiation Shielding, Rept. AMRL-TDR-64-11, *Biophys. Lab., U.S. Air Force, Dayton, Ohio* (1964).

31.  J. F. Perkins, Monte Carlo Calculation of Transport of Fast Electrons, *Phys. Rev.* **126**, 1781 (1962).
32.  A. T. Nelms, Energy Loss and Range of Electrons and Positrons, Circular 577, *Natl. Bur. Std., Washington, D.C.* (1956).
33.  H. A. Bethe, Moliere's Theory of Multiple Scattering, *Phys. Rev.* **89**, 1256 (1953).
34.  H. A. Bethe and W. Heitler, Moliere's Theory of Multiple Scattering, *Proc. Roy. Soc.* (*London*) A **146**, 83 (1934).
35.  W. R. Yucker and J. R. Lilley, Space Radiation Shielding Analysis by Program CHARGE, *Trans. Am. Nucl. Soc.* **8**, 196 (1965).
36.  H. Kulenkampf and S. Schmidt, The Energy Distribution in the Spectrum of X-Ray Bremsstrahlung, *Ann. Physik* **43**, 494 (1943).
37.  W. R. Yucker, Secondary Nucleons Produced in High Energy Nuclear Reactions, Rept. SM-46334, *Douglas Aircraft Co.* Santa Monica, California (1964).
38.  D. L. Dye and G. Butler, Computer Calculations of Doses from Protons in Space, *J. Astron. Sci.* **9**, 63 (1962).
39.  H. J. Schaefer, Local Dose from Proton and Alpha Particle Enders behind Complex Shield Systems, pp. 507 ff., *Second Symp. Protection against Radiations in Space*, NASA-SP-71 (1964).
40.  R. Wallace, P. G. Steward, and C. Sondhaus, Primary and Secondary Proton Dose Rates in Spheres and Slabs of Tissue, pp. 301 ff., *Second Symp. Protection against Radiations in Space*, NASA-SP-71 (1964).
41.  R. A. Blaine and H. Alter, Apollo Radiation Shielding Analysis I—Basic Physics Data and Proton Source Information, *Trans. Am. Nucl. Soc.* **6**, 431 (1963).
42.  K. L. Rooney, W. J. Roberts and R. S. Hubner, Apollo Radiation Shielding Analysis II—A Program to Calculate the Penetration of Primary and Secondary Radiations in the Apollo Geometry, *Trans. Am. Nucl. Soc.* **6**, 432 (1963).
43.  F. Raymes, Appollo Spacecraft Radiation Protection Status Report, pp. 365 ff., *Second Symp. Protection against Radiations in Space*, NASA-SP-71 (1964).
44.  B. Liley and G. C. Schaedle, An Examination of the Relative Merits of Stochastic and Nonstatistical Methods of Computing Primary Ionization Doses, pp. 527 ff., *Second Symp. Protection against Radiations in Space*, NASA-SP-71 (1964).
45.  A. D. Krumbein, P. S. Mittelman, E. S. Troubetzkoy, F. Nakache, and J. Celnik, Synthesis of Minimum Weight Proton Shields, pp. 773 ff., *Proc. Symp. Protection against Radiation Hazards in Space*, TID-7652 (1962).
46.  J. Celnik, A. D. Krumbein, and F. R. Nakache, Synthesis of Spherical Minimum Weight Proton Shields, pp. 225 ff., *Second Symp. Protection against Radiations in Space*, NASA-SP-71 (1964).
47.  F. L. Bouquet, A Space Radiation Protection System for Near-Earth Manned Orbital Space Stations, pp. 397 ff., *Second Symp. Protection against Radiations in Space*, NASA-SP-71 (1964).

# VIII

## DOSES DUE TO NUCLEAR
## SPACE RADIATIONS

### SPACECRAFT SHIELDING

In this section of this chapter the doses and dose rates due to the various natural sources of nuclear radiation in space are discussed. The situation considered is (in most cases) a point tissue-equivalent dosimeter centered inside a spherical aluminum shell of constant thickness. The space radiation environment is considered to be isotropic.

### A. Solar Flares

As was discussed in Chapter I, the first systematic attempt to construct a model of the solar flare radiation was by D. K. Bailey. This leads to the following mathematical expression for the proton fluxes [1]:

$$\phi(E > E_0, t) = \frac{at \exp[-\alpha' E_0 t]}{E_0^2} \tag{8.1}$$

$$\phi(E, t)\, dE = \frac{at \exp[-\alpha' E t](\alpha' E t + 2)}{E^3} \tag{8.2}$$

$$\phi(E > E_0) = \frac{a}{(\alpha')^2 E_0^4} \tag{8.3}$$

$$\phi(E)\, dE = \frac{4a}{(\alpha')^2 E^5} \tag{8.4}$$

where $a = 1 \times 10^{10}$, $\alpha' = 8 \times 10^{-4}$, $t =$ time (hr), and $E =$ proton energy (Mev).

These expressions are the integral energy spectrum as a function of time, the differential energy spectrum as a function of time, and the corresponding time-integrated energy spectra.

From the range-energy relation $(R = \delta E^n)$ it is seen that a charged particle with initial energy $E_0$ (Mev) will emerge with energy $E$ (Mev) after penetrating a shield of thickness $x$ (gm/cm²), where

$$E = \left[ E_0^n - \frac{x}{\delta} \right]^{1/n} \qquad (8.5)$$

$n, \delta$ = constants associated with the shield material.

For a solar flare (e.g., the Bailey model event), which exhibits an $AE^{-\alpha}$ integral energy spectrum prior to penetrating a shield, the differential energy spectrum after penetrating a shield of thickness $x$ is

$$\phi(E) \, dE = A\alpha E^{-(\alpha+1)} \left[ 1 + \left( \frac{E'}{E} \right)^n \right]^{-[(\alpha/n)+1]} \qquad (8.6)$$

where $E' = (x/\delta)^{1/n}$ = shield cutoff energy (Mev). This expression exhibits an energy peak flux of

$$\phi(E) \, dE = A\alpha \left( \frac{\delta}{x} \right)^{(\alpha+1)/n} \left[ \frac{(n-1)^{(n-1)/n}(\alpha+1)^{(\alpha+1)/n}}{(n+\alpha)^{(\alpha+n)/n}} \right] \qquad (8.7)$$

at

$$E = \frac{x}{\delta} \left( \frac{n-1}{\alpha+1} \right)^{1/n} \qquad (8.8)$$

For the Bailey model event $A = 1.56 \times 10^{16}$ and $\alpha = 4$ *(note, $A = a/(\alpha')^2$)*.

If the shield is $x$ gm/cm² aluminum $(n = 1.73; \delta = 3.47 \times 10^{-3})$, Eq. (8.6) reduces to

$$\phi(E) \, dE = \frac{6.25 \times 10^{16} E^{0.73}}{[E^{1.73} + 288x]^{3.3}} \qquad (8.9)$$

This function is shown in Fig. 8-1 for $x = 1, 2,$ and 3 gm/cm². For other materials, the shape is quite similar.

In order to obtain the dose $(D)$ behind 1 gm/cm² aluminum due to primary protons for the Bailey model event, the following integral is evaluated:

$$D = \int_0^\infty \phi(E')C(E') \, dE' \qquad (8.10)$$

where $D$ = primary proton dose (Rad), $C(E)$ = flux-to-dose conversion

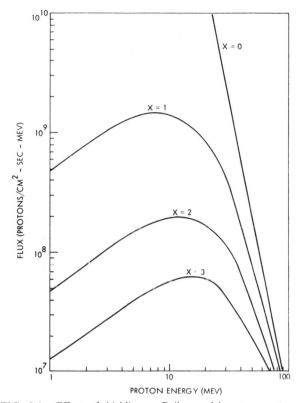

FIG. 8-1.  Effects of shielding on Bailey model proton spectrum.

function $= B_1 E^{-C_1} + B_2 E^{C_2}$, and $\phi(E) =$ expression given by Eq. 8-9. Values of $B_1, B_2, C_1$, and $C_2$ are listed in Table 4-3.

Unfortunately, due to the nonintegral power of $E$, the expression cannot be integrated in closed form and leads to the Beta function. A nomogram [2] and a circular slide rule [3] based upon the Beta function have been prepared. However, for thin shields, essentially (within $\pm 20\%$) the same answer is obtained by using the following relationship [1, 4]:

$$D(x) = 2 \int_{E_{\text{cutoff}}}^{\infty} \phi(E)C(E)\, dE \qquad (8.11)$$

where $\phi(E)$ is the primary spectrum prior to penetrating the shield, $E_{\text{cutoff}} = (x/\delta)^{1/n}$, and $x =$ shield thickness.

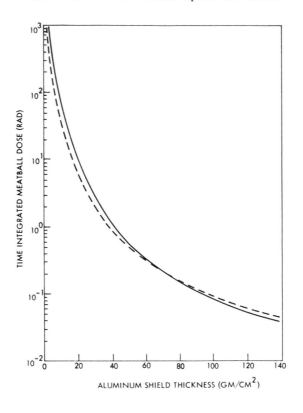

FIG. 8-2. Effects of shielding on Bailey model proton dose.

By using the above shortcut, one obtains

$$D_{\text{Rad}} = \frac{1 \times 10^{11}}{(E')^{4.8}} + \frac{2.4 \times 10^7}{(E')^{3.15}} \qquad (8.12)$$

$$D_{\text{Rad}} = \frac{1.5 \times 10^4}{x^{2.78}} + \frac{8 \times 10^2}{x^{1.82}} \quad \text{for aluminum}$$

This function (shown in Fig. 8-2) agrees well with the computer calculations for shields $\lesssim 30$ gm/cm². For thicker shields, it predicts high, reaching a factor of 2 at 60 gm/cm$^2$. Since most spacecraft designs employ $\lesssim 10$ gm/cm$^2$ shielding, this is not a serious limitation.

It is interesting to calculate the proton dose rates (D.R.) due to the Bailey model flare. Here the straightforward approach would be to evaluate the integral,

$$\text{D.R.}(t, x) = \int_0^\infty \phi(E', t, x)C(E')\,dE'$$

where $\phi(E', t, x)$ is obtained by substituting Eq. 8-5 in Eq. 8-2.

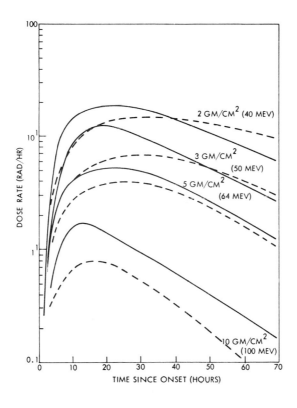

CALCULATED BY COMPUTER
CALCULATED ANALYTICALLY

FIG. 8-3.  Proton dose rates for Bailey model event.

Again, since this leads to a complicated expression, it is tempting to try a similar shortcut. By analogy one could write

$$\text{D.R.}(x, t) = 2 \int_{E_{\text{cutoff}}}^{\infty} \phi(E, t) C(E)\, dE$$

where $\phi(E, t)$ is given by Eq. 8.2.

However the results are less satisfactory than expected (Fig. 8-3). The advantage of the shortcut (making the integrand simple enough to be evaluated in closed form) is not apparent when dealing with dose rates. Fortunately the dose rates due to solar flares are sufficiently small that it is the total dose that is of primary concern.

The Bailey model is for a very large event ($> 10^{10}$ protons/cm$^2$ above 30 Mev), and no single flare of this magnitude has ever been observed. The characteristics of the nuclear radiation (protons and alpha particles) of flares which have been observed for the period 1956–1961 has been tabulated by Webber [5] and others.

An analysis of this data obtained for individual solar flares leads to the following mathematical expressions [6]:

$$\phi(E > E_0, t) = \frac{At \exp[-\alpha E_0^n t]}{E_0^m} \tag{8.13}$$

$$\phi(E, t)\, dE = \frac{At \exp[-\alpha E^n t](\alpha nt E^n + m)}{E^{m+1}} \tag{8.14}$$

$$\phi(E > E_0) = \frac{A}{\alpha^2 E^{m+2n}} = \frac{2100\, A}{E_0^{1.55}} \tag{8.15}$$

$$\phi(E)\, dE = \frac{(m + 2n)\, A}{\alpha^2 E^{m+2n+1}} = \frac{3200\, A}{E_0^{2.55}} \tag{8.16}$$

$$\hat{\phi}(E > E_0) = \frac{17\, A}{E_0^{1.15}} \tag{8.17}$$

where $\alpha = 0.022$, $m = 0.75$, $n = 0.4$—and all three are constants, and $A$ = normalization constant.

In order to calculate the primary proton dose due to a flare, the procedure is (as before) to evaluate the integral:

$$D(X) = \int_0^\infty \phi(E', x)C(E')\,dE'$$

where

$$\phi(E', x) = \frac{3200\,A\,(E')^{n-1}}{\left[(E')^n + \dfrac{x}{\delta}\right]^{1+(1.55/n)}}$$

$$C(E') = B_1(E')^{-C_1} + B_2(E')^{C_2}$$

However, (as before), the foregoing may be closely approximated by the integral,

$$D(X) = 2 \int_{E_c = (x/\delta)^{1/n}}^\infty \phi(E, 0)C(E)\,dE$$

The result of evaluating the above equation is

$$\frac{D}{A} - \frac{1.1 \times 10^{-2}}{(x/\delta)^{2.35/n}} + \frac{5.6 \times 10^{-6}}{(x/\delta)^{0.7/n}} \tag{8.18}$$

For aluminum, the above expression reduces to

$$\frac{D}{A} = \frac{5 \times 10^{-6}}{x^{1.35}} + \frac{5.6 \times 10^{-7}}{x^{0.4}}$$

For an event of $10^{10}$ protons/cm$^2$ above 30 Mev ($A = 9.3 \times 10^8$), the point dosimeter proton dose expected inside a uniform spherical shield of aluminum is shown in Fig. 8-4. The proton doses expected for events of other sizes may be obtained by scaling.

There is a simple relationship between proton dose due to solar events and the proton flux above the shield cutoff energy. This relationship, obtained by substituting Eq. 8-15 into Eq. (8-18) is

$$\frac{D(\text{Rad})}{\phi(E > E_c)\,(\text{protons/cm}^2)} = \frac{5.2 \times 10^{-6}}{(x/\delta)^{0.8/n}} + 2.7 \times 10^{-9} \left(\frac{x}{\delta}\right)^{0.85/n} \tag{8.19}$$

For aluminum, the relationship is shown in Fig. 8-5.

Other analytical approaches have been developed for calculating the proton doses inside spherical shields due to solar flares. Burrell [7] uses an improved fit to the range-energy relation, viz.,

$$R(E) = \frac{a}{2b}\ln(1 + 2bE^r) \tag{8.20}$$

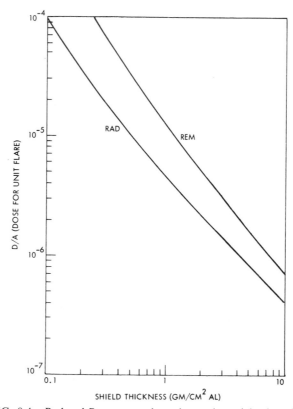

FIG. 8-4.   Rad and Rem proton doses due to size-weighted model flare.

where $a$, $b$, and $r$ are constants. Either a differential power law spectrum or an integral rigidity spectrum can be combined with the above range-energy relation to yield the degraded proton spectrum after passage through the shield. Nuclear interactions are taken into account by an exponential term employing an energy-independent inelastic cross section. The flux-to-dose conversion function is based upon the proton stopping power of tissue. The proton Rad doses as a function of aluminum shield thickness have been obtained in this manner for flares and trapped radiation. The application of the method to multilayer shields is also discussed.

A different analytical approach was taken by Nakache [8] who considered a spherical tissue phantom centered inside a spherical shield composed of

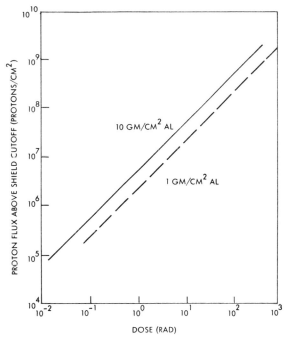

FIG. 8-5.    Relationship between flare dose and flux above shield cutoff for protons.

concentric layers. The conventional fit to the proton range-energy relation was used, but the shield thickness as a function of angle $t(\phi)$ was approximated by an expression of the form,

$$t = t_0 + K \sin^2 \phi$$

where $\phi$ is the polar angle and $t_0$ and $K$ are constants. A power law incident spectrum was assumed. The primary proton dose as a function of radius inside the spherical phantom was calculated analytically for the flare of May 10, 1959, and compared with computer calculations. The agreement was very good so long as the radius of the phantom did not approach that of the shield. For such situations the approximation used to obtain the shield thickness as a function of angle introduces errors.

In dealing with effects of radiation on humans, it is necessary to obtain doses in Rem rather than rad. The relationship is

$$Rem = rad \times RBE$$

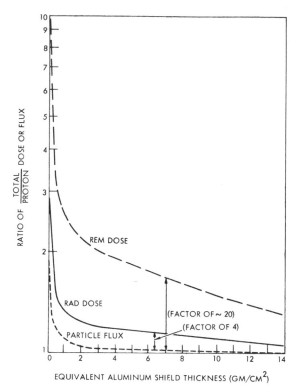

FIG. 8-6.   Alpha particle correction factors for solar flares.

where the RBE (relative biological effectiveness) is as discussed in Chapter IV. For protons which exhibit $E^{-\alpha}$ energy spectra, an expression for the RBE as a function of the exponent $\alpha$ and the shield thickness $x$ (gm/cm$^2$) was obtained. Applying that relationship to the solar flare analysis presented above ($\alpha = 1.55$) leads to values of the RBE from which rem doses due to flares can be calculated. The results of such calculations are also shown in Fig. 8-4.

In this chapter so far, only protons arising from solar flares have been considered. A considerable amount of data shows that alpha particles are also emitted [6]. A recent study [10] of such data as tabulated by Webber [5] shows that protons and alpha particles emitted during solar flares have essentially the same spectral shape, with 1.2 protons/alpha particle being emitted at any given energy. The rise and characteristic decay times appear to be identical, and the peak flux rates also show the ratio of 1.2. Thus, in the absence of any shielding, the particle flux at any energy is increased 83 %.

However, the relative importance of solar flare alpha particles is decreased by shielding. An alpha particle requires four times the energy of a proton to have the same range as the proton. Since the ratio of protons of energy $E$ to alpha particles of energy $4E$ increases as $E$ increases, the ratio of protons/ alpha particles increases as does the shielding thickness. Because of the specific ionization ratio the rad dose contribution of each penetrating alpha particle will be four times that of each penetrating proton, however. There- fore, the ratio of rad dose due to penetrating alpha particles to that due to penetrating protons is four times the corresponding particle flux ratio. When the RBE is taken into account, it is seen that the Rem dose effectiveness of an alpha particle of energy $4E$ is about 20 times that of a proton of energy $E$. Thus, to take account of the alpha particles emitted during solar flares, it is necessary to multiply the proton fluxes and doses by a factor which depends upon the quantity considered (particle flux, rad dose, or Rem dose) and upon the equivalent aluminum shielding thickness present. These factors are shown in Fig. 8-6.

This analysis of solar flare nuclear radiation has been used to calculate the rad and rem doses produced by the eight largest events of the 1956–1961 period. The proton rad doses were calculated using the following relation- ships, which were derived from Eq. 8-18.

$$\text{rad dose } (1 \text{ gm/cm}^2) = 5 \times 10^{-7} \phi \left( \frac{P}{\text{cm}^2} > 30 \text{ Mev} \right)$$

$$\text{rad dose } (10 \text{ gm/cm}^2) = 2 \times 10^{-7} \phi \left( \frac{P}{\text{cm}^2} > 100 \text{ Mev} \right)$$

(8.21)

Proton rad doses for shield thicknesses between 1–10 gm/cm$^2$ were obtained by interpolation. Proton Rem doses were obtained by multiplying the proton rad doses by appropriate RBE factors (Table 8-1).

Alpha particle rad and rem doses were obtained from the corresponding proton quantities by using the calculations presented in Fig. 8-6. The alpha particle portion is, of course, the additive amount by which the factors shown exceed unity.

The proton and alpha particle rad and rem doses calculated this way are

TABLE 8-1

MULTIPLICATIVE FACTORS FOR SOLAR FLARE DOSE CONVERSION

|  | 0.1 gm/cm$^2$ | 1 gm/cm$^2$ | 10 gm/cm$^2$ |
|---|---|---|---|
| rad $(P)$ to rad $(P + \alpha)$ | 4.2 | 1.45 | 1.1 |
| rad $(P)$ to Rem $(P)$ | 2.2 | 1.5 | 1.1 |
| rad $(P)$ to Rem $(P + \alpha)$ | 18 | 4.0 | 1.65 |
| Rem $(P)$ to Rem $(P + \alpha)$ | 8.3 | 2.7 | 1.5 |
| rad $(P + \alpha)$ to Rem $(P + \alpha)$ | 4.3 | 3.0 | 1.5 |
| Rem $(P)$ to rad $(P + \alpha)$ | 1.9 | 0.9 | 1.0 |

listed in Table 8-2. Since the present analysis was based largely on the work of Webber [5], the rad results are generally in good agreement with his. The one exception is for the flare of 2/23/56, for which the present analysis indicates a higher proton dose (500 rad versus 280 rad) and a lower alpha particle dose (160 rad versus 710 rad) [9]. This is probably due to the relativistic (nontypical) characteristics of that flare, while the present analysis was based on the weighted statistical averages of forty-three large flares (mostly nonrelativistic). Rem flare doses have not been published, so no comparisons with the calculated Rem doses of Table 8-2 were possible.

The role of alpha particles in solar flare dose calculations inside a typical spacecraft has been investigated by Schaefer [11], Robbins [12], and Raymes [13]. Schaefer [11] used a spherical approximation to the command module and a 30 cm diameter spherical phantom for his calculations. For the Bailey model flare, he calculated that $\sim 10\%$ of the skin dose rate of $\sim 1$ rad/hr was due to alpha particles. His calculations showed that this fraction decreased monotonically as tissue depth increased. Robbins [12] also used a spherical geometry code to approximate the Apollo command module. An exponential rigidity flare spectrum was assumed, yielding skin (surface) and blood-forming-organ ($\sim 5$ cm) doses for both protons and alpha particles as a function of the characteristic rigidity $P_0$. For values of $P_0 \gtrsim 160$ Mv, Robbins found that the alpha particle skin dose exceeded the proton skin dose. The fraction of the blood-forming-organ dose due to alpha particles also increased with characteristic rigidity, reaching $\sim 20\%$ for $P_0 = 160$. Corresponding calculations for the LEM showed that the alpha particles were relatively even more important. These conclusions are supported by the work of Raymes [13] who used a modified Monte Carlo

TABLE 8-2

RAD AND REM DOSES FOR EIGHT LARGE OBSERVED FLARES[a]

| Event date | Rad doses | | | | Rem doses | | | |
|---|---|---|---|---|---|---|---|---|
| | 1 gm/cm² | 2 gm/cm² | 5 gm/cm² | 10 gm/cm² | 1 gm/cm² | 2 gm/cm² | 5 gm/cm² | 10 gm/cm² |
| 2/23/56 | 500 | 250 | 120 | 70 | 750 | 325 | 145 | 77 |
| | 160 | 58 | 20 | 7 | 1200 | 370 | 115 | 39 |
| 5/10/59 | 480 | 145 | 37 | 17 | 720 | 190 | 44 | 19 |
| | 152 | 34 | 6.1 | 1.7 | 1080 | 220 | 35 | 10 |
| 7/10/59 | 500 | 185 | 56 | 28 | 750 | 240 | 67 | 31 |
| | 160 | 44 | 9.3 | 2.8 | 1200 | 280 | 53 | 16 |
| 7/14/59 | 650 | 200 | 45 | 20 | 980 | 260 | 54 | 22 |
| | 200 | 47 | 7.5 | 2.0 | 1560 | 300 | 43 | 11 |
| 7/16/59 | 455 | 145 | 47 | 26 | 680 | 190 | 56 | 29 |
| | 144 | 34 | 7.8 | 2.6 | 1020 | 220 | 45 | 15 |
| 11/12/60 | 650 | 270 | 100 | 50 | 980 | 350 | 120 | 55 |
| | 200 | 63 | 17 | 5.0 | 1560 | 400 | 100 | 28 |
| 11/15/60 | 360 | 145 | 50 | 24 | 540 | 190 | 60 | 26 |
| | 115 | 34 | 8.3 | 2.4 | 865 | 220 | 48 | 13 |
| 11/18/61 | 150 | 58 | 19 | 8 | 225 | 75 | 23 | 8.8 |
| | 48 | 14 | 3.1 | 0.8 | 360 | 86 | 18 | 4.4 |

[a] The top number is the proton dose, the bottom is the alpha particle dose

program which described the Apollo command module rather accurately. His calculations also showed that even allowing for various secondary radiations the skin and blood-forming-organ doses expected on the Apollo mission are appreciably less than the allowable limits.

One other aspects of the calculations must be considered—the doses upon human beings in an actual spacecraft as contrasted to the doses at the center of a uniform spherical shield. Since the dose inside the latter is a maximum at the center (the focusing effect), off-center points will receive a lower dose. However, an analysis [14] shows that the focusing effect is < 10% for points < 70% off center (100% off center is against the inside

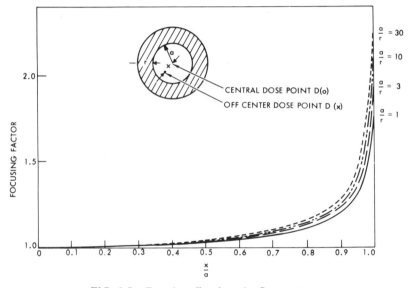

FIG. 8-7.   Focusing effect for solar flare protons.

wall; see Fig. 8-7). While actual spacecraft will generally have complicated shapes if the walls are of uniform equivalent thickness, it is a good approximation to consider the dose inside everywhere the same. For spacecraft whose walls vary in equivalent thickness, this is not true, since the solid angle of the thin section depends upon position considered inside the spacecraft. In this case, the interior dose will, in general, depend upon the thinnest section of the spacecraft.

Only primary particles (protons and alpha particles) due to solar flares have been considered so far. It is necessary to consider the role that secondary nucleons (cascade and evaporation neutrons and protons) play in contributing to the doses. Most calculations involving secondaries have been carried out using computer programs based upon differential cross sections and particle multiplicities. The results generally show that secondary particles are relatively unimportant from the standpoint of tissue rad dose for shield thicknesses $\lesssim 30$ gm/cm$^2$. A possible exception may occur when the primary protons have a range $< 30$ gm/cm$^?$, so that any dose received beyond the proton range is due to secondaries. Such a situation could occur when

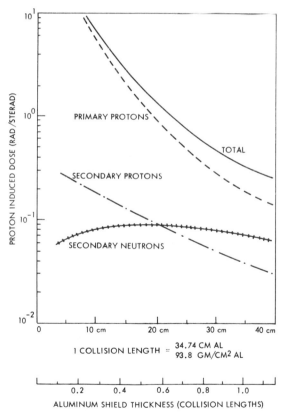

FIG. 8-8. Primary and secondary doses due to protons of 5/10/59 flare.

dealing with monoenergetic incident protons. For solar flare protons, which exhibit a continuous spectrum, there will always be some protons penetrating any reasonable spacecraft shielding, and these penetrating protons will usually be more important in producing a rad dose than the secondaries. This is shown in Fig. 8-8, which presents the results of a computer dose calculation for the solar flare of May 10, 1959 [15]. Other solar flare calculations exhibit similar dose-versus-distance relationships. Thus secondary nucleons may generally be neglected in rad dose calculations for shields $\lesssim 30$ gm/cm$^2$.

Secondary gamma rays due to solar flare protons are probably not a major threat, although the exact magnitude of the doses they produce is unknown at the present time. The calculations of Madey *et al.* [16] indicated

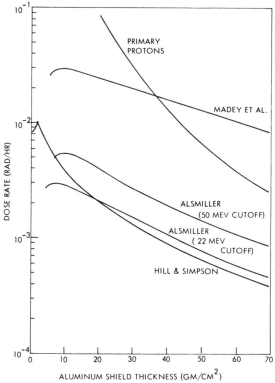

FIG. 8-9.  Secondary gamma ray doses for flare of 5/10/59.

that for aluminum shields of $\sim 30$ gm/cm$^2$ the gamma ray rad dose might equal the proton dose. Alsmiller *et al.* [17] carried out a similar calculation for aluminum shields, obtaining gamma ray dose rates approximately an order of magnitude lower. Deutsch [18] calculated the secondary gamma ray dose rate for a carbon shield and also obtained lower results. All three groups apparently used the same proton source spectrum but different inelastic scattering cross sections.

More recently Hill and Simpson [19] applied a modification of the LIGHT code (the DLIGHT code) to the secondary gamma ray problem. Their results agree fairly well with those of Alsmiller *et al.* [17] (Fig. 8-9). The DLIGHT code has also been used to calculate the gamma ray spectra obtained by Zobel *et al.* [20] from $\sim 160$ Mev protons on C, O, and Al with very good results. It would therefore appear that the gamma rays constitute at most a slight percentage of the total dose for spacecraft $< 20$ gm/cm$^2$.

It must be pointed out that the calculations of secondaries due to solar flare particles are almost always concerned with proton-induced reactions. The substructure of the alpha particle makes theoretical analysis of alpha particle secondaries difficult, and the lack of suitable accelerators has prevented the experimental work necessary to establish cross sections, energy thresholds, particle multiplicities, and so forth. It is quite possible that alpha particle secondaries may be important dose contributors, as the various $(\alpha, n)$ reactions known at low energies suggest [21]. More work is obviously needed to clarify the dose role of solar flare alpha particles.

The doses so far have been point doses—the dose a point isotropic tissue equivalent dosimeter would read if centered inside a spherical shield of uniform thickness. From the biological standpoint, the point dosimeter doses are obviously higher than the doses to any portion of the human body because of the self-shielding of the latter. For the skin, the point dosimeter doses should be divided by a factor of 2. For the blood-forming organs, which lie on the average 4–5 cm below the surface of the skin, the doses may be found by adding this thickness of tissue to the shielding of the spacecraft and taking 50% of the doses thus obtained. While some radiation will reach the skin and the blood-forming organs from all directions, the bulk ($\sim 90\%$) of the dose will come from a $2\pi$ solid angle. A series of calculations by Dye show the dose distribution as a function of tissue depth behind 1, 2, 5, and 10 gm/cm$^2$ of aluminum [22]. The results are presented for various $E^{-n}$ differential energy spectra with values of $n$ from 2 to 5. While individual solar flare radiations detected at the earth exhibit a range of *n*-values, the size-weighted solar proton fluxes appear to have an *n*-value of ~2.5. Taking the depth of the blood-forming organs to be 4 cm leads to the ratios shown in Fig. 8-10. Thus the skin dose can be taken as ~0.5 the point dose and the blood-forming-organ dose can be estimated using the ratios of Fig. 8-10. While the results are only approximate and the complicated geometry of a typical spacecraft often makes use of the worst point concept necessary, estimating skin and blood-forming-organ doses this way is useful for mission analysis.

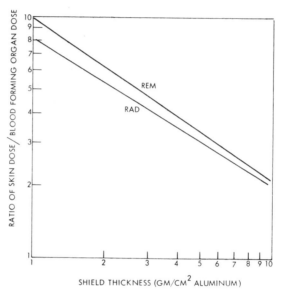

FIG. 8-10.   Ratio of skin-to-blood-forming-organ dose for protons of size-weighted model flare.

## B.   Trapped (Van Allen) Radiation

As discussed in the chapter on the Van Allen belts, the proton differential energy spectra have been mathematically fitted by expressions of the form [23, 24],

$$\phi(E)\,dE = \text{const} \exp[-E/E_0]\,dE \qquad (8.22)$$

where $E_0 = c_1 L^{-c_2}$, $L$ is the McIlwain coordinate, and $c_1$ and $c_2$ are constants.

The difficulty with such expressions is that using them to calculate electron doses requires a computer, because they cannot be integrated by hand in closed form. Electron Van Allen spectra have not been found to be describable by any simple relationship. Since the spatial dependence of the energy spectra is not great and there are theoretical reasons for expecting the electrons and protons at a given spatial location for having the same $E/m$ dependence, one can write [25]

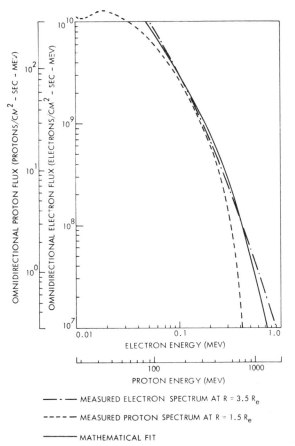

FIG. 8-11. Fit to differential $p^+$ and $e^-$ Van Allen energy spectra.

$$\phi(E)\,dE = \frac{4.5 \times 10^8}{m^{2.31}} \left[ \left(\frac{E}{m}\right)^{-1.5} - \left(\frac{E}{m}\right)^{-1.4} \right] \qquad (8.23)$$

where $m$ is the particle mass (in units of $m_0$).

As can be seen in Fig. 8-11, this expression fits the peak spectra fairly well. The somewhat different shapes of the proton and electron spectra may be due to neglecting the spatial ($L$) dependence. By integrating this expression from $E_0$ to the upper limit at which it goes to zero (1 Mev for electrons, 1836 Mev for protons), the following expression is obtained:

$$\phi(E > E_0) = \frac{9.0 \times 10^8}{m^{1.31}} \left[ \left(\frac{E_0}{m}\right)^{-0.5} - 1.25 \left(\frac{E_0}{m}\right)^{-0.4} + 0.25 \right] \qquad (8.24)$$

For electrons $m = 1$, so this reduces to

$$\phi(E > E_0) = \frac{9.0 \times 10^8}{E_0^{0.5}} - \frac{1.125 \times 10^9}{E_0^{0.4}} + 2.25 \times 10^8$$

For protons $m = 1836$, so the result becomes

$$\phi(E > E_0) = \frac{2.0 \times 10^6}{E_0^{0.5}} - \frac{1.2 \times 10^6}{E_0^{0.4}} + 1.2 \times 10^4$$

These equations predict an electron flux of $6.2 \times 10^8$ electrons/cm$^2$ above 40 kev and a proton flux of $2.4 \times 10^4$ proton/cm$^2$ above 100 Mev. As can be seen, these correspond to conservative peak values for the respective belts.

The dose calculation consists of evaluating the integral,

$$D(x) = 2 \int_{E' = (x/\delta)^{1/n}}^{(E/m) = 1} \phi(E)C(E)\,dE \qquad (8.25)$$

where $\phi(E)$ is the differential energy spectrum and $C(E)$ is the flux-to-dose conversion function. The logic for this approach is discussed in the preceding section on doses due to solar flares. The integral yields

$$D_p \left(\frac{\text{rad}}{\text{sec}}\right) = \frac{3.38}{(E')^{1.3}} - \frac{1.73}{(E')^{1.2}}$$
$$+ 7 \times 10^{-4}(E')^{0.45} - 1.9 \times 10^{-3}(E')^{0.35} + 5.8 \times 10^{-3}$$

$$\qquad (8.26)$$

$$D_e \left(\frac{\text{rad}}{\text{sec}}\right) = \frac{1.93}{(E')^{1.4}} - \frac{2.08}{(E')^{1.3}} + \frac{32}{(E')^{0.35}} - \frac{44.8}{(E')^{0.25}} + 12.95$$

where $D_p$ is the proton dose rate at peak of proton belt ($r = 1.5 R_e$), $D_e$ the electron dose rate at peak of electron belt ($r = 3.5 R_e$), and $E'$ the shield cutoff energy (Mev) $= (x/\delta)^{1/n}$.

The particle dose rates are plotted in Fig. 8-12 for aluminum. The electron

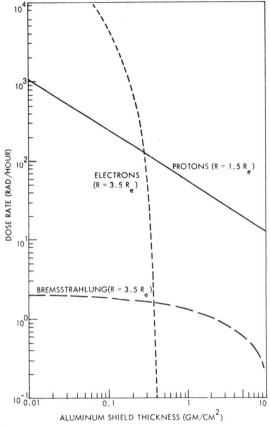

FIG. 8-12.   Dose rates due to $p^+$ and $e^-$ Van Allen radiation.

dose rate drops off rapidly as the shield cutoff energy approaches 1 Mev (0.4 gm/cm² aluminum). The proton dose rate behaves similarly for shield thicknesses on the order of a few hundred gm/cm² aluminum.

While proton-induced secondary radiations may be neglected for shields whose thicknesses are on the order of 10 gm/cm$^2$ or less, the electron-produced bremsstrahlung becomes important for shields $\gtrsim 0.5$ gm/cm$^2$. The bremsstrahlung energy flux $[\phi_\gamma(E)]$ is:

$$E_\gamma \phi_\gamma(E_\gamma) = \int E_e \phi_e(\widehat{E}_e) \, \mathscr{E} \, (E_e, Z) \, dE_e = 1.2 \times 10^6 \frac{\text{Mev}}{\text{cm}^2 \text{sec}} \quad (8.27)$$

where $\mathscr{E} \, (E_e, Z) \cong 7 \times 10^{-3} Z E_e$.

The bremsstrahlung dose rate is obtained by attenuating this energy flux through the spacecraft wall. Due to the $1/\lambda^2$ distribution, the average energy of each bremsstrahlung photon is

$$\bar{E}_\gamma \sim \tfrac{3}{4} \bar{E}_e$$

where $\bar{E}_e$ is the average energy of the electrons producing it. The average energy of the electrons producing bremsstrahlung is

$$E_e \cong \frac{\int E_e^2 \phi_e(E_e) \, dE_e}{\int \phi_e(E_e) \, dE_e} \cong 90 \text{ kev}$$

The extra factor of $E_e$ in the numerator is due to the linear dependence of bremsstrahlung production with electron energy. The relaxation length of the 67 kev bremsstrahlung photons in aluminum is $\sim 4.2$ gm/cm$^2$. Therefore, if the electron flux is entirely converted to bremsstrahlung photons at the outer surface of an aluminum spacecraft, the bremsstrahlung dose rate inside is

$$DR \cong E_\gamma \phi_\gamma C_\gamma(E_\gamma) e^{-x/\lambda} = 2.0 e^{-x/4.2} \text{ rad/hr} \quad (8.28)$$

where $x$ is the shield thickness (gm/cm$^2$).

This function is also shown in Fig. 8-12. As can be seen, the assumption that all electrons produced bremsstrahlung photons at the outer surface of the spacecraft is conservative, since the electron energy flux is attenuated more rapidly than the photon energy flux.

Several other calculations of dose rates due to the trapped (Van Allen) radiation have been carried out. Most of them deal with specific orbits; these are discussed in the last chapter, since the radiation environment over any gravitational orbit is not a constant.

Burrell [7] calculated the proton rad dose due to the Freden–White spectrum. His analytical approach has been described earlier in this chapter.

He obtained $\sim 10$ rad/hr at 3 gm/cm$^2$ tissue and $\sim 4$ rad/hr at 10 gm/cm$^2$ tissue, which corresponds to $\sim 5$ gm/cm$^2$ aluminum and $\sim 18$ gm/cm$^2$ aluminum respectively. This is roughly a factor of 2 lower than the calculations presented earlier (Fig. 8-12). This affords an estimate of the errors introduced by the approximate fit to the Freden–White spectrum.

A series of computer calculations of the Van Allen electron and bremsstrahlung dose rates have been carried out by Russak [26] for six different incident electron spectra. The bremsstrahlung was considered to be produced continuously throughout the shield, and the calculated dose rates showed that the relative importance of the bremsstrahlung is quite dependent upon the shape of the electron spectrum used. Since a fission electron spectrum is appreciably harder than the natural electron spectrum, a nuclear detonation in the Van Allen belts may increase the dose rates expected as much as an order of magnitude or more.

Focusing factors for fission (e.g., Starfish) electrons have been calculated for spherical shields by Moshofsky [27]. He assumed an exponential transmission dependence $(e^{-\beta t})$ on aluminum thickness $(t)$ to calculate the absorbed rad dose at a point. His results show a focusing factor which can be very approximately fit by the function,

$$\frac{D}{D_0} = 1 - \frac{\beta t}{8} \sin\left(\frac{\pi x}{2r}\right) \tag{8.29}$$

where $D$ is the dose at a distance $X$ from center of the shield (rad), $D_0$ the dose at the center of the shield (rad), $r$ the inner radius of the shield, and $\beta \sim 3$ cm$^2$/gm.

For natural (nonfission) Van Allen electrons, the focusing factor would be much greater, because their energy spectrum is softer. However for shields $\gtrsim 1$ gm/cm$^2$ the bremsstrahlung dose rates exceed the electron dose rates, and the bremsstrahlung will exhibit a focusing factor of $\sim 1$ for essentially every case.

The RBE of the electrons and the bremsstrahlung photons they produce is unity. For the protons, the RBE is a function of shield thickness. For shields $> 1$ gm/cm$^2$, the RBE can be taken as unity with an error of $\lesssim 15\%$.

## C. Galactic (Cosmic) Radiation

The energy spectra of the components of galactic radiation have been measured by various means [28, 29]. The integral proton energy spectrum may be fit by

$$\phi(E > E_0) = \frac{20}{5 + E_0^{1.5}} \tag{8.30}$$

where $E$ is in Bev. The corresponding proton differential energy spectrum then is

$$\phi(E)\,dE = \frac{30\sqrt{E}}{[5 + E^{\frac{3}{2}}]^2}\,dE \tag{8.31}$$

This function exhibits a peak at $E = 1$ Bev which agrees with the few available measurements of the differential energy spectrum. As $E$ becomes large, the integral spectrum becomes an $E^{-\alpha}$ type, where $\alpha = 1.5$.

The free-space unshielded dose rate due to the galactic radiation may be computed by evaluating the integral

$$D = \int_0^\infty \phi(E)C(E)\,dE$$

where $C(E)$ is the flux to dose conversion factor (rad–cm$^2$/proton).

While the energy region over which $C(E)$ is known to apply for protons is 1–1000 Mev, it was assumed that the flux-to-dose conversion function held above that. The integral was evaluated graphically, because analytical integration in closed form was not possible. The result was 50 mrad/day, in good agreement with the measured value of 45 mrad/day during periods of minimum solar activity [29]. This indicates that the neglect of the other components of the galactic radiation is approximately balanced by the conservatism of the extrapolated flux-to-dose conversion function.

The energies of the galactic protons are so high that nuclear interactions rather than ionization are the major attenuation mechanism. At 1 Bev, for example, a range of $\gtrsim 500$ gm/cm$^2$ in aluminum would result if ionization were the only attenuation mechanism, while nuclear interactions yield a range of $\sim 110$ gm/cm$^2$ aluminum.

The dose rate to primary galactic protons is

$$D \cong 50e^{-n\sigma x}$$

where $D$ is the dose rate (mrad/day), $\sigma$ the cross section due to nuclear interactions (cm$^2$/atom), $n$ the number of nuclei/gm, and $x$ the shield thickness (gm/cm$^2$).

To obtain the above equation, integration over energy was not necessary, because the cross sections for nuclear interactions are essentially constant above $\sim 150$ Mev [30, 31]. The neglect of the disturbance of the low-energy portion of the galactic spectrum due to ionization results in an error $\lesssim 10\%$ in the dose rate.

Since nuclear (cascade and evaporation) interactions are the main attenuation mechanisms [32], the interaction products (protons and neutrons) must also be taken into account. The flux of each component of the nuclear secondaries is

$$\phi_i(E', x) = \int_0^x v n \sigma \phi(E, x)\, dx \qquad (8.32)$$

where $\phi_i(E', x)$ is the flux (particles/cm$^2$–Mev) of one type of secondary particles of energy $E'$ at a shield depth of $x$ (gm/cm$^2$), $v$ the number of one type of secondary particles per interaction, and $\phi(E, x)$ the primary galactic flux (proton/cm$^2$–Mev).

For aluminum,

$$
\begin{array}{lll}
v(\text{cascade protons}) & = \ \sim 1.8 & (0.3\ E_p) \\
v(\text{cascade neutrons}) & = \ \sim 1.5 & (0.3\ E_p) \\
v(\text{evaporation protons}) & = \ \sim 0.8 & (8.8\ \text{Mev}) \\
v(\text{evaporation neutrons}) & = \ \sim 2.5 & (4.0\ \text{Mev})
\end{array}
$$

The cascade products in aluminum have an energy of $\sim 30\%$ of the primary protons, while the evaporation products have the energies given above.

In any material, the number of secondary protons will increase approximately linearly until those born at the outer shield surface have reached their range $(R)$, whereupon the number of secondary particles will decrease exponentially at the same rate as the primary protons. For secondary neutrons, the behavior is similar, except that their attenuation after being born is approximately exponential. At shield penetrations on the order of a relaxation length, neutrons will begin showing the exponential decrease governed by the attenuation of the primary protons. The mathematics is quite similar to the Bateman equations which describe the formation and decay of products in a radioactive series [33].

The equation describing the secondary dose rates due to galactic protons is

$$D_i(x) = \int_0^E \phi(E', x) C(E')\, dE'$$

where $i$ is the type of secondary (evaporation neutrons, cascade protons, and so on).

A reasonable approximation is to assume that the secondary dose contributions vary like the flux of the secondaries, since all but the evaporation proton component are attenuated by having the number flux, rather than the particle energy, decreased.

For aluminum, use of the assumption yields [34]

$$D_{\text{cascade protons}} = 95\,(1 - e^{-\Sigma x})\,\frac{\text{mrad}}{\text{day}}\,(0 \leqslant x \leqslant 65)$$

$$D_{\text{evaporation protons}} = 190\,(1 - e^{-\Sigma x})\,\frac{\text{mrad}}{\text{day}}\,(0 \leqslant x \leqslant 0.15)$$

$$D_{\text{cascade neutrons}} = 23\,(1 - e^{-\Sigma x})\,\frac{\text{mrad}}{\text{day}}\,(0 \leqslant x \leqslant 65)$$

$$D_{\text{evaporation neutrons}} = 10\,(1 - e^{-\Sigma x})\,\frac{\text{mrad}}{\text{day}}\,(0 \leqslant x \leqslant 19)$$

where $\Sigma = 9.1 \times 10^{-3}$ cm$^2$/gm.

For shield thicknesses greater than $R$, the exponential decrease of the primary protons is controlling. This results in secondary particle spectra whose shape does not change appreciably with increased shield penetration but whose magnitude decreases exponentially. The invariance of the spectral shape with distance results in the following relation:

$$D_i(x) = D_i(R)e^{-\Sigma(x-R)} \qquad (x \geqslant R)$$

For aluminum, the equations become [34]

$$D_{\text{cascade protons}} = 43\,e^{-\Sigma(x-65)}\ \text{mrad/day} \qquad (x \geqslant 65)$$
$$D_{\text{evaporation protons}} = 0.26\,e^{-\Sigma(x-0.15)}\ \text{mrad/day} \ (x \geqslant 0.15)$$
$$D_{\text{evaporation protons}} = 10\,e^{-\Sigma(x-65)}\ \text{mrad/day} \qquad (x \geqslant 65)$$
$$D_{\text{evaporation protons}} = 0.9\,e^{-\Sigma(x-19)}\ \text{mrad/day} \qquad (x \geqslant 19)$$

The primary proton and secondary particle dose rates are plotted in Fig. 8-13. It is seen that the total dose rate increases with shielding thickness until $\sim 80$ gm/cm$^2$ aluminum is reached. While for most materials the dose rate behaves similarly, using the usual relationship based on the range-energy relationship to convert to equivalent aluminum thickness is not valid

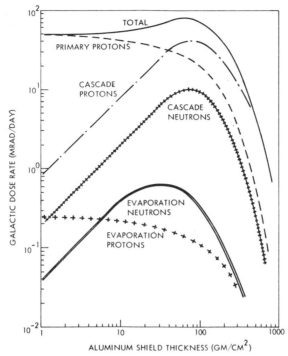

FIG. 8-13.  Galactic dose rate as a function of shield thickness.

here because the nuclear interaction properties do not follow any such simple law. For galactic radiation, the attenuation must be calculated for each different material. However, for typical spacecraft (1–10 gm/cm$^2$), the galactic radiation may be considered to contribute a dose rate of ∼50 mrad/day.

More and Tiffany have calculated the energy removal (rad) dose rates inside aluminum [35] and copper [36] shields due to galactic and solar flare proton-induced showers. The calculations were based on Monte Carlo techniques, although comparison calculations based upon simplified proton attenuation mechanisms were also carried out. Unfortunately the results presented do not separate galactic proton doses from solar flare proton doses, so not direct comparisons with the galactic doses calculated is here possible.

Due to the very high energy of the galactic radiation and the fact that secondary radiations are not important for shield thicknesses of the sort that will be encountered on spacecraft in the near future, the RBE of galactic radiation is often taken as unity. The very high energy removes the effects of geometry, and the focusing factor may be set equal to one for all positions within the spacecraft.

## EARTH SHIELDING

Two mechanisms act to limit the solar flare and galactic radiation arriving at any point within the Earth's atmosphere.

The first mechanism which acts to limit the radiation arriving at any point is the atmosphere itself. The protons and alpha particles which constitute the primary space radiations lose energy by ionization in the atmosphere. In this regard the atmosphere acts like any spacecraft shield of $\sim 1000$ gm/cm$^2$ (Fig. 8-14).

The second mechanism is the geomagnetic field which deflects charged particles not arriving along the earth's magnetic axis. The result is that there is a minimum momentum/unit charge which a particle must possess if it is to reach any given altitude and latitude [37]. Particles arriving at any point in question still possess (in the absence of the atmosphere) their original energy, however. The flux of such particles is only a fraction of the total which would otherwise be able to reach the point in question.

At any altitude and latitude, the actual energy spectrum is the result of the effects of both factors. These factors are discussed in the following sections of this chapter.

### A.   Atmospheric Effects

The Earth's atmosphere may be considered as a material shield against radiation in space. At the geomagnetic poles it is the only shield.

The attenuation of nuclear space radiation in the atmosphere is due to two mechanisms—atomic ionization and nuclear reactions. At low energies ($\lesssim 200$ Mev) atomic ionization predominates. For the attenuation of nuclear space radiation in the Earth's atmosphere, this corresponds to an altitude of $\sim 80,000$ feet. For protons which penetrate below this altitude, nuclear interactions become increasingly more important.

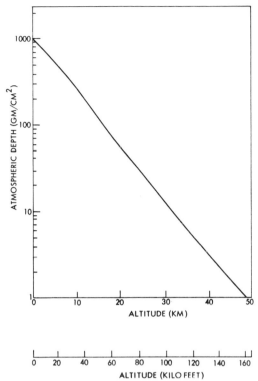

FIG. 8-14.   Thickness (gm/cm²) of Earth's atmosphere vs. altitude.

Nuclear reactions will produce secondary particles in the atmosphere. For protons in air, the nonelastic cross section (Fig. 8-15) and nuclear multiplicities (Figs. 8-16 and 8-17) are largely based on Bertini's theoretical work [38]. The cross section and the nuclear multiplicities become essentially constant above a few hundred million electron volts and were therefore extrapolated. The atmosphere was assumed to have a constant composition of 20% oxygen and 80% nitrogen, independent of altitude.

Two differences between the atomic ionization and the nuclear reaction attenuation mechanism should be noted. Ionization reduces the energy of each primary particle without affecting the flux of such particles, while nuclear reactions produce just the opposite effect. This is a consequence of the deterministic (i.e., good statistics) of the atomic ionization attenuation

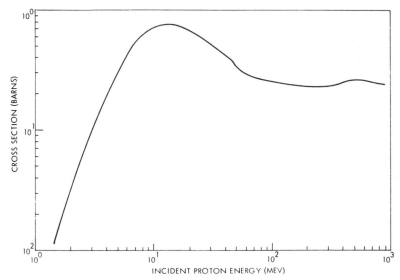

FIG. 8-15.    Proton nonelastic cross section for air.

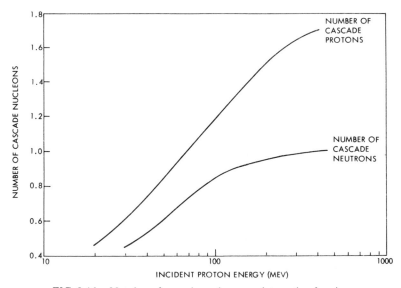

FIG. 8-16.    Number of cascade nucleons per interaction for air.

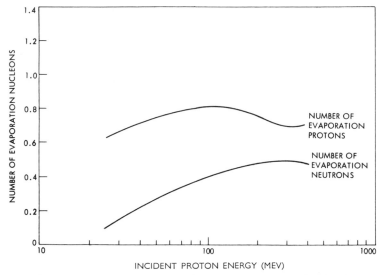

FIG. 8-17. Number of evaporation nucleons per interaction for air.

versus the probabilistic (i.e., poor statistics) of the nuclear reaction attenuation.

In order to facilitate the calculations, the attenuation of the atmosphere in the absence of the geomagnetic field is considered here. The flux ($\phi$) of the primary protons at any atmospheric depth was calculated from the relation,

$$\phi = \phi_0 e^{-n\sigma x/\rho} \text{ (protons/cm}^2\text{–hr–Mev)}$$

where $\phi$ is the incident flux, $n$ the nuclear density in the sea level atmosphere ($5 \times 10^{19}$ nuclei/cm$^3$), $\rho$ the sea level atmospheric density ($1.2 \times 10^{-3}$ gm/cm$^2$), and $x$ the atmospheric depth (gm/cm$^2$).

The surviving primary protons at any atmospheric depth will possess only approximately their incident energy, since ionization losses decrease it.

The dose rate $DR(X)$ due to primary galactic protons was calculated by using the expression,

$$DR(X) = \int_0^\infty \phi(E)C(E)\, dE$$

where $X$ is the atmosphere depth (gm/cm$^2$), and $C(E)$ the flux-to-rad-dose conversion factor.

In order to take the secondary nuclear products (cascade and evaporation nucleons) into account, it was necessary to evaluate expressions of the form,

$$\phi_{\text{secondary}}(E'', x) = \int_0^x v n \sigma(E' \to E'') \phi(E', x) \, dx$$

where $v$ is the number of one type of secondary particle per interaction (Figs. 8-16 and 8-17), $n$ the density of nuclei in the atmosphere, $\sigma(E' \to E'')$ the nonelastic number cross section (Fig. 8-15), and $\phi(E', x)$ the flux of primary protons.

For cascade products the nucleons were each assigned an energy $E'' = 0.3E'$ based upon the behavior of neighboring nuclei of carbon and aluminum [39]. For evaporation products, the proton energy was taken as 8 Mev, and the neutron energy as 4.5 Mev. Since the nuclear reaction products are less energetic than the primary protons, the fluxes and doses due to the secondaries will increase with atmospheric depth until an equilibrium is reached. For secondary protons, this equilibrium will occur at atmospheric depths equal to the ranges of these particles. For secondary neutrons, the equilibrium will occur near an atmospheric depth on the order of a collision-free path. Considering galactic protons whose primary energy spectrum has a maximum at $\sim 1$ Bev, the cascade and evaporation secondary protons peak at $\sim 50 \, \text{gm/cm}^2$ ($\sim 70,000$ feet) and $\sim 0.07 \, \text{gm/cm}^2$ ($\sim 150,000$ feet), respectively, while the secondary neutrons peak in the neighborhood of $\sim 70 \, \text{gm/cm}^2$ ($\sim 63,000$ feet) and $\sim 20 \, \text{gm/cm}^2$ ($\sim 88,000$ feet) respectively.

So far the attenuation calculations have been carried out for a point tissue-equivalent dosimeter centered inside a sphere composed of 80% nitrogen and 20% oxygen. For dose points in the Earth's atmosphere, the space radiations do not arrive isotropically but arrive in a vertical cone whose solid angle is $\sim 2\pi$ above the atmosphere and decreases as atmospheric depth increases. To a first approximation the cone is limited to those angles for which the slant path exceeds the vertical path by a relaxation length for the primary radiation. For a galactic protons, which have a relaxation length of $\sim 90 \, \text{gm/cm}^2$ in air, the effective solid angle was calculated using this approximation.

The galactic dose rates thus calculated as a function of atmospheric depth at the geomagnetic poles of the Earth are shown in Fig. 8-18 [39]. It is seen that secondary nucleons are calculated to be the chief dose contributors for atmospheric depths greater than $\sim 30 \, \text{gm/cm}^2$, and that at a depth of $\sim 50 \, \text{gm/cm}^2$ the calculated galactic dose rate is actually greater than that above the atmosphere.

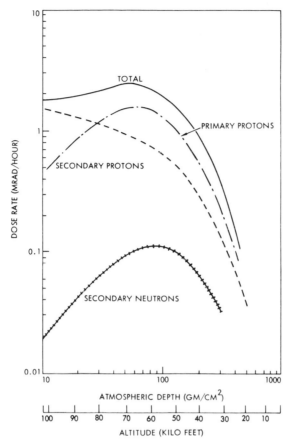

FIG. 8-18.  Calculated galactic radiation dose rate in Earth's atmosphere if no geomagnetic field.

A great many measurements of dose rates in the Earth's atmosphere have been carried out by balloon flights. For geomagnetic latitudes $\gtrsim 60$ deg the results obtained during solar minimums appear to be a function of atmospheric depth if isotropic detectors are used (so the east-west effect is averaged out). The measured particle fluxes are grouped into three classes— primary nucleons, hard secondaries, and soft secondaries. The soft secondaries are the most numerous for atmospheric depths $\lesssim 750 \, \mathrm{gm/cm^2}$ ($\gtrsim 10,000$ feet altitude), where the hard component takes over (Fig. 8-19) [29]. This soft component is composed of electron-positron showers which are pro-

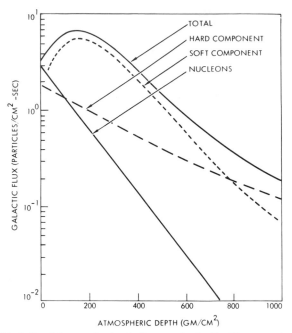

FIG. 8-19.   Measured galactic flux rate in the Earth's atmosphere.

duced by, and in turn produce, gamma rays. Such showers are produced from nucleon-nucleon collisions which yield unstable mesons decaying to initiate the electrons, positrons, and gamma rays.

The hard component consists mostly of those mesons which do not initiate electron-positron showers. Due to their greater penetrating capabilities, they are responsible for most of the observed sea level galactic dose rate.

In the absence of accurate energy spectra measurements, it is difficult to compare the measured particle fluxes with the calculated dose rates. However, if an average flux to dose conversion factor $\sim 1 \times 10^{-8}$ rad–cm$^2$/particle is used for the soft component, the peak dose rate is $\sim 45$ mrad/day, or $\sim 45$ mRem/day, since the RBE of the soft component is unity.

The choice of $1 \times 10^{-8}$ for the flux-to-dose conversion factor appears reasonable because photons do not reach this value $\lesssim 100$ Mev, while electrons do not fall below $3 \times 10^{-8}$ for any energy $\gtrsim 0.1$ Mev. In spite of the uncertainties involved in attempting this sort of comparison, it is reassuring to conclude that one obtains approximately the same peak measured and calculated galactic dose rates. The locations of the measured and calculated dose rate peaks do not agree nearly as well. The calculated peak at $\sim 60$ gm/cm$^2$ occurs at less than half the atmospheric depth of $\sim 150$ gm/cm$^2$ at which the peak was measured. Thus one may conclude that the neglect of mesons and their secondaries in the calculation involved compensating errors which do not cancel out at all atmospheric depths.

## B. Magnetic Field Effects

The magnetic field of the Earth is essentially that of a dipole, which drops off with the inverse cube of the distance from the Earth. The Earth's magnetic field strength at the surface is only $\sim 0.3$ gauss, but the effects of the field extend for thousands of miles into space. It is this vast extent that compensates for the low field strength and causes deflection of the incident cosmic ray primaries.

Primary particles that arrive vertically at the poles are moving parallel to the Earth's field and are thus not deflected; but primaries arriving vertically at the equator are moving at right angles to the field and will experience a large deflection force unless their momentum exceeds a certain value. This critical or cutoff momentum depends on the charge of the particle as well as on the geomagnetic latitude. To a first approximation, the smallest momentum, $P$, needed by a primary particle of an effective charge $Z_{\text{eff}}$ to enter the atmosphere vertically at a particular geomagnetic latitude, $\lambda$, is given by [40]:

$$P \cong \tfrac{1}{4} P_c Z_{\text{eff}} \cos^4 \lambda \qquad (8.33)$$

where $P_c = 59.3$ Bev/$c$.

In terms of energy the magnetic cutoff for protons (using the dipole approximation) is given by the expression [37]:

$$E(\text{Bev}) = M_0 C^2 \left\{ -1 + \sqrt{1 + \left(\frac{60}{r^2}\right) \frac{\cos^8 \lambda}{(M_0 C^2)^2 [\sqrt{1 + \cos \theta \cos^3 \lambda} + 1]^4}} \right\} \qquad (8.34)$$

where $r = (R_e + h)/R_e$ and $R_e$ is the earth's radius (6371 km), $M_0 C^2$ the rest energy of proton (0.938 Bev), $\lambda$ the geomagnetic latitude, and $\theta$ the angle of incidence ($\theta = 0$, horizontal incidence; $\theta = \pi/2$, vertical incidence).

Thus there is an altitude and a geomagnetic latitude that a proton with a given energy and angle of incidence cannot exceed. This relationship is shown graphically in Fig. 8-20. It is seen that for geomagnetic latitudes $\gtrsim 60$ deg the cutoff energy is rather small (it is identically zero at $\lambda_{mag} = 90$ deg).

The geomagnetic latitude is different from the geographic latitude by approximately 8 deg to the south in the western hemisphere and is a function

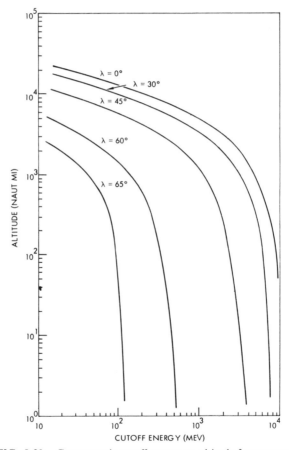

FIG. 8-20.   Geomagnetic cutoff energy vs. altitude for protons.

of time, since the magnetic field of the Earth is slowly moving. The minimum galactic radiation intensity above the earth's atmosphere does not occur at either the geographic nor the geomagnetic equators, but $\sim 7$ deg north of the former and $\sim 15$ deg north of the latter [41].

In addition to the geomagnetic latitude effect there is an east-west effect of the galactic radiation near the Earth. As a positively charged particle approaches the Earth at the equator, it is deflected toward the east. The same phenomenon applies to negatively charged particles, but the direction is reversed. The east-west effect is very small at sea level, but becomes in-

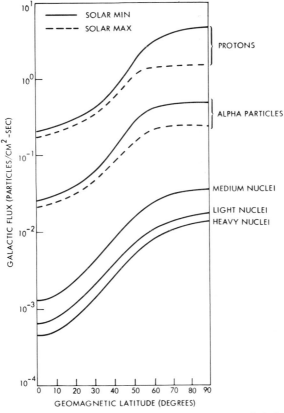

FIG. 8-21. Galactic flux rate as a function of geomagnetic latitude.

creasingly significant at higher altitudes. It also increases with proximity to the geomagnetic equator.

The effect of the geomagnetic field on galactic radiation present above the Earth's atmosphere is shown in Fig. 8-21 [29, 42]. As expected all components of the galactic radiation are affected approximately the same, exhibiting a factor of around 10 reduction in flux at the geomagnetic equator during solar maximum, and a factor of about 20 during solar minimum. This leads to measured latitude dose rates due to galactic radiation as shown in Fig. 8-22 [29, 43]. The effects of solar activity are seen to be important.

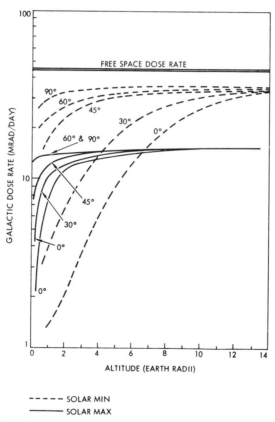

FIG. 8-22.   Galactic dose rates in vicinity of Earth above the atmosphere.

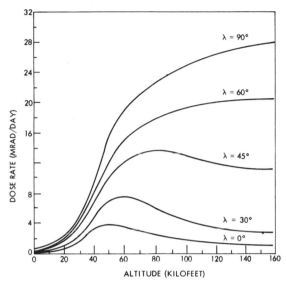

FIG. 8-23.   Galactic dose rates in Earth's atmosphere at solar min.

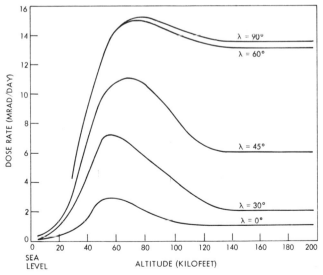

FIG. 8-24.   Galactic dose rates in Earth's atmosphere at solar max.

Kuhn *et al.* [44] have developed a computer program for calculating the solar flare hazard to Earth-orbiting vehicles. The effects of the geomagnetic field on the incident protons and the shadow effect of the Earth are specifically evaluated using the Stormer integral. For 200 nautical mile 70 deg orbits, dose rate reductions of $\geqslant 2$ orders of magnitude over the free space dose rate were obtained for the flare of 2/23/56. For a "softer" flare, such as that of 11/12/60, a reduction of $\geqslant 3$ orders of magnitude was calculated. Since the proton spectrum becomes softer with time, these reduction factors increase with time.

The significance of the geomagnetic field upon the evolution of life on Earth should be mentioned. It has been proposed that this field (which is believed to arise from the convection currents in the molten core which in turn are due to the rotation of the earth) made possible the development of life on this planet. Had there been no magnetic field the entire surface of the lifeless Earth (which may have had no life-supporting atmosphere) would have been exposed to galactic and solar radiation. This would probably have impeded the development of life, and it has been proposed that our atmosphere is the result of eons of plant life activity. If this hypothesis is correct then the occurrence of life on planets is directly related to planetary magnetic fields and may be less common than was once thought.

## C. Combined Atmospheric-Geomagnetic Effects

At any point in the Earth's atmosphere both geomagnetic deflection and atmospheric attenuation act to limit the space radiation dose rates. A summary of the balloon dose rate measurements is contained in Figs. 8-23 and 8-24 [29, 43]. Again the profound effects of the solar activity on the dose rates is observed. The peaks in the galactic dose rates are due to soft secondaries.

So far the discussion of dose rates in the Earth's atmosphere has been concerned essentially with galactic radiations. This is due to the relative lack of such data on solar flare dose rates and the far less penetrating power of solar flare radiations. However at sufficient altitudes and latitudes solar flare radiations are important. A series of calculations have been carried out to yield solar flare dose rates in the Earth's atmosphere [39]. The flare model used was the envelope of the largest observed flares, having an integral energy spectrum given by

$$\phi(E > E_0, t) = \frac{1.5 \times 10^8 t \exp[-0.022E_0^{0.4}t]}{E_0^{0.75}}$$

where $t$ is the time (in hours) from flare onset. The maximum flux rate occurs at

$$t_{max} = \frac{45}{E_0^{0.4}} \text{ (hr)}$$

which leads to peak flux rates given by

$$\hat{\phi}(E) = \frac{2.9 \times 10^9}{E^{2.15}} \quad \text{(proton/cm}^2\text{–hr–Mev)} \qquad (8.35)$$

To calculate the flare dose the above expression was multiplied by the flux-to-rad-dose conversion factor and integrated from the appropriate geomagnetic or atmospheric cutoff energy (whichever was greater) to infinity. The desired rem doses were obtained by multiplying by the appropriate RBE factor for $E^{-2.15}$ spectra and the alpha particle rem dose correction factor for each latitude and atmospheric depth. The effective solid angle as a function of atmospheric depth was calculated using the ± relaxation length limit. The results are contained in Tables 8-3 and 8-4. The Rem doses of Table 8-4 show that for altitudes $\gtrsim 40,000$ feet and geomagnetic latitudes $\gtrsim 60$ deg the peak solar flare dose rates may exceed the galactic dose rates.

A number of excellent and detailed calculations of the space radiation hazards at SST (supersonic transport) altitudes ($\sim 70,000$ feet) have been reported in the literature. Shen [45] analyzed the neutron and proton data of several high-altitude balloon flights to obtain dose and star production estimates. He concluded that there would be relatively little hazard except for chance star events in sensitive regions of the body. The effects of nitrous oxide and ozone at SST altitudes were also considered as part of the same study effort. Flamm and Lingenfelter [46] used a rigidity differential proton energy spectrum to calculate rad and rem solar flare dose rates in the atmosphere as a function of altitude and characteristic rigidity. Secondary dose contributions were included by assuming equal cross sections for proton and neutron secondaries. A comprehensive review of previous work, coupled with an evaluation of the biological hazards due to both flare and galactic radiation, was carried out by Foelsche [47]. Stars and heavy primary hits were considered in estimating that neither the crew members

## TABLE 8-3

MAXIMUM DOSE RATES EXPECTED AS FUNCTION OF LATITUDE AND ALTITUDE DUE TO NATURAL SPACE RADIATION (MRAD$^a$HR)

(THESE NUMBERS HAVE $1\sigma$ LIMITS OF $\pm$ A FACTOR OF 2)

| Altitude (feet) | | Geomagnetic latitude (deg) | | | | | |
|---|---|---|---|---|---|---|---|
| | | 0° | 30° | 45° | 60° | 75° | 90° |
| 10,000 | Flare | $1.0 \times 10^{-2}$ | $1.1 \times 10^{-2}$ | $1.3 \times 10^{-2}$ | $1.6 \times 10^{-2}$ | $1.9 \times 10^{-2}$ | $2 \times 10^{-2}$ |
| | No flare | $1.3 \times 10^{-2}$ | $1.3 \times 10^{-2}$ | $1.6 \times 10^{-2}$ | $2.1 \times 10^{-2}$ | $2.5 \times 10^{-2}$ | $2.8 \times 10^{-2}$ |
| 20,000 | Flare | $1.3 \times 10^{-2}$ | $3.0 \times 10^{-2}$ | $4.5 \times 10^{-2}$ | $5.5 \times 10^{-2}$ | $7.5 \times 10^{-2}$ | $8 \times 10^{-2}$ |
| | No flare | $2.1 \times 10^{-2}$ | $3.3 \times 10^{-2}$ | $4.6 \times 10^{-2}$ | $5.8 \times 10^{-2}$ | $8.0 \times 10^{-2}$ | $9.0 \times 10^{-2}$ |
| 30,000 | Flare | $4.0 \times 10^{-2}$ | $9.0 \times 10^{-2}$ | $1.1 \times 10^{-1}$ | $7.0 \times 10^{-2}$ | $9.0 \times 10^{-2}$ | $1 \times 10^{-1}$ |
| | No flare | $6.3 \times 10^{-2}$ | $9.0 \times 10^{-2}$ | $1.3 \times 10^{-1}$ | $1.7 \times 10^{-1}$ | $2.0 \times 10^{-1}$ | $2.1 \times 10^{-1}$ |
| 40,000 | Flare | $6.0 \times 10^{-2}$ | $2.0 \times 10^{-1}$ | $2.7 \times 10^{-1}$ | $3 \times 10^{-1}$ | $5 \times 10^{-1}$ | $5 \times 10^{-1}$ |
| | No flare | $1.3 \times 10^{-1}$ | $2.0 \times 10^{-1}$ | $2.8 \times 10^{-1}$ | $3.2 \times 10^{-1}$ | $3.7 \times 10^{-1}$ | $3.9 \times 10^{-1}$ |
| 50,000 | Flare | $1.2 \times 10^{-1}$ | $2.8 \times 10^{-1}$ | $3.8 \times 10^{-1}$ | $0.8$ | $1.8$ | $2.5$ |
| | No flare | $1.5 \times 10^{-1}$ | $3.0 \times 10^{-1}$ | $4.0 \times 10^{-1}$ | $5.2 \times 10^{-1}$ | $6.2 \times 10^{-1}$ | $6.4 \times 10^{-1}$ |
| 60,000 | Flare | $1.3 \times 10^{-1}$ | $3.0 \times 10^{-1}$ | $4.7 \times 10^{-1}$ | $1.0$ | $8$ | $12$ |
| | No flare | $1.4 \times 10^{-1}$ | $3.1 \times 10^{-1}$ | $5.0 \times 10^{-1}$ | $6.3 \times 10^{-1}$ | $7.5 \times 10^{-1}$ | $7.7 \times 10^{-1}$ |
| 70,000 | Flare | $1.1 \times 10^{-1}$ | $2.8 \times 10^{-1}$ | $5.2 \times 10^{-1}$ | $2.8$ | $40$ | $50$ |
| | No flare | $1.3 \times 10^{-1}$ | $3.0 \times 10^{-1}$ | $5.5 \times 10^{-1}$ | $7.1 \times 10^{-1}$ | $8.3 \times 10^{-1}$ | $8.7 \times 10^{-1}$ |
| 80,000 | Flare | $8.0 \times 10^{-2}$ | $2.4 \times 10^{-1}$ | $5.0 \times 10^{-1}$ | $4.5$ | $150$ | $170$ |
| | No flare | $1.0 \times 10^{-1}$ | $2.5 \times 10^{-1}$ | $5.7 \times 10^{-1}$ | $7.5 \times 10^{-1}$ | $9.2 \times 10^{-1}$ | $9.5 \times 10^{-1}$ |
| 90,000 | Flare | $7.5 \times 10^{-2}$ | $2.0 \times 10^{-1}$ | $4.2 \times 10^{-1}$ | $7$ | $480$ | $500$ |
| | No flare | $9.0 \times 10^{-2}$ | $2.2 \times 10^{-1}$ | $5.6 \times 10^{-1}$ | $8.0 \times 10^{-1}$ | $9.5 \times 10^{-1}$ | $1.0$ |
| 100,000 | Flare | $7.0 \times 10^{-2}$ | $1.7 \times 10^{-1}$ | $3.3 \times 10^{-1}$ | $8$ | $1400$ | $1500$ |
| | No flare | $7.5 \times 10^{-2}$ | $2.0 \times 10^{-1}$ | $5.4 \times 10^{-1}$ | $8.0 \times 10^{-1}$ | $1.0$ | $1.1$ |

TABLE 8-4

Maximum Dose Rates Expected as a Function of Latitude and Altitude Due to Natural Space Radiation (mrem[a]hr)
(These Numbers Have $1\sigma$ Limits of $\pm$ a Factor of 2)

| | | Geomagnetic latitude (deg) | | | | | |
|---|---|---|---|---|---|---|---|
| | | 0° | 30° | 45° | 60° | 75° | 90° |
| 10,000 | Flare | $1.0 \times 10^{-2}$ | $1.1 \times 10^{-2}$ | $1.3 \times 10^{-2}$ | $1.6 \times 10^{-2}$ | $1.9 \times 10^{-2}$ | $2 \times 10^{-2}$ |
| | No flare | $1.3 \times 10^{-2}$ | $1.3 \times 10^{-2}$ | $1.6 \times 10^{-2}$ | $2.1 \times 10^{-2}$ | $2.5 \times 10^{-2}$ | $2.8 \times 10^{-2}$ |
| 20,000 | Flare | $1.3 \times 10^{-2}$ | $3.0 \times 10^{-2}$ | $4.5 \times 10^{-2}$ | $5.5 \times 10^{-2}$ | $7.5 \times 10^{-2}$ | $8 \times 10^{-2}$ |
| | No flare | $2.1 \times 10^{-2}$ | $3.3 \times 10^{-2}$ | $4.6 \times 10^{-2}$ | $5.8 \times 10^{-2}$ | $8 \times 10^{-2}$ | $9 \times 10^{-2}$ |
| 30,000 | Flare | $4.0 \times 10^{-2}$ | $9.0 \times 10^{-2}$ | $1.1 \times 10^{-1}$ | $7 \times 10^{-2}$ | $9 \times 10^{-2}$ | $1 \times 10^{-1}$ |
| | No flare | $6.3 \times 10^{-2}$ | $9.0 \times 10^{-2}$ | $1.3 \times 10^{-1}$ | $1.7 \times 10^{-1}$ | $2.0 \times 10^{-1}$ | $2.1 \times 10^{-1}$ |
| 40,000 | Flare | $6.0 \times 10^{-2}$ | $2.0 \times 10^{-1}$ | $2.7 \times 10^{-1}$ | $3 \times 10^{-1}$ | $5 \times 10^{-1}$ | $5 \times 10^{-1}$ |
| | No flare | $1.3 \times 10^{-1}$ | $2.0 \times 10^{-1}$ | $2.8 \times 10^{-1}$ | $3.2 \times 10^{-1}$ | $3.7 \times 10^{-1}$ | $4 \times 10^{-1}$ |
| 50,000 | Flare | $1.2 \times 10^{-1}$ | $2.8 \times 10^{-1}$ | $3.8 \times 10^{-1}$ | 0.8 | 1.8 | 2.5 |
| | No flare | $1.5 \times 10^{-1}$ | $3.0 \times 10^{-1}$ | $4.0 \times 10^{-1}$ | $5.2 \times 10^{-1}$ | $6.2 \times 10^{-1}$ | $6.5 \times 10^{-1}$ |
| 60,000 | Flare | $1.3 \times 10^{-1}$ | $3.0 \times 10^{-1}$ | $4.7 \times 10^{-1}$ | 1.0 | 8 | 12 |
| | No flare | $1.4 \times 10^{-1}$ | $3.1 \times 10^{-1}$ | $5.0 \times 10^{-1}$ | $6.3 \times 10^{-1}$ | $7.5 \times 10^{-1}$ | $8 \times 10^{-1}$ |
| 70,000 | Flare | $1.1 \times 10^{-1}$ | $2.8 \times 10^{-1}$ | $5.2 \times 10^{-1}$ | 3 | 40 | 50 |
| | No flare | $1.3 \times 10^{-1}$ | $3.0 \times 10^{-1}$ | $5.5 \times 10^{-1}$ | $7.1 \times 10^{-1}$ | $8.5 \times 10^{-1}$ | $9 \times 10^{-1}$ |
| 80,000 | Flare | $8.0 \times 10^{-2}$ | $2.4 \times 10^{-1}$ | $5.0 \times 10^{-1}$ | 5 | 160 | 180 |
| | No flare | $1.0 \times 10^{-1}$ | $2.5 \times 10^{-1}$ | $5.7 \times 10^{-1}$ | $7.7 \times 10^{-1}$ | $9.5 \times 10^{-1}$ | 1.0 |
| 90,000 | Flare | $7.5 \times 10^{-2}$ | $2.0 \times 10^{-1}$ | $4.2 \times 10^{-1}$ | 8 | 550 | 600 |
| | No flare | $9.0 \times 10^{-2}$ | $2.2 \times 10^{-1}$ | $5.6 \times 10^{-1}$ | $8.5 \times 10^{-1}$ | 1.0 | 1.1 |
| 100,000 | Flare | $7.0 \times 10^{-2}$ | $1.7 \times 10^{-1}$ | $3.4 \times 10^{-1}$ | 10 | 2000 | 2500 |
| | No flare | $7.5 \times 10^{-2}$ | $2.0 \times 10^{-1}$ | $5.5 \times 10^{-1}$ | $9.0 \times 10^{-1}$ | 1.1 | 1.2 |

(allowed 5 Rem/year) nor the passengers (allowed 0.5 Rem/year) would be likely to exceed the allowable limits. The major uncertainties deal with pregnant women and growing children, where rapid cell division is taking place. All researchers agree that on-board radiation monitoring is desirable so that the pilot will known when and if to descend to lower altitudes.

REFERENCES

1.  J. W. Haffner, An Attenuation Kernel for the Bailey Model Event, *Trans. Am. Nucl. Soc.* **7,** 16 (1964).
2.  R. A. Weagant, Nomogram for Heavy Charged Particle Shielding Calculations, Rept. SID 64–10, *North American Aviation, Downey, California* (1964).
3.  R. A. Weagant, Proton Shielding Slide Rule, *Space and Inform. Syst. Div., North American Aviation Downey, California* (1964).
4.  R. A. Madey, A Useful Formula for Calculating Space Proton Dose Rates, *Trans. Am. Nucl. Soc.* **6,** 194 (1963).
5.  W. R. Webber, An Evaluation of the Radiation Hazard due to Solar Particle Events, Rept. D2-90469, *Boeing Co., Seattle,* Washington (1963).
6.  J. W. Haffner, Shielding Analysis of 1956–1961 Solar Proton Event Data, Rept. SID 64–1295, *North American Aviation, Downey California* (1964).
7.  M. O. Burrell, The Calculation of Proton Penetration and Dose Rates, p. 493, *Second Symp. Protection against Radiations in Space,* NASA-SP-71 (1964).
8.  F. R. Nakache, Analytical Formulation of Proton Dose Rates behind Spherical Multilayer Shields, p. 485, *Second Symp. Protection against Radiations in Space,* NASA-SP-71 (1964).
9.  P. Frier and W. R. Webber, Radiation Hazard in Space from Solar Particles, *Science* **142,** 1591 (1963).
10. J. W. Haffner, The Role of Alpha Particles in Shielding against Solar Event Radiation, Rept. SID 64-1297, *North American Aviation, Downey, California* (1964).
11. H. J. Schaefer, Local Dose from Proton and Alpha Particle Enders behind Complex Shield Systems, p. 507, *Second Symp. Protection against Radiations in Space,* NASA-SP-71 (1964).
12. D. E. Robbins, Apollo Shielding Analysis, p. 143 ff., *Second Symp. Protection against Radiations in Space,* NASA-SP-71 (1964).
13. F. Raymes, Apollo Spacecraft Nuclear Radiation Protection Status Report, p. 365 ff., *Second Symp. Protection against Radiations in Space,* NASA-SP-71 (1964).
14. J. W. Haffner, Geometrical Factors in Space Radiation Shielding, Rept. SID 64–1296, *North American Aviation, Downey, California* (1964).
15. R. G. Alsmiller and J. E. Murphy, Space Vehicle Shielding Studies—Calculations of the Attenuation of a Model Solar Flare and Monoenergetic Proton Beams by Aluminum Shield, Rept. ORNL-3317, *Oak Ridge Natl. Lab.,* Oak Ridge, Tennessee (1963).

16. R. Madey, A. G. Duneer, and T. J. Krieger, Gamma Dose from Solar Flare Protons Incident on an Aluminum Shield, *Trans. Am. Nucl. Soc.* **5**, 213 (1962).

17. F. S. Alsmiller, R. G. Alsmiller, and D. K. Trubey, Comparison of Primary Proton Dose with the Dose from Gamma Rays Produced by Inelastic Scattering of Solar Flare Protons, p. 225, Rept. ORNL 3360, *Oak Ridge Natl. Lab.*, Oak Ridge, Tennessee (1962).

18. R. W. Deutsch, Gamma Dose Resulting from Inelastic Scattering of Solar Flare Protons Incident on a Carbon Shield, *Trans. Am. Nucl. Soc.* **5**, 405 (1962).

19. C. W. Hill and K. M. Simpson, Calculation of Proton-Induced Gamma Ray Spectrum and Comparison with Experiment, p. 351 ff., *Second Symp. Protection against Radiations in Space*, NASA-SP-71 (1964).

20. W. Zobel, F. C. Maienschein, and R. J. Scroggs, Spectra of Gamma Rays Produced by Interaction of 160 MeV Protons with Be, C, Al, Co, and Bi, p. 341 ff., *Second Symp. Protection against Radiations in Space*, NASA-SP-71 (1964).

21. J. B. Marion and J. L. Fowler, "Fast Neutron Physics I." Wiley (Interscience), New York, 1963.

22. D. L. Dye, Space Proton Doses at Points within the Human Body, Rept. D2-90106, *Boeing Co., Seattle, Washington* (1962).

23. C. E. McIlwain and G. Pizzella, On the Energy Spectrum of Protons Trapped in the Earth's Inner Van Allen Zone, *J. Geophys. Res.* **68**, 1811 (1963).

24. W. L. Imhof and R. R. Smith, Proton Intensities and Energy Spectra in the Inner Radiation Belt, *J. Geophys. Res.* **65**, 1377 (1960).

25. J. W. Haffner, Calculations of Dose Rates due to Van Allen Radiation, Rept. SID 64-2035, *North American Aviation, Downey, California* (1964).

26. S. L. Russak, Radiation Dosages from Electrons and Bremsstrahlung in the Van Allen Belt, p. 760 ff., *Symp. Protection against Radiation Hazards in Space*, TID-7652 (1962).

27. R. P. Moshofsky, Errors from Geometric Approximations Introduced in Three Computational Models for Space Vehicle Electron Dose Prediction, p. 465 ff., *Second Symp. Protection against Radiations in Space*, NASA-SP-71 (1964).

28. A. Rosen and J. Vogl, Cosmic Rays in Space, *in*: "Space Physics" (D. P. LeGalley and A. Rosen, eds.), Chap. 17. Wiley, New York, 1964.

29. W. P. Saylor, D. E. Winer, C. J. Eiwen and A. W. Carriker, "Space Radiation Guide," Chap. 4, Rept. AMRL-TDR-62-86, *Biomed. Lab., U.S. Air Force, Dayton, Ohio* (1962).

30. H. W. Bertini, Parametric Study of Calculated Cascade and Evaporation Reactions for 25–400 MeV Nucleons, Rept. ONRL-3499, *Oak Ridge Natl. Lab.*, Oak Ridge, Tennessee (1963).

31. H. Alter, Basic Microscopic Data for Space Shielding Analysis, Memo 8853, *North American Aviation., At. Intern. Div., Canoga Park, California* (1963).

32. N. Metropolis, R. Bivins, M. Storm, A. Turkevich, J. Miller, and G. Friedlander, Monte Carlo Calculations of Intranuclear Processes, I and II, *Phys. Rev.* **110**, 185 (1958).

33. R. D. Evans, "The Atomic Nucleus," Chap. 15, McGraw-Hill, New York, 1955.

34. J. W. Haffner, The Role of Galactic Protons in Shielding against Space Radiation, Rept. SID 64–2036, *North American Aviation, Downey, California* (1964).

35. K. A. More and O. L. Tiffany, Comparison of Monte Carlo and Ionization Calculations for Spacecraft Shielding, pp. 682 ff., *Proc. Symp. Protection against Radiation Hazards in Space*, TID-7652 (1962).

36. K. A. More and O. L. Tiffany, Cosmic Ray Shower Production in Manned Space Vehicles —Copper, pp. 183 ff., *Second Symp. Protection against Radiations in Space*, NASA-SP-71 (1964).

37. R. W. Williams, Cosmic Rays and High Energy Phenomena, *in*: "Fundamental Formulae of Physics," (D. H. Menzel, ed.) Vol II. Dover, New York, 1960.

38. H. W. Bertini, Monte Carlo Calculations on Intranuclear Cascades, Rept. ORNL-3383, *Oak Ridge Natl. Lab.*, Oak Ridge, Tennessee (1963).

39. J. W. Haffner, Space Radiation Dose Rates in the Earth's Atmosphere, Paper 65–511, *Second Ann. AIAA Meeting, San Francisco, California* (1965).

40. B. Peters, Progress in Cosmic Ray Research Since 1947, *J. Geophys. Res.* **64**, 155 (1959).

41. A. E. Sandstrom, Some Geophysical Aspects of Cosmic Rays, *Am. J. Phys.* **29**, 187 (1961).

42. H. V. Neher, The Primary Cosmic Radiation, *Ann. Rev. Nucl. Sci.* **8**, 217 (1958).

43. S. W. Leeper, Biological Hazards from Space Radiation Based on Tissue Equivalent Ion Chamber Measurements, *Proc. Inst. Environmental Sci. Washington, D.C.* (1961).

44. E. Kuhn, F. E. Schwamb, and W. T. Payne, Solar Flare Hazard to Earth Orbiting Vehicles. pp. 429 ff., *Second Symp. Protection against Radiations in Space*, NASA-SP-71 (1964).

45. S. P. Shen, Space Radiation and the Hypersonic Transport, Rept. R-64 SD1, *General Electric Co., Missile and Space Vehicle Dept., Philadelphia, Pennsylvania* (1964).

46. E. J. Flamm and R. E. Lingenfelter, Neutron and Proton Dosages in the Upper Atmosphere from Solar Flare Radiation, *Science* **144**, 1566 (1964).

47. T. Foelsche, The Ionizing Radiations in Supersonic Transport Flights, pp. 287 ff., *Second Symp. Protection Against Radiations in Space*, NASA-SP-71 (1964).

# IX

## MISSION ANALYSIS
## CONSIDERATIONS

In the preceding chapters the various parameters associated with the three types of space nuclear radiation (Van Allen, flare, and galactic) have been discussed. The information ultimately desired concerns the particle fluxes and doses to be expected on a given mission. If this information is available for a sufficient number of parameters, then the trade-off studies between radiation shielding and such factors as life support system weight, $\Delta v$ (incremental velocity) for the mission and the propulsion system to obtain it, and so forth can be carried out. In this chapter various mission analysis studies are discussed.

### A. Mission Timing

As expected, since solar flares are often the greatest source of space radiation dose on an extraterrestrial mission, the timing of a mission usually has a major effect upon the doses expected. On the average the lowest flare doses will be received on missions undertaken during solar minimums (e.g., 1965, 1976, et seq.), the largest during solar maximums (e.g., 1970–71, 1981–82, et seq.). The magnitude of future solar cycles can only be estimated from those of past ones, and on this basis the sunspot number (and presumably the solar flare annual doses) vary by greater than or equivalent to a factor of 10 from solar maximum to solar minimum. The electron fluxes in the outer portions of the Earth's trapped radiation belts vary in phase with solar activity by approximately this factor, while the galactic radiation at 1 A.U. is believed to vary by about a factor of 1.5–2.0 out of phase with the solar cycle. This solar flare and galactic dose behavior is shown in Fig. 9-1.

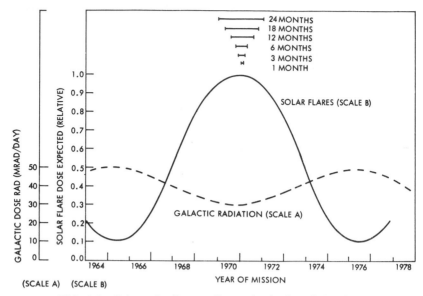

FIG. 9-1.   Solar cycle effects on flare and galactic radiation doses.

However, since solar flares apparently occur semirandomly, it is not possible to predict what flares of what size will take place. It is only possible to predict what the probability is that a given total solar flux or dose will be exceeded during a specified period. These flux versus probability and dose versus probability relationships have been compiled by Webber [1], Modisette *et al.* [2] and others [3–5] based upon the 1956–1961 solar flare data. For probabilities $\gtrsim 10\%$ the various computations agree fairly well, but for probabilities $\lesssim 10\%$ there are appreciable (approaching an order of magnitude) disagreements, simply because the $\sim 60$ events do not permit accurate statistical analyses in this region. A fairly conservative average of such analyses has been used to compute the flare proton flux probabilities per month, shown in Fig. 9-2. Based upon this flux-probability relationship, dose-probability relationships have been obtained. The results of one such study are shown in Fig. 9-3. Other similar curves can be generated mathematically by noting that the flare proton flux probability curves can be approximately fit by the expression,

$$P = e^{-\beta\sqrt{\mathcal{J}\phi/t}} \tag{9.1}$$

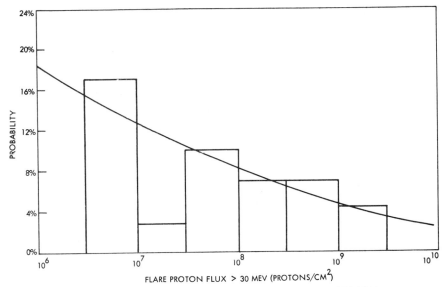

FIG. 9-2.  Flare flux probability by size averaged over 1956–1961.

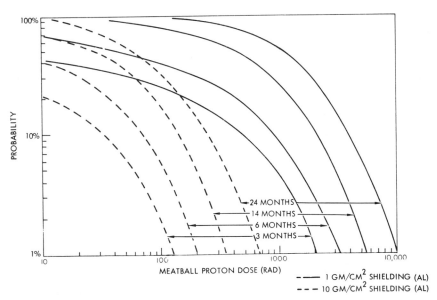

FIG. 9-3.  Flare proton dose probability curves averaged over 1956–1961.

where $P$ is the probability of exceeding $\int\phi$ (protons/cm$^2$ > 30 Mev), $t$ the mission duration (weeks), and

$$\beta = \left\{5.5 + 3\cos\left[\frac{2\pi}{11}(\text{YEAR}-1954)\right]\right\}\Big/10^4$$

The factor $\beta$ is treated as a variable to take account of the effects of the solar cycle. For missions longer than about two years, this relationship is not accurate, because the mission duration is not short compared with the solar cycle.

Previous studies [6] of solar flare doses have established the following approximate relationships:

$$D_p^1(\text{rad}) = 5 \times 10^{-7}\phi(\text{protons/cm}^2 > 30\text{ Mev}) \qquad (9.2)$$

$$= 0.75\, X^{1.2} D_{p+\alpha}^x \text{ (rad)}$$

$$= 0.38\, X^{1.4} D_{p+\alpha}^x \text{ (Rem)} \qquad (1 \leqslant X \leqslant 10)$$

where $D_p^1$ is the point flare dose due to protons behind 1 gm/cm$^2$ aluminum, $D_{p+\alpha}^1$ is the corresponding quantity when both protons and $\alpha$ particles are taken into account, and $X$ is the aluminum equivalent shield thickness (gm/cm$^2$).

By combining these equations and solving for $X$ one obtains

$$X\left(\frac{\text{gm}}{\text{cm}^2}\right) = 33\left[\frac{t(\text{weeks})}{D(\text{rad})}\right]^{0.83}\left\{\frac{-\ln P}{5.5 + 3\cos[2\pi/11\,(\text{YEAR}-1954)]}\right\}^{1.67}$$

$$X\left(\frac{\text{gm}}{\text{cm}^2}\right) = 33\left[\frac{t(\text{weeks})}{D(\text{Rem})}\right]^{0.71}\left\{\cdots\right\}^{1.43} \qquad (9.3)$$

Thus given the mission duration ($t$), the calendar year in which it largely falls (YEAR), the solar flare dose limit $D$ (rad or Rem), and the probability ($P$) acceptable for exceeding this dose limit, the above formulas give the equivalent aluminum shield thickness $X$(gm/cm$^2$) required. This applies only outside the Earth's magnetosphere in the vicinity of 1 A.U. The major effects of mission timing are apparent in this analysis.

Another effect of timing on the solar flare dose expected in deep space concerns the month the mission falls in. While it may be fortuitous, the 1956–1961 flare data show that the periods May 15–July 5 and December 1–January 15 were essentially free of serious flares. On the other hand, the months of February, March, July, and November were especially bad (Fig.

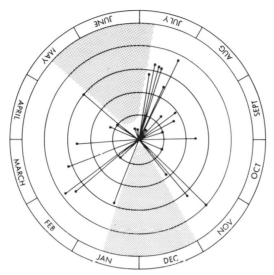

FIG. 9-4. Distribution of solar flare events by month, showing two essentially flux-free periods for 1956–1961.

9-4) [7]. These considerations would only be of interest for missions lasting less than about a month, but, until further flare data are available, one cannot assume that the month in which a mission is undertaken has no effect on the solar flare doses to be expected.

It must be pointed out that while the space radiation doses expected are a function of mission timing, so may be the $\Delta v$ required of the rocket propulsion unit. If another planet or astronomical body is to be explored (either by a flyby or a lander), there are good years (relatively low $\Delta v$ required) and bad years (high $\Delta v$ required) [8, 9]. Since $\Delta v$ considerations for such missions generally are overriding, the space radiation environment expected during the good years (from a $\Delta v$ standpoint) must simply be accepted. However, if there is little or no difference between two or more missions on a $\Delta v$ basis, the effects of the solar cycle may tip the scales in favor of a mission at or near solar minimum if the vehicle is to be manned.

## B.  Doses on Earth Orbital Missions

Since the majority of the unmanned space missions and all of the manned space flights (as of January, 1966) have taken place in an Earth orbit, there has been considerable interest in the space radiation dose expected for such missions. Such doses are obviously a function of orbit altitude and inclination, since the trapped (Van Allen) radiation generally constitutes the major source of space radiation here. The timing of the mission and possibly vehicle orientation also play a role.

A number of studies have been carried out yielding particle fluxes and/or doses for various Earth orbital missions. The electron and bremsstrahlung rad dose rates expected during 12 hours in earth orbit as a function of aluminum shield thickness were calculated by Russak [10], using the electron spectrum of Pizzella et al. [11]. Altitudes of 300, 400, 600, and 1000 nautical miles were considered at inclinations of 0 (equatorial), 40, and 90 (polar) deg. More recently, Russak and Richardson [12] have calculated the daily proton rad doses for various orbits as a function of aluminum shield thickness, using the energy spectrum of Imhof and Smith [13]. An extensive series of calculations of proton and electron (natural and fission) fluxes and rad doses has been carried out by Keller and Pruett [14]. Power law $(E^{-\alpha})$ fits to the energy spectra obtained by Explorers XII, XIV, XV, and Telstars I and II were used, yielding results for 16 orbits from 400 nautical miles to 10,000 as a function of orbit inclination and aluminum shield thickness. Eye, skin, and blood-forming-organ doses as a function of aluminum shield thickness inside 2- and 6-man spacecraft were computed by Jordan et al. [15] for 100, 200, and 400 nautical mile orbits at inclinations of 29, 60, and 90 deg. Bouquet [16] calculated electron and proton fluxes and doses as a function of shield thickness inside a 24-man space station for various orbit altitudes and inclinations. The solar flare hazards to an orbiting space station were explicitly calculated by Kuhn et al. [17], while Mar [18], and Fortney and Duckworth [19] investigated the effects of the trapped radiation particle flux anisotropy on dose calculations. Undoubtedly there have been other calculations of the doses and dose rates expected inside a vehicle in Earth orbit. Comparisons of results obtained by different groups is difficult because of differences in environment model used, vehicle considered, and quantity calculated.

The point rad and Rem doses expected for various earth orbital missions have been calculated [6], using the environmental models and analytical techniques discussed in earlier chapters. High-trust trips to and from circular Earth orbits were assumed. Doses due to the trapped radiations, and contributions made by solar flare and galactic radiations were included.

For equatorial orbits the dose contributions due to solar and galactic particles above the geomagnetic cutoff energy were readily obtained. For polar orbits the fraction of the free space dose rate was based upon the fraction of the time the orbiting vehicle would spend above the latitude where the geomagnetic cutoff energy and the shield cutoff energy were equal. For both equatorial and polar orbits solar flare dose rates were calculated on the basis of 1 % probability averaged over six months. Since

TABLE 9-1

SPACE RADIATION DOSE RATES (RAD/DAY) EXPECTED FOR ORBITAL MISSIONS[a]

| Orbital altitude (km) | 0.1 gm/cm$^2$ | | 1.0 gm/cm$^2$ | | 10 gm/cm$^2$ | |
|---|---|---|---|---|---|---|
| | Van Allen | Other[b] | Van Allen | Other | Van Allen | Other |
| 300 Equator | $3 \times 10^2$ | <0.1 | <0.1 | <0.1 | <0.1 | <0.1 |
| Polar | $5 \times 10^1$ | 90 | 0.1 | 3 | <0.1 | 0.2 |
| 400 Equator | $2 \times 10^3$ | <0.1 | 1 | <0.1 | 0.3 | <0.1 |
| Polar | $4 \times 10^2$ | 100 | 0.2 | 3 | <0.1 | 0.2 |
| 600 Equator | $1 \times 10^4$ | <0.1 | 5 | <0.1 | 2 | <0.1 |
| Polar | $3 \times 10^3$ | 150 | 1 | 4 | 0.4 | 0.2 |
| 1000 Equator | $1 \times 10^5$ | <0.1 | 50 | <0.1 | 15 | <0.1 |
| Polar | $3 \times 10^4$ | 200 | 15 | 4 | 5 | 0.2 |
| 3000 Equator | $3 \times 10^5$ | <0.1 | 1000 | <0.1 | 300 | <0.1 |
| Polar | $1 \times 10^5$ | 300 | 300 | 5 | 100 | 0.3 |
| 10,000 Equator | $1 \times 10^6$ | <0.1 | 30 | <0.1 | 10 | <0.1 |
| Polar | $4 \times 10^5$ | 400 | 10 | 6 | 3 | 0.4 |
| 31,000 Equator | $4 \times 10^5$ | 16 | 3 | 16 | 0.5 | 0.8 |
| Polar | $1 \times 10^5$ | 800 | 0.6 | 16 | 0.1 | 0.8 |

[a] All entries have 1σ limits of ± a factor of 3. Van Allen dose rates calculated for orbits in 1970, active Sun, assuming no more high altitude nuclear detonations. Galactic and flare doses calculated for solar maximum, 1 % flare probability, averaged over 6 months.
[b] Other: includes flare and galactic radiation.

the 1 % probable flare doses do not increase linearly with mission duration, the extrapolated flare dose rates will be high for missions longer than six months, low for those less than six months. By using Fig. 9-3 the flare dose rates for any mission duration may be readily calculated.

The calculated rad and Rem dose rates for various orbital missions are listed in Tables 9-1 and 9-2. The Van Allen dose rates were based on the

TABLE 9-2

SPACE RADIATION DOSE RATES (REM/DAY) EXPECTED FOR ORBITAL MISSIONS[a]

| Orbital altitude (km) | 0.1 gm/cm$^2$ | | 1.0 gm/cm$^2$ | | 10 gm/cm$^2$ | |
|---|---|---|---|---|---|---|
| | Van Allen | Other[b] | Van Allen | Other | Van Allen | Other |
| 300 Equator | $3 \times 10^2$ | <0.1 | <0.1 | <0.1 | <0.1 | <0.1 |
| Polar | $5 \times 10^1$ | 250 | <0.1 | 6 | <0.1 | 0.2 |
| 400 Equator | $2 \times 10^3$ | <0.1 | 1.3 | <0.1 | 0.3 | <0.1 |
| Polar | $4 \times 10^2$ | 300 | 0.3 | 8 | <0.1 | 0.2 |
| 600 Equator | $1 \times 10^4$ | <0.1 | 6.5 | <0.1 | 2 | <0.1 |
| Polar | $3 \times 10^3$ | 500 | 1.3 | 10 | 0.4 | 0.2 |
| 1000 Equator | $1 \times 10^5$ | <0.1 | 65 | <0.1 | 16 | <0.1 |
| Polar | $3 \times 10^4$ | 800 | 20 | 12 | 5 | 0.2 |
| 3000 Equator | $3 \times 10^5$ | <0.1 | 1300 | <0.1 | 330 | <0.1 |
| Polar | $1 \times 10^5$ | 1200 | 400 | 15 | 110 | 0.3 |
| 10,000 Equator | $1 \times 10^6$ | <0.1 | 35 | <0.1 | 10 | <0.1 |
| Polar | $4 \times 10^5$ | $2 \times 10^3$ | 12 | 18 | 3 | 0.4 |
| 31,000 Equator | $4 \times 10^5$ | 50 | 3 | 50 | 0.5 | 0.9 |
| Polar | $1 \times 10^5$ | $4 \times 10^3$ | 0.6 | 50 | 0.1 | 0.9 |

[a] All entries have $1\sigma$ limits of $\pm$ a factor of 3. Van Allen dose rates calculated for orbits in 1970, active Sun, assuming no more high altitude nuclear detonations. Galactic and flare doses calculated for solar maximum, 1% flare probability, averaged over 6 months.
[b] Other: includes flare and galactic radiation.

expected environment in 1970 (solar maximum) assuming no further high-altitude nuclear detonations take place.

The effects of the use of the ERD concepts upon the shielding required were considered. A simple geometry was used—a point dosimeter centered inside a uniform aluminum spherical shell. Two dose limits (100 and 300 Rem) were taken as perhaps being representative for space missions, remembering that these are dosimeter limits (the skin dose would be approximately half the dosimeter dose, and the blood-forming organs would receive 15–25% the dosimeter dose).

The shielding thicknesses (gm/cm$^2$ aluminum equivalent) required for the 100 and 300 Rem dose limits are listed in Table 9-3 for the ERD and no-ERD conditions. These numbers were calculated by assuming that the radiation was received uniformly over the six-month period. By ratioing the entries of Tables 9.1 and 9.2 an effective RBE for each orbital mission was obtained. This then was used to estimate the recoverable and nonrecoverable

TABLE 9-3

| Orbit altitude | | If 100 Rem limit | | If 300 Rem limit | |
|---|---|---|---|---|---|
| | | No ERD | With ERD | No ERD | With ERD |
| | | gm/cm$^2$ | gm/cm$^2$ | gm/cm$^2$ | gm/cm$^2$ |
| 300 km | Equator | 1.0 | 0.8 | 0.8 | 0.5 |
| | Polar | 5.5 | 3 | 3 | 1.5 |
| 400 kev | Equator | 4 | 0.9 | 0.9 | 0.7 |
| | Polar | 6 | 4 | 4 | 2 |
| 600 km | Equator | 14 | 11 | 11 | 8 |
| | Polar | 10 | 7 | 7 | 4 |
| 1000 km | Equator | 21 | 18 | 18 | 15 |
| | Polar | 17 | 14 | 14 | 11 |
| 3000 km | Equator | 31 | 28 | 28 | 25 |
| | Polar | 27 | 24 | 24 | 21 |
| 10,000 km | Equator | 20 | 16 | 16 | 13 |
| | Polar | 16 | 13 | 13 | 10 |
| 31,000 km | Equator | 13 | 9 | 9 | 6 |
| | Polar | 12 | 8 | 8 | 7 |

[a] All entries have $1\sigma$ limits of $\pm 3$ gm/cm$^2$ or $\pm 30\%$, whichever is larger.

portions of the doses for each mission (the recoverable fraction was taken as 0.9/RBE the mission dose). The effective rem dose thus received was $\sim$ RBE/3 the total rem dose. Therefore the calculated shielding thicknesses required for each orbital mission if the ERD concept is used is that required for the same mission without the ERD concept for a dose limit $\sim 3$/RBE times as large.

As Tables 9-1–3 show, orbital missions in the region above 500 km altitude will require shielding thicknesses which are excessive by today's spacecraft standards (typical spacecraft have shielding effectiveness equivalent to 3–5 gm/cm$^2$ aluminum). The use of the "storm cellar" concept does not help much either, since the radiation is chronically present. While an astronaut could sleep in the small heavily shielded "storm cellar," he would probably not be able to carry out his mission without leaving it.

A corollary situation concerns the use of low-thrust, high-specific-impulse propulsion units, such as ion engines. For missions of long duration they offer definite advantages because they can operate for weeks, months, or years, and thereby achieve large $\Delta v$'s. However to use such a propulsion unit inside the Earth's magnetosphere to transform from an Earth orbit to a planetary trajectory will involve a tightly coiled spiral path through the Van Allen radiation belts. To a first approximation this is equivalent to a series of Earth orbits, some of which will pass through the heart of the radiation belts. For manned missions the shielding requirements are considerable, since such spiraling away from the Earth may require several weeks to pass through the Van Allen belts. This is one example where space radiation considerations have a major effect on overall mission feasibility [20].

Most of the United States Earth orbital missions involve orbit inclinations of $\sim 28$ deg because the Atlantic Missile Range islands where tracking radar and communications stations are located lie approximately in this direction from Cape Kennedy, Florida. This permits launchings over water which take advantage of the Earth's rotation to reduce the $\Delta v$ requirements to achieve orbit and escape velocities. (Polar—90 deg—orbit vehicles are launched from Vandenburg Air Force Base in California.) From a space radiation analysis standpoint most of the 28 deg orbits will experience

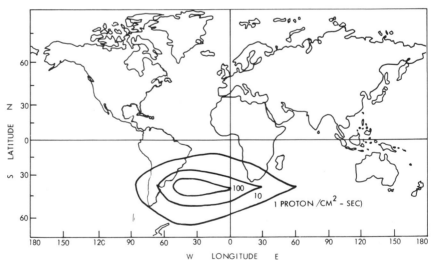

FIG. 9-5.   Van Allen protons $(40 < E < 110 \text{ Mev})$ at 200 naut. mi, showing location and extent of the South Atlantic anomaly.

essentially the same doses and dose rates as equatorial orbits. For low-lying orbits the 28 deg orbit doses will be greater due to the South Atlantic anomaly [15]. This anomaly is due to the fact the geomagnetic field is slightly off center, leading to higher *L*-values (McIlwain coordinate) for a given altitude in the vicinity of ∼ 30 deg south latitude, 15 deg west longitude, than elsewhere. The proton flux contours at 200 nautical miles altitude show this anomaly very clearly (see Fig. 9-5) [15]. On a Mercator projection a 28 deg orbit describes approximately a sine wave between + 28 and − 28 deg latitude. Therefore the South Atlantic anomaly will contribute the bulk of the flux and dose received at low altitudes ($\lesssim$ 400 km). Since successive orbits will ultimately traverse all points between the limiting latitudes, this anomaly is more important for extended duration orbital missions than for short ones. For this reason there are advantages to orbit at as low an altitude as possible. Radiation monitors carried by the Mercury [21] and Vostok [22] astronauts have indicated low (mrad) radiation doses, but for future orbital missions, such as the MOL (Manned Orbiting Laboratory), space radiation considerations will play an important part in determining the orbit.

## C. Deep Space Missions

A deep space mission is one which extends beyond the Earth's magnetosphere, and generally involves transferring from an Earth orbit to a solar orbit. Such missions will probably involve first achieving a low-altitude Earth orbit, but a direct passage from launch to deep space mission is possible.

For a deep space mission the first radiations encountered are the Van Allen belts. For the passage through these a high-thrust (probably chemical) vehicle is desirable to minimize the time spent and to prevent radioactive contamination of the near-Earth environment. The trajectory of a typical high-thrust chemical rocket is shown in Fig. 9-6 [23]. If this trajectory is equatorially superimposed on the spatial distribution of the Van Allen belts and the time integral of the particle fluxes evaluated, the result is ∼ $1 \times 10^{12}$ electrons/cm$^2$ > 40 kev and ∼ $6 \times 10^6$ protons/cm$^2$ > 100 Mev. For a shield of 5 gm/cm$^2$ aluminum, the electron- and proton-produced doses are (neglecting the spatial dependence of the energy spectra) 0.27 and 1.4 rad respectively. The RBE for Van Allen protons attenuated through 5 gm/cm$^2$

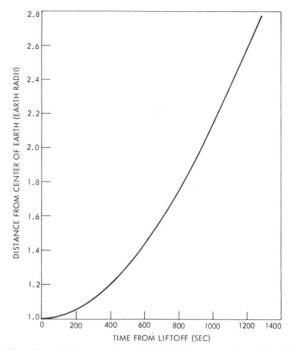

FIG. 9-6.  Position-time trajectory of typical high-thrust rocket rising from the Earth.

aluminum is calculated to be 1.1. Therefore, a high-thrust equatorial passage through the Van Allen belts yields a point dose of only 1.8 Rem behind a 5 gm/cm² aluminum shield. This is sufficiently low that modifying the mission trajectory to avoid the belts is probably not desirable.

Beyond the belts solar flare and galactic (cosmic) radiations are the only known sources of space radiation to contend with. Their relative importance depends upon the shield thickness (Fig. 9-7) [24]. For shields $\gtrsim 20$ gm/cm² the galactic radiation contributes the larger portion of the Rem dose. However, Fig. 9-7 also shows that if the deep space mission begins with a low thrust passage through the Van Allen belts the solar and galactic radiations are relatively unimportant for all shield thicknesses.

The solar and galactic doses expected as a function of mission duration, mission timing, and shield thickness have all been discussed previously. In order to summarize this material, the rad and Rem doses expected on various deep space missions are listed in Tables 9-4 and 9-5 [6]. Here the outbound

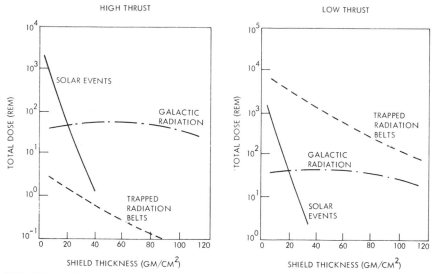

FIG. 9-7.  Relative importances of the three sources of space radiation for a deep space mission.

and inbound trips through the Van Allen belts were assumed to involve the same dose accumulation. It was assumed that the entire mission took place at approximately 1 A.U. Theoretical estimates have been made of the effects of distance from the Sun on galactic and solar radiations expected. The effects on solar flare radiations depend upon what theoretical models one uses and the parameters of the solar flare [25, 26].

The effects of the ERD concept on shielding required for a deep space mission were calculated on the assumption that the radiation doses were received uniformly during the mission. The only alternative was to postulate a specific flare history, and this involves even greater assumptions. So long as the flare doses are not essentially due to one or two large flares the assumption is not serious. The resulting point doses are listed in Table 9-6 [27], and show the definite advantages of deep space missions during solar minimums as well as the increasing effect of the use of the ERD concept with increasing mission duration.

As a detailed example of a space mission which would include space radiation shielding considerations involving most of the technical material presented, consider a manned round trip to Mars. From energy con-

TABLE 9-4

SPACE RADIATION rad DOSES EXPECTED FOR DEEP SPACE MISSIONS[a]

| Shielding | Source | 1 month | 3 months | 6 months | 12 months | 18 months | 24 months |
|---|---|---|---|---|---|---|---|
| 0.1 gm/cm² | Van Allen | $4 \times 10^3$ | $4 \times 10^3$ | $4 \times 10^3$ | $4 \times 10^3$ | $4 \times 10^3$ | $4 \times 10^3$ |
| | | $3.5 \times 10^3$ | $3.5 \times 10^3$ | $3.5 \times 10^3$ | $3.5 \times 10^3$ | $3.5 \times 10^3$ | $3.5 \times 10^3$ |
| | Flares (1%) | $1.1 \times 10^5$ | $1.5 \times 10^5$ | $1.8 \times 10^5$ | $2.2 \times 10^5$ | $2.9 \times 10^5$ | $3.6 \times 10^5$ |
| | | $1.1 \times 10^4$ | $1.5 \times 10^4$ | $2.2 \times 10^4$ | $2.9 \times 10^4$ | $4.4 \times 10^4$ | $7.3 \times 10^4$ |
| | Galactic | 0.9 | 2.7 | 5.4 | 11 | 16 | 22 |
| | | 1.5 | 4.5 | 9.0 | 18 | 27 | 36 |
| 1.0 gm/cm² | Van Allen | 6.8 | 6.8 | 6.8 | 6.8 | 6.8 | 6.8 |
| | | 6.5 | 6.5 | 6.5 | 6.5 | 6.5 | 6.5 |
| | Flares (1%) | 1500 | 2000 | 2500 | 3000 | 4000 | 5000 |
| | | 150 | 210 | 300 | 400 | 600 | 1000 |
| | Galactic | 0.9 | 2.7 | 5.4 | 11 | 16 | 22 |
| | | 1.5 | 4.5 | 9.0 | 18 | 27 | 36 |
| 10 gm/cm² | Van Allen | 1.5 | 1.5 | 1.5 | 1.5 | 1.5 | 1.5 |
| | | 1.5 | 1.5 | 1.5 | 1.5 | 1.5 | 1.5 |
| | Flares (1%) | 75 | 100 | 125 | 150 | 200 | 250 |
| | | 7.5 | 11 | 15 | 20 | 30 | 50 |
| | Galactic | 0.9 | 2.7 | 5.4 | 11 | 16 | 22 |
| | | 1.5 | 4.5 | 9.0 | 18 | 27 | 36 |

[a] Van Allen doses calculated on basis of two high-thrust trips in plane geomagnetic equator (1 outbound, 1 inbound), in 1970, assuming no more high-altitude nuclear detonations. Flare doses based upon 1% probability, include effects of protons and alpha particles. Top numbers are for solar max, bottom for solar min.

TABLE 9-5

SPACE RADIATION REM DOSES EXPECTED FOR DEEP SPACE MISSIONS[a]

| Shielding | Source | 1 month | 3 months | 6 months | 12 months | 18 months | 24 months |
|---|---|---|---|---|---|---|---|
| 0.1 gm/cm² | Van Allen | $4 \times 10^3$ <br> $3.5 \times 10^3$ | $4 \times 10^3$ <br> $3.5 \times 10^3$ | $4 \times 10^3$ <br> $3.5 \times 10^3$ | $4 \times 10^3$ <br> $3.5 \times 10^3$ | $4 \times 10^3$ <br> $3.5 \times 10^3$ | $4 \times 10^3$ <br> $3.5 \times 10^3$ |
|  | Flares (1 %) | $4.8 \times 10^5$ <br> $4.8 \times 10^4$ | $6.6 \times 10^5$ <br> $6.6 \times 10^4$ | $8 \times 10^5$ <br> $1 \times 10^5$ | $1 \times 10^6$ <br> $1.3 \times 10^5$ | $1.3 \times 10^6$ <br> $1.9 \times 10^5$ | $1.6 \times 10^6$ <br> $3.2 \times 10^5$ |
|  | Galactic | 0.9 <br> 1.5 | 2.7 <br> 4.5 | 5.4 <br> 9.0 | 11 <br> 18 | 16 <br> 27 | 22 <br> 36 |
| 1.0 gm/cm² | Van Allen | 7.5 <br> 7.2 | 7.5 <br> 7.2 | 7.5 <br> 7.2 | 7.5 <br> 7.2 | 7.5 <br> 7.2 | 7.5 <br> 7.2 |
|  | Flares (1 %) | 5000 <br> 500 | 6600 <br> 700 | 8,200 <br> 1,000 | 10,000 <br> 1,300 | 13,000 <br> 2,000 | 16,500 <br> 3,300 |
|  | Galactic | 0.9 <br> 1.5 | 2.7 <br> 4.5 | 5.4 <br> 9.0 | 11 <br> 18 | 16 <br> 27 | 22 <br> 36 |
| 10 gm/cm² | Van Allen | 1.6 <br> 1.6 | 1.6 <br> 1.6 | 1.6 <br> 1.6 | 1.6 <br> 1.6 | 1.6 <br> 1.6 | 1.6 <br> 1.6 |
|  | Flares (1 %) | 110 <br> 11 | 150 <br> 17 | 190 <br> 22 | 225 <br> 30 | 300 <br> 45 | 375 <br> 75 |
|  | Galactic | 0.9 <br> 1.5 | 2.7 <br> 4.5 | 5.4 <br> 9.0 | 11 <br> 18 | 16 <br> 27 | 22 <br> 26 |

[a] Van Allen doses calculated on basis of two high-thrust trips in plane of geomagnetic equator (1 outbound, 1 inbound) in 1970, assuming no more high-altitude nuclear detonations. Flare doses based on 1% probability, include effects of proton and alpha particles. Top numbers are for solar max, bottom for solar min.

TABLE 9-6

EFFECT OF ERD ON SHIELDING REQUIRED FOR VARIOUS DEEP SPACE MISSIONS[a]

| Deep space mission duration | If 100 Rem limit | | If 300 Rem limit | |
|---|---|---|---|---|
| | No ERD (gm/cm²) | With ERD (gm/cm²) | No ERD (gm/cm²) | With ERD (gm/cm²) |
| 1 mo. (solar max) | 10.0 | 9.6 | 6.4 | 6.0 |
| (solar min) | 3.4 | 3.2 | 1.5 | 1.4 |
| 3 mo. (solar max) | 11.5 | 10.0 | 7.6 | 6.4 |
| (solar min) | 4.0 | 3.6 | 2.0 | 1.6 |
| 6 mo. (solar max) | 13.2 | 10.5 | 8.8 | 6.8 |
| (solar min) | 4.8 | 4.0 | 2.5 | 1.9 |
| 12 mo. (solar max) | 14.4 | 11.3 | 9.8 | |
| (solar min) | 5.8 | 4.7 | 3.2 | 2.4 |
| 18 mo. (solar max) | 14.7 | 11.5 | 10.0 | 7.6 |
| (solar min) | 6.8 | 5.3 | 3.9 | 2.8 |
| 24 mo. (solar max) | 15.4 | 12.0 | 10.4 | 7.8 |
| (solar min) | 8.5 | 6.6 | 5.0 | 3.8 |

[a] All entries have $1\sigma$ limits of $\pm 3$ gm/cm² or $\pm 30\%$, whichever is larger.

siderations, a trip of approximately 480 days appears desirable because a shorter trip would require that a larger $\Delta v$ be supplied to the spacecraft while a longer trip would increase the weight of the life support systems (including meteoroid and radiation shielding) required. The outbound leg of the trip will require 220 days; a stay on Mars of 30 days is desired; and the inbound leg of the trip will require 230 days [8]. The vehicle used would be a high-thrust chemical rocket.

The first space radiation encountered will be the Van Allen belts. As calculated previously the total point dosimeter dose received inside a 5 gm/cm² aluminum shield due to outward passage through the Earth's Van Allen belts is ~1.8 Rem. The return trip through the belts would be of a similar magnitude, and was chosen as ~2.0 Rem to allow for delays due to selection of the optimum reentry window. The recoverable portion of the ~1.8 Rem on the outgoing leg of the mission is ~1.5 Rem, and it is ~1.7 Rem on the return portion.

The galactic radiation will amount to ~50 mrad/day for shields up to

10 gm/cm$^2$ aluminum. Since the RBE of the primary protons (the only important component for shields $\lesssim 10$ gm/cm$^2$) is unity, the mission dose for 450 days in space will be $\sim 22.5$ Rem. However, the dose is chronic, and after 450 continuous days of exposure, the ERD will be $\sim 4.2$ Rem.

The galactic radiation received while on the surface of Mars depends upon the composition and depth of the Martian atmosphere and the strength of the Martian magnetic field. Since the Mariner IV data showed a very thin ($\lesssim 10$ gm/cm$^2$) atmosphere and essentially no magnetic field, the galactic radiation at the surface is $\sim 0.5$ that of free space. The solar radiation is estimated to be half that expected behind a 10 gm/cm$^2$ aluminum shield.

The major source of radiation will be solar flares. If 99% reliability is desired, a 1 gm/cm$^2$ shield will result in an average meatball proton dose of $\sim 2500$ rad for the mission while a 10 gm/cm$^2$ shield will reduce this to $\sim 150$ rad. Interpolating between these figures, using the curve for an expected large event, yields $\sim 500$ rad for 5 gm/cm$^2$. The RBE for solar flare protons attenuated through 5 gm/cm$^2$ is $\sim 1.15$. Therefore, the proton dose is $\sim 575$ Rem. The alpha particle contribution increases this by a factor of 1.8 to $\sim 1030$ Rem.

It must be remembered that this dose was obtained by averaging the available data over that portion of the 11-year solar cycle between 1956 and 1961. By making the trip during a period of low solar activity, this may be reduced by a factor of $\sim 3$ to $\sim 345$ Rem. For a very long mission, e.g., seven years or more, such reduction cannot be made. While a dose of 345 Rem due to solar flares looks high, it would not be received all at once. It would probably be received in a few (2–10) large flares plus a larger number of smaller ones.

In order to take the ERD into account, the 345 Rem was assumed to be received in seven large events distributed as follows:

30 Rem at 30  days after start of mission
50 Rem at 100 days after start of mission
95 Rem at 185 days after start of mission
50 Rem at 195 days after start of mission
 5 Rem at 300 days after start of mission
100 Rem at 380 days after start of mission
15 Rem at 450 days after start of mission
___
345 Rem total

The ratio of protons to alpha particles for a 5 gm/cm$^2$ shield is 24 (i.e., the alpha particles add $\sim 4\%$ to the penetrating flux), but the penetrating alpha particles add $\sim 80\%$ to the Rem dose. Therefore, the RBE of the alpha particles is effectively 20 ($= 80\%/4\%$). The recoverable portion of the dose is therefore

$$\text{protons} \qquad \frac{90\% \times 575 \text{ Rem}}{1.15 \times 3} = 150 \text{ Rem}$$

$$\text{alpha particles} \qquad \frac{90\% \times 575 \times 0.8}{20 \times 3} = 7 \text{ Rem}$$

The remaining 188 Rem due to the solar flares may be considered as causing permanent damage. For each flare, 45% ($= 157/345$) of the Rem dose damage then is considered as reparable, half of this (22.5%) within 30 days.

The point dosimeter ERD inside a 5 gm/cm$^2$ aluminum shield due to 2 passages through the Earth's trapped radiation belts, the galactic flux while outside the Earth's atmosphere, and the expected solar event activity during solar minimum are shown in Fig. 9-8. As can be readily seen, the solar flare activity is by far the largest source of dose for this sort of mission.

In order to convert point dosimeter rem doses to rem doses received by various portions of the astronaut, the following factors can be used:

Skin dose = 1/2 point dosimeter dose
Blood-forming-organ dose = 1/4 point dosimeter dose (for 5 gm/cm$^2$ shielding)

This second factor is an average for the large solar flares (average rigidity = 100). The resulting total mission doses are

$$\begin{array}{ll} \text{skin} & 186 \text{ Rem} \\ \text{blood-forming organs} & 93 \text{ Rem} \end{array}$$

These numbers are within the limits of what, it is generally agreed, a man can take with at most temporary discomfort. These ERD values will decrease to 96 and 48 rem respectively, after the mission is completed. For this example, a spacecraft with shielding equivalent to 5 gm/cm$^2$ aluminum appears to be satisfactory for a manned Mars mission during solar minimums (e.g., 1975–1977).

The effects of the space radiation encountered on the spacecraft materials

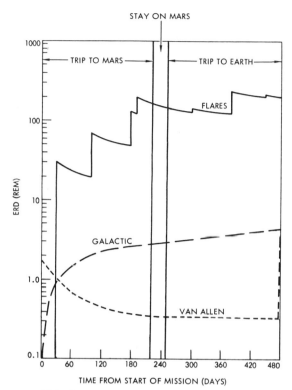

STAY ON MARS

FIG. 9-8. ERD expected for a Mars mission.

need to be considered. While inside the 5 gm/cm$^2$ spacecraft the mission point dose is 219 rad, outside (e.g., 0.1 gm/cm$^2$ shielding), the mission doses are

Van Allen 18 rad protons
2 × 10$^3$ rad electrons } outgoing leg of trip

20 rad protons
2.2 × 10$^3$ rad electrons } return leg of trip

Galactic 22.5 rad during trip
1.2 rad on surface of Mars

Flares 1 × 10$^4$ rad protons
3 × 10$^4$ rad alpha particles

The total mission dose of $4 \times 10^4$ rad is largely due to alpha particles emitted in solar flares. Alpha particles are the major contributors because they are almost as numerous as the protons and have much higher flux-to-rad-dose conversion factors. More important, an examination of the data shows that exposed ($< 0.1$ gm/cm$^2$ shielding) semiconductors will probably not continue to function for the duration of the mission, organic electrical insulation should be avoided, and even more rugged electronic components should be chosen with care. Transparent windows and elastic door seals should have a protective coating when possible.

It thus is apparent that, while the primary concern of space radiation shielding analysis is the protection of the astronauts, radiation-sensitive spacecraft components should also be avoided or protected (perhaps by placing them inside the craft). Considering that meteoroids as well as nuclear radiation will be encountered on the mission, an integrated approach to shielding against the space environment is desirable.

## D. Shield Weight Considerations, Optimization

The mission doses and space radiation shield thicknesses have been considered in previous sections. It is interesting to examine the weights of space radiation shields in comparison with the weights of meteoroid shielding and life support system weights. A study has been carried out by Beever and Rusling [28] based upon the following parameters:

| | |
|---|---|
| Mission dose | 100 rem (point, no ERD) |
| Spacecraft volume | 700 ft$^3$/man, cylindrical |
| Storm cellar volume | 50 ft$^3$/man, cylindrical |

Life support systems comprise those assemblies of subsystems which provide for atmospheric control, food, and water. They range in degree of closure from essentially open to almost full ecological systems. Of particular importance to the shield designer is the fact that these systems contain substantial amounts of storables for which there is a measure of flexibility in the location of storage.

Several life support systems were analyzed [29]. Designated systems A through F, they varied from "open" (high makeup requirements) to closed (no makeup requirements). System C was considered to be based on state-of-the-art technology, with only about a third the makeup requirements of system A. In system C wash water, perspiration, and urine water are re-claimed, $CO_2$ is reduced by hydrogenation, and thermal control is performed by radiators using recycle coolant. The weight, volume, and heat loads of system C are approximately:

$$\text{Weight (lb)} = 2.25\,N\tau + 158\,N + 0.009\,q + 120$$
$$\text{Volume (ft}^3) = 0.166\,N\tau + 3.05\,N + 2.40$$
$$\text{Heat Load (Btu/hr)} = 843.4\,N$$

where $N$ is the crew size (number of men), $\tau$ the mission duration (days), and $q$ the process heat load (Btu/hr).

In addition, any leakage of food, air, or water must be added to the life support system weights. While no leakage was assumed, it is difficult to keep leakage (especially oxygen) below $\sim 10$ lb/day.

Meteoroid protection is of prime importance to the radiation shield designer because it constitutes a mass envelope which is fully effective in radiation protection. From a space meteoroid shielding standpoint the important parameters are the mass and velocity distributions of the meteoroids. The measurements do not provide such information directly, and therefore it must be inferred. The so-called "Ames criteria" was used for this study, which yields (for single sheets of aluminum) [30, 31].

$$t = 2.7 \times 10^{-6} \left( \frac{AT}{P} \right)^{\frac{1}{3}}$$

where $t$ is the meteoroid shield thickness (meters), $T$ the mission duration (sec), $A$ the area of spacecraft surface ($m^2$), and $P$ the probability of no penetration.

The calculated meteoroid shield, radiation shield, and life support system weights for various missions are listed in Table 9-7 [28]. It should be pointed out that the meteoroid shielding weights involves shielding the entire spacecraft (700 ft$^3$/man) while the space radiation shield weight is that additional weight which must be provided around a 50 ft$^3$/man, 6-ft-long storm cellar. Thus full advantage of the meteoroid shielding is taken in calculating the space radiation shield weights. For a MOL in the Van Allen belts the radiation shield weights would climb considerably.

One striking conclusion from Table 9-7 is that the weight of the life support system appreciably exceeds that of the radiation shield for long duration missions with large crews (seven or more men). A considerable portion of

TABLE 9-7

SYSTEM WEIGHTS[a]

| Mission duration (days) | Life support system "C" | Meteoroid shielding (Ames criterion single sheet) | Net radiation shielding (radiation shield- meteoroid shield) |
|---|---|---|---|
| | | 3-man crew | |
| 30 | 1,500 | 4,038 | 1,890 |
| 100 | 3,300 | 6,020 | 2,200 |
| 300 | 6,700 | 8,680 | 2,440 |
| 1000 | 18,200 | 12,950 | 2,530 |
| | | 7-man crew | |
| 30 | 4,100 | 8,600 | 3,100 |
| 100 | 5,700 | 12,840 | 3,520 |
| 300 | 10,600 | 18,500 | 3,810 |
| 1000 | 27,600 | 28,800 | 3,520 |
| | | 10-man crew | |
| 30 | 6,100 | 12,500 | 3,530 |
| 100 | 8,300 | 17,650 | 4,190 |
| 300 | 14,500 | 25,500 | 4,440 |
| 1000 | 36,000 | 38,100 | 4,180 |

[a] Weights are in pounds.

this weight involves storables whose placement is not critical. By judicious placement of these around the storm cellar, most if not all the required radiation shielding can be provided at no increase in weight. Waste products can be stored in the same containers once the consumables have been used, thus maintaining the radiation shielding.

Space radiation shielding weight optimization studies have been carried out only for simple spacecraft geometries and relatively simple environments. Krumbein et al. [32] adapted an optimization procedure developed for nuclear proton shields. The procedure was to select those materials which had the greatest stopping power at the cutoff shield energy. Celnik et al. [33] extended the method by showing that by the neglect of secondary neutrons the best materials could be selected through using a Young diagram. Optimum thicknesses of materials to yield a 20 cm radius spherical void with a central dose constraint of 25 Rem in flares of May 10, 1959, and February 23, 1956, were calculated.

An optimization study of solar cell shielding for the Advanced Orbiting Solar Observatory (AOSO) was carried out by Weiner [34]. The problem was to provide the necessary power from the minimum weight of silicon solar cells. If unshielded, the environmental radiation (Van Allen belt particles and solar flare protons) would damage the solar cells directly; if shielded by transparent coverings, these coverings would darken, decreasing solar cell output. For the 300 nautical mile 97.6 deg orbit of the AOSO, Weiner concluded that by using $N/P$-10 ohm-cm solar cells unshielded the weight would be a minimum. For this orbit, if the area of solar cells is unrestricted, the weight is reduced by using more solar cells than by providing transparent coverings. This way the power requirements at the end of the AOSO's expected operational life of a year can be met.

## E.  Dose Reduction via Operational Procedures

Once the spacecraft is launched the mass of shielding present cannot be increased if an emergency (e.g., a large flare) arises. However, there are certain operational procedures available which can be used to limit the dose received.

One operational procedure for reducing the space radiation dose is to modify the mission trajectory. For spacecraft not too far from Earth this may take the form of aborting the mission to return to earth before the solar flare dose exceeds desired limits [35]. For high flying aircraft ( > 70,000 feet) at polar latitudes the philosophy is similar—simply reduce altitude to take advantage of the shielding of the earth [36]. It will be noted, however, that for the spacecraft it is a geomagnetic field which provides the shielding while for the aircraft the atmosphere does so.

Another possible operational procedure which may reduce the space radiation dose is to orient the spacecraft so that the heavily shielded portions face the incoming particles. Since spacecraft are generally quite heterogeneous, this will help, provided the radiation environment is anisotropic. For some solar flares the first portion of the incident radiation appears to be anisotropic. A model anisotropic flare has been used to calculate that a ~20% reduction in dose may be possible by orientation of the Apollo capsule [37].

A third operational procedure is to use any movable material present to provide "spot" shielding. For a given mass of material the most efficient shield is a uniform distribution over all $4\pi$ solid angles. Any departure from this will increase the dose, since the increased contributions from the thin spots will exceed the decreased contributions from the thick spots. Therefore the placement of movable material against the spacecraft windows, for example, will reduce the dose inside. This is the logical extension of the storm cellar concept. As in the latter concept its utility is greatest for transient radiation environments, least for continuous radiation environments (e.g., equatorial orbits in the Van Allen belts).

## F.  Other Shielding Concepts

This book has been essentially concerned with the attenuation of space nuclear radiation by material (passive) shielding. An alternative kind of shielding based upon the creation of a magnetic field around the spacecraft (active shielding) has been proposed. While at the present the sizes of the spacecraft and the mission durations considered favor passive shielding, in the future the technology will probably advance until active shielding becomes preferable under certain conditions [38].

Two considerations concerning active shielding favor it for long missions. One is that it can be turned on and off, so that it is used only when needed (e.g., during solar proton events). The other is that the weight of active shielding increases more slowly with spacecraft size than that of passive shielding [39].

The usual manner of creating a magnetic field is by use of superconducting coils of niobium-zirconium alloy, since these materials have been shown to retain their superconductivity in a magnetic field up to $\sim 10^5$ gauss. Future nuclear and chemical rockets will probably use liquid hydrogen for fuel, and this can also be used to cool the magnetic coils [40, 41]. Two problems exist —the mechanical strength required to preserve the integrity of the magnet becomes very large at high magnetic fields, and safeguards must be maintained to prevent the magnet coils from leaving the superconducting state suddenly, for the heat released will boil the cooling liquid hydrogen with explosive suddenness.

A modification of the usual magnetic shielding has been proposed by Levy and Janes [42]. This modification involves creating an electron plasma around a toroid-shaped spacecraft to shield it against the solar wind. With the electrical discharging effects of the solar wind eliminated, electrostatic shielding (raising the spacecraft potential to several million volts) may be possible. In this way the magnetic field required has only to contain low-energy electrons instead of excluding high-energy protons.

Other types of active shielding have been proposed, but these appear much less promising than superconducting magnetic shielding. Among these are electrostatic shielding (it may be essentially impossible to achieve the electric fields required to deflect the energetic protons enough to miss even a small space capsule) and magnetic shielding by a plasma created by the detonation of a nuclear weapon (the radiation from the detonation is an additional hazard and the plasma will probably not remain effective for shielding for the several hours required). For the time being superconducting magnets appear to offer the only alternative to bulk material shielding against the radiation in space, and the technology of the former requires further development before its use will be feasible.

## REFERENCES

1. W. R. Webber, An Evaluation of the Radiation Hazard due to Solar Particle Events, Rept. D2-90469, *Boeing Airplane Co.*, Seattle, Washington (1963).
2. J. L. Modisette, T. M. Vinson, and A. C. Hardy, Model Solar Proton Environments for Manned Spacecraft Design, NASA-TN-D-2746 (1963).
3. H. H. Malitson, Predicting Large Solar Cosmic Ray Events, *Astronaut. Aerospace Eng.* **1,** 70 (1963).
4. J. B. Weddell and J. W. Haffner, Statistical Evaluation of Proton Radiation from Solar Flares, Rept. SID-66-421, *North American Aviation, Corp.* Los Angeles, Calif. (1966).
5. D. L. Dye and M. Wilkinson, Radiation Hazards in Space, *Science* **147,** 19 (1965).
6. J. W. Haffner, A Study of Space Radiation Shielding, Rept. SID-64-2037, *North American Aviation, Corp.* Los Angeles, Calif. (1964).
7. R. Pay, Apollo Astronauts Are Painstakingly Protected from Solar-Flare Protons, *Missiles Rockets*, p. 22 (1964).
8. A. L. Jones and W. V. McRae, Manned Mars Landing and Return Mission Study, Rept. SID 64-619, *North American Aviation, Corp.* Los Angeles, Calif. (1964).
9. A. L. Jones and W. V. McRae, Manned Mars and/or Venus Flyby Vehicle Systems Study, Rept. SID 65-761, *North American Aviation, Corp.* Los Angeles, Calif. (1965).
10. S. L. Russak, Radiation Dosages from Electrons and Bremsstrahlung in the Van Allen Belt, pp. 760 ff., *Proc. Symp. Protection against Radiation Hazards in Space*, TID-7652 (1962).

11.  G. Pizzella, C. D. Laughlin, and B. J. O'Brien, Note on the Electron Energy Spectrum in the Inner Van Allen Belt, *J. Geophys. Res.* **67,** 3281 (1962).
12.  S. Russak and K. Richardson, Proton Flux, Dosage, and Damage Estimates in the Van Allen Belt, pp. 251 ff., *Second Symp. Protection against Radiations in Space,* NASA-SP-71 (1964).
13.  W. L. Imhof and R. R. Smith, Proton Intensities and Energy Spectrums in the Inner Van Allen Belt, *J. Geophys. Res.* **69,** 91 (1964).
14.  F. L. Keller and R. G. Pruett, The Effect of Charged-Particle Environments on Manned Military Space Systems, pp. 265 ff., *Second Symp. Protection against Radiations in Space,* NASA-SP-71 (1964).
15.  T. M. Jordan, E. F. Koprowski, and R. W. Langley, Shielding Requirements for Manned Orbiting Space Stations, pp. 415 ff., *Second Symp. Protection against Radiations in Space,* NASA-SP-71 (1964).
16.  F. L. Bouquet, A Space Radiation Protection System for Near-Earth Manned Orbital Space Stations, pp. 397 ff., *Second Symp. Protection against Radiations in Space,* NASA-SP-71 (1964).
17.  E. Kuhn, F. E. Schwamb, and W. T. Payne, Solar Flare Hazard to Earth-Orbiting Vehicles, pp. 429 ff., *Second Symp. Protection against Radiations in Space,* NASA-SP-71 (1964).
18.  B. W. Mar, An Evaluation of Radiation Shielding by Vehicle Orientation, pp. 413 ff., *Second Symp. Protection against Radiations in Space,* NASA-SP-71 (1964).
19.  R. E. Fortney and G. D. Duckworth, The Importance of Radiation Anisotropy in Dose Calculations, pp. 477 ff., *Second Symp. Protection against Radiations in Space,* NASA-SP-71 (1964).
20.  J. W. Keller, Long Range NASA Shielding Requirements, pp. 663 ff., *Proc. Symp. Protection against Radiation Hazards in Space,* TID-7652 (1962).
21.  G. W. Crawford, Space Dosimetry, *in*: "Space Physics" (D. P. LeGalley and A. Rosen, eds.), Chap. 18. Wiley, New York, 1964.
22.  Y. M. Volynkin, A. V. Antipov, V. A. Guda, M. D. Nikitin, and P. P. Saksonov, The Biological Evaluation of Radiation Conditions on the Path between the Earth and the Moon, NASA Tech. Transl. TT-F-279 (1964).
23.  J. W. Haffner and E. R. Beever, Effective Mars Mission Radiation Doses, Rept. SID 64-1298, *North American Aviation, Corp.* Los Angeles, Calif. (1964).
24.  H. Elliot, Cosmic Ray Intensity in Interplanetary Space, *Nature* **186,** 299 (1960).
25.  J. B. Weddell, Interaction of Hydrodynamic Shocks with Charged Particles in the Solar Corona, Rept. SID 64-1500, *North American Aviation, Corp.* Los Angeles, Calif. (1964).
26.  K. A. Anderson, Energetic Solar Particles, *in*: "Space Physics" (D. P. LeGalley and A. Rosen, eds.), Chap. 16. Wiley, New York, 1964.
27.  J. W. Haffner, The ERD Concept in Space Radiation Shielding, Paper 65-497, *Second Ann. AIAA Meeting, San Francisco, California* (1965).
28.  E. R. Beever and D. H. Rusling, The Importance of Space Radiation Shielding Weight, pp. 407 ff., *Second Symp. Protection against Radiations in Space,* NASA-SP-71 (1964).
29.  F. I. Honea, Life Support Systems, *in*: "Manned Mars Landing and Return Mission Study" (A. L. Jones and W. V. McRae, eds.), Sect. 3.1.1. Rept. SID 64-619, *North American Aviation, Corp.* Los Angeles, Calif. (1964).

30. The Meteoroid Environment for Project Apollo, Annex C, Bellomm Rept. Washington, D.C. (1963).
31. C. T. D'Aiutolo, First Meteoroid Penetration Data for SNAP Designs, *Nucleonics* **21,** No. 11, 51 (1963).
32. A. D. Krumbein *et al.*, Synthesis of Minimum Weight Proton Shields, pp. 760, *Proc. Symp. Protection against Radiation Hazards in Space*, TID-7652 (1962).
33. J. Celnik, A. D. Krumbein, and F. R. Nakache, Synthesis of Spherical Minimum Weight Proton Shields, pp. 225 ff., *Second Symp. Protection against Radiations in Space*, NASA-SP-71 (1964).
34. H. Weiner, Optimum Solar Cell Shielding for the Advanced Orbiting Solar Observatory, pp. 511 ff., *Second Symp. Protection against Radiations in Space*, NASA-SP-71 (1964).
35. P. W. Higgins, Operational Procedures for Apollo Dose Reduction, pp. 151 ff., *Second Symp. Protection against Radiations in Space*, NASA-SP-71 (1964).
36. T. Foelsche, The Ionizing Radiations in Supersonic Transport Flights, pp. 287 ff., *Second Symp. Protection against Radiations in Space*, NASA-SP-71 (1964).
37. F. Raymes, Apollo Spacecraft Nuclear Radiation Protection Status Report, pp. 365 ff., *Second Symp. Protection against Radiations in Space*, NASA-SP-71 (1964).
38. R. H. Levy, The Prospects for Active Shielding, pp. 794 ff., *Proc. Symp. Protection against Radiation Hazards in Space*, TID-7652 (1962).
39. R. E. Bernert and Z. J. J. Stekly, Magnetic Radiation Shielding Using Superconducting Coils, pp. 199 ff., *Second Symp. Protection against Radiations in Space*, NASA-SP-71 (1964).
40. A. D. Prescott, E. W. Urban, and R. D. Shelton, The Application of the Liouville Theorem to Magnetic Shielding Problems, pp. 189 ff., *Second Symp. Protection against Radiations in Space*, NASA-SP-71, (1964).
41. N. Edmonson, Shielding of Space Vehicles by Magnetic Fields, pp. 808 ff., *Proc. Symp. Protection Against Radiation Hazards in Space*, TID-7652, (1962).
42. R. H. Levy and G. S. Janes, Plasma Radiation Shield, pp. 211 ff., *Second Symp. Protection against Radiations in Space*, NASA-SP-71 (1964).

# AUTHOR INDEX

Numbers in parentheses are reference numbers and indicate that an author's work is referred to although his name is not cited in the text. Numbers in italic show the page on which the complete reference is listed.

## A

Abbott, L. S., 197, 203 (47), *213*
Aizu, H., 49, *71*
Ajzenberg-Selove, F., 182 (11), *212*
Albert, R. D., 197 (52), *213*, 224, *251*
Alderman, I. M., 135 (106), *149*
Alfvén, H., 69 (125), 75, 78, *102*
Allen, L., 101, *106*
Allen, R. G., 121, 126 (54), *146*
Allen, R. I., 222 (17), *251*
Allison, S. K., 169 (41), *176*
Alpen, E. L., 126 (72), 127 (77), 128 (82), *147*, *148*
Alper, T., 110 (9), 111 (9), *144*
Alsmiller, F. S., 269, *297*
Alsmiller, R. G., 171 (47), *177*, 268 (15), 269, *296*, *297*
Alter, H., 159 (18), *175*, 233, *252*, 277 (31), *297*
Amazeen, P. G., 87, *103*
Amster, H., 180, *211*
Anderson, H. R., 26, 33, 42, 43, 56 (63), 61, *73*, *74*
Anderson, K. A., 12 (15), 19, 40, 42, 66, 75, 87, *103*, 311;(26), *324*
Anger, C. D., 19 (51), *42*

Anger, H. O., 119 (47), 126 (47), *146*
Antipov, A. V., 309 (22), *324*
Antipov, V. V., 119 (45), 120 (45), 126 (45), *146*
Antonov, A. V., 181, *211*
Antrack, D., 13 (24), *41*
Armstrong, A. H., 85, 91, *102*, *104*
Arnold, D. M., 139 (121), *150*
Arnold, J. R., 55 (55), *72*
Arnoldy, R. L., 19 (50), 33, 42, 43, 57 (67), *73*
Aron, W. A., 167, *176*
Ashe, J. B., 185 (21), *212*
Ashikawa, J. K., 120, 126 (51), *146*
Ashkin, J., 155, *175*
Atwood, K. C., 110 (8), *144*
Avery, A. F., 200 (56), *214*
Axford, W. I., 13 (22, 25), *41*

## B

Babcock, H. D., 59 (75), *73*
Babcock, H. W., 59 (75), *73*
Baggerly, L. L., 173 (53), *177*
Baicker, J. A., 139 (121, 125), *150*

327

# SUBJECT INDEX

## A

Absorptions, polar cap, 35
Acceleration
  betatron, 69
  Fermi, 69
Activation
  cross section, 185
  radioactive, of material, 140
Active shielding, 322
Advanced Orbiting Solar Observatory
  (AOSO), 321
Agassiz experiment, 46
Age
  galactic, 48
  neutron, 180
Air showers, cosmic ray, 46, 51, 65, 66, 285
Albedo theory, neutron, 37, 65, 96
Albert-Welton kernel, 197, 201, 224
Alpha particles
  galactic radiations, 47–53
  solar flare radiations, 22–25, 262–265
Ames criteria, micrometeorite, 319
Angular distributions, source, 211
Anisotropy, flux of solar particles, 33, 304, 321
Annular duct leakage, 209–211
Anomaly, South Atlantic, 88, 98, 308
Apollo spacecraft, 230–236, 264
Approximation
  Born, 226, 228

diffusion, 193–195
line of sight, 207
  $P$, 193
  $S_n$, 193
Argonne Code Center, 216
Argus experiments, 98
Artificial radiation belt, 97–102
  decay of, 100–102
Astronomical unit (A.U.), 12
Atlantic missile range, 308
Atomic displacements, 107, 109
Atomic ionization, 107–108, 283
Atomic shell correction, 153
Attenuation, point kernel, 195–200
Attenuation coefficient
  linear, 171, 190, 195
  mass, 142, 190, 226
Attenuation length, 171, 190, 277
Aurorae, polar, 13, 97

## B

B–L Coordinates, 89–91
Bailey model event, 27–29, 253–258
Barn (definition of unit), 183
Belts
  artificial radiation, 97–102
  Van Allen, 12, 36, 76ff, 227
Beta decay, 185
Beta functions, 255